W9-BKD-162

The Human Body

Auguste Rodin's "The Thinker"—*Homo sapiens sapiens.*

The World Book
Encyclopedia of Science

Volume
7

The Human Body

World Book, Inc.
a Scott Fetzer company
Chicago

Acknowledgments

Consultant Editors
Mike Janson and Joyce Pope

Consultants and Contributors
Ray Aldridge
Nicole Bechirian
Robert Burton
Jonathan Elphick
Thom Henvey
Casey Horton
Dorothy Jackson
Mike Janson
Ginny Johnson
Nick Law
Jane Mainwaring
Joyce Pope
Nora Spears
John Stidworthy
Jude Welton
Peter White

Artists and Designers
Eric Drewery
Mick Gillah
Nicki Kemball
Aziz Khan
David Parker
Roberta Polfus
Mick Saunders
Charlotte Styles
Alan Suttie

Bull Publishing Consultants Ltd
Wendy Allen
Harold Bull
John Clark
Eric Drewery
Kate Duffy
Ursula Fifield
Nicola Okell
Martyn Page
Polly Powell
Hal Robinson
Sandy Shepherd

Published by World Book, Inc., Chicago 1989
1992 printing.

Printed in the United States of America
Library of Congress Catalog Card No. 90-70521
ISBN: 0-7166-2600-4
O/IB

Contents

Preface

The Human Body, like the other volumes in this series of publications about the sciences, deals with a specific scientific area. The human body is introduced through its anatomy and physiology. Growth and development and the causes and treatment of illness extend this study. Finally, it describes the characteristics of adaptation, socialization, and the ability to modify or control the environment, which make human beings the dominant species of our planet.

The editorial approach

The object of the series is to explain for an average family readership, adults and children alike, the many aspects of science that are not only fascinating in themselves but are also vitally important for an understanding of the world today. To achieve this, the books have been made straightforward and concise, accurate in content, and are clearly and attractively presented. They are also a readily accessible source of scientific information.

The often forbidding appearance of traditional science publications has been completely avoided. Approximately equal proportions of illustrations and text make even the most unfamiliar subjects interesting and attractive. Even more important, all of the drawings have been created specially to complement the text, each explaining a topic that can be difficult to understand through the printed word alone.

The application of these principles thoroughly and consistently has created a publication that encapsulates its subject in an interesting and stimulating way, and that will prove to be an invaluable work of reference and education for many years to come.

The advance of science

One of the most exciting and challenging aspects of science is that its frontiers are constantly being revised and extended and new developments are occurring all the time. Its advance depends largely on observation, experimentation, and debate, which generate theories that have to be tested and even then stand only until they are replaced by better concepts. For this reason, it is difficult for any science publication to be completely comprehensive. It is possible, however, to provide a thorough foundation that ensures any such advances can be comprehended—and it is the purpose of each book in this series to create such a foundation, by providing all the basic knowledge in the particular area of science it describes.

How to use this book

This book can be used in two basic ways.

The first, and more conventional, way is to start at the beginning and to read through to the end, which gives a coherent and thorough picture of the subject and opens a resource of basic information that can be returned to for re-reading and reference.

The second allows the book to be used as a library of information presented subject by subject, which the reader can consult piece by piece as required.

All articles are prepared and presented so that the subject is equally accessible by either. Topics are arranged in a logical sequence, outlined in the contents list. The index allows access to more specific points.

Within an article, scientific terms are explained in the main text where an understanding of them is central to the understanding of the subject as a whole. Fact entries giving technical, mathematical, or biographical details are included, where appropriate, at the end of the article to which they relate. There is also an alphabetical glossary of terms at the end of the book, so that the reader's memory can be refreshed and so that the book can be used for quick reference whenever necessary.

All articles are relatively short, but none has been condensed artificially. Most articles occupy two pages, but some are four pages long.

The sample two-page article *(right)* shows the important elements of this editorial plan and illustrates the way in which this organization permits maximum flexibility of use.

(A) **Article title** gives the reader an immediate reference point.

(B) **Section title** shows the part of the book in which a particular article falls.

(C) **Main text** consists of approximately 850 words of narrative information set out in a logical manner, avoiding biographical and technical details that might tend to interrupt the story line and hamper the reader's progress.

(D) **Illustrations** include specially commissioned drawings and diagrams and carefully selected photographs, which expand, clarify, and add to the main text.

(E) **Captions** explain the illustrations and make the connection between the textual and the visual elements of the article.

(F) **Annotation** of the drawings allows the reader to identify the various elements referred to in the captions.

(G) **Theme images,** where appropriate, are included in the top left-hand corner of the left-hand page, to emphasize a central element of information or to create a visual link between different but related articles.

(H) **Fact entries** are added at the foot of the last page of certain articles to give biographical details, chemical or mathematical formulas, or additional information relating to the article but not essential to an understanding of the main text itself.

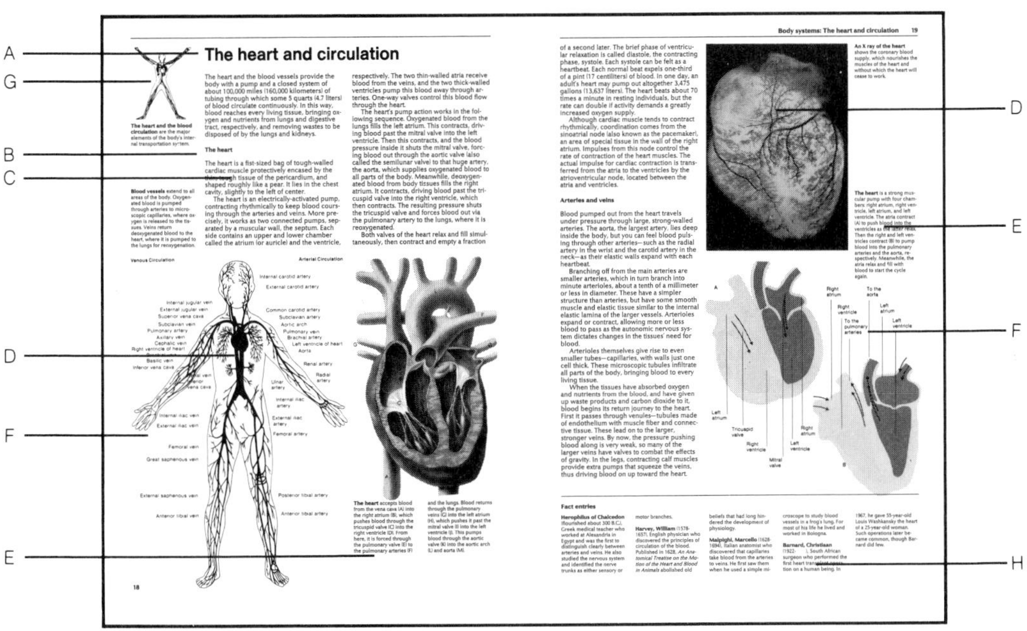

Introduction

The human body is a marvel. It starts out as a single cell and in time develops into a body consisting of trillions of cells that can perform an astonishing variety of physical and mental activities. The human body can also replace certain worn-out parts and defend itself against hundreds of diseases. The outer layer of the skin, for example, our first line of defense against disease, is entirely replaced every 15 to 30 days.

The human brain, the most remarkable part of the human body, is what distinguishes people from all other living things. It enables them to delve into the secrets of the living cell, create beautiful poetry and other works of art, and send sophisticated spacecraft to the moon and beyond. Nothing else—no other animal, no machine—can think like a human being.

The human sciences, as they are sometimes called, attempt to encompass an approach to humankind that includes the study of our origins, our structure, our functioning, our inherited characteristics, and our behavior, both as individuals and as members of human society. Taken together, these broad areas of knowledge form the basis of the humanitarian applied science of medicine—which itself forms the focus of a modern caring society in which the young are nurtured, the adult kept strong and healthy, and the elderly and the sick given relief and rest.

The need for knowledge of ourselves becomes increasingly apparent as medicine becomes more specialized and our world becomes more complex. To be a survivor in this modern age demands judgments from all of us about such things as what to eat and drink, how much exercise to take, how many children to bear, or how much stress to accept. Such judgments can be made easier by the knowledge about ourselves revealed in this book.

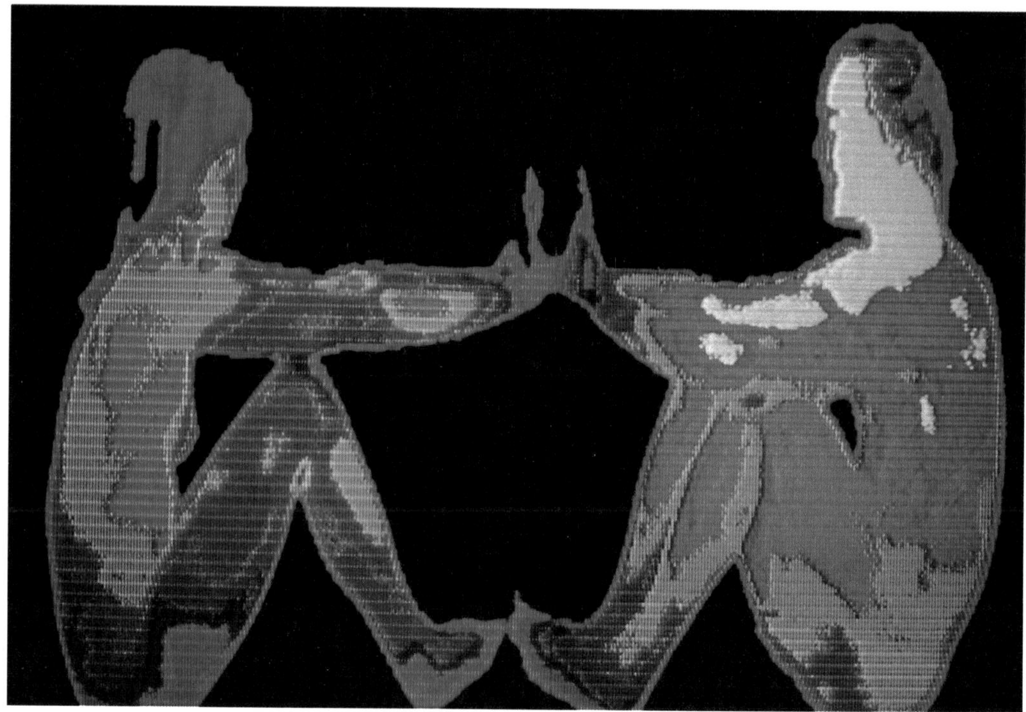

The human body gives off heat through the skin. This thermograph shows how the temperature varies over different parts of the body surface.

Growing up is a physical and mental process that relies on diet and activity, the care of other people—especially the parents—and the environment, from which all things are learned.

The basic human sciences

The oldest of the human sciences is anatomy, the study of human structure, which was founded on the basis of observation at Alexandria in about 300 B.C. (although the embalmers of ancient Egypt had acquired a rudimentary knowledge of human anatomy). Herophilus of the Alexandrian School studied the brain and spinal cord, identified tendons and nerves, and discovered that the nerves and brain direct movements. He was probably the first anatomist who learned by carrying out dissections of cadavers rather than by merely reading ancient texts.

The most famous anatomist of the Middle Ages was Leonardo da Vinci. His enquiring mind and his skill as an artist have left us an unrivaled collection of anatomical drawings. Unfortunately, his notebooks were lost for two centuries, but now we can see that Leonardo—the artist and engineer—was perhaps the father of scientific anatomy. Traditionally, this title goes to Andreas Vesalius, a Flemish anatomist who studied at Louvain in 1537. It was commonly held at that time that nothing could be added to the conclusions of the Greek physician Galen, who died at the end of the second century A.D., and whose theories combine anatomical and medical observation with a belief in the existence of "humors" that influence the body and its health. When Vesalius was appointed professor at Padua, he carried out dissections in public and wrote his masterpiece *On the Fabric of the Human Body*, or *Fabrica,* which established the scientific basis of anatomy.

Knowledge of physiology was increased at about the time that the Englishman William Harvey went to study at Padua in 1598. When he returned to Britain he taught anatomy and surgery at St. Bartholomew's Hospital in London, and in 1628, published his book on the circulation of the blood. This work refuted Galenic doctrine and continued the scientific revolution in our understanding of human anatomy and physiology. The modern era of physiology expanded with the use of the experimental method, while in anatomy, the invention of the microscope led to an appreciation of cellular theory and tissue structure and function. The modern basic sciences include relative newcomers, such as biochemistry, which developed out of physiological chem-

Human beings are set apart from other animals by their ability to use intellect and tools (the combination we now call technology) to conquer or modify the environment. Humans have learned to make wheeled vehicles to improve their mobility on land, build boats to cross oceans, and construct aircraft—from hang gliders to supersonic jet planes—to fly through the air.

istry, and pharmacology (the study of drug actions), which developed out of pharmacy and materia medica (the branch of medical study that deals with drugs, their sources, preparations, and uses).

The latest additions to these basic human studies are human genetics, psychology, and sociology. Human genetics as a science has led to a greater understanding of the mechanisms of inherited characteristics and disorders and to the ability to counsel prospective parents on their chances of having normal babies even if there is a history of genetic problems in the family. The study of psychology has allowed a better understanding of the functioning of the mind and human behavior, which in turn is the basis of our appreciation of mental illness and mental subnormality. And advances in sociology, the study of human societies in towns and cities or in the countryside, may lead to better use of our human resources, with reduced conflict between societies' divisions and classes.

Human adaptability

Divisions of mankind are obvious in the differing physical features of the populations in various parts of the world. Some of these racial characteristics are the result of useful environmental adaptations during the later stages of human evolution. Other physical characteristics, such as physiological adaptations to high altitude in mountain-dwelling peoples, show more immediate examples of physical adaptability.

Human culture, however—with the use of clothes, fire, travel, warfare, and so on—has tended to blunt the edge of the selective processes that led to evolutionary differences, and marriages across racial groups have blurred the boundaries in many parts of the world. Racial mixtures are diffuse in South America, for example.

When the human machine breaks down

There are thousands of separate disorders listed in medical dictionaries, but there are just a few basic categories into which nearly all illnesses can be classified. These are deficiencies (of diet, vitamins, hormones, and so on), infections (by bacteria, viruses, or fungi), tumors (such as cancers resulting from uncontrolled growth), allergies (such as hay fever and asthma), and lastly, the degenerative processes that affect the heart, arteries, and joints of older people.

The Western system of medicine is based on the attempt to understand the human body by means of science and then to apply this knowledge to the alleviation—or, better, prevention—of the disorders that physicians are called upon to treat. Thus, deficiency diseases are diagnosed and then treated by replacement therapy; infections are treated using antibiotics that kill the invading microorganisms; allergies are treated by desensitization; and tumors by surgery to remove the tissues whose growth has gotten out of hand. Degenerative processes cannot be completely halted, but some of their effects can be relieved, by the replacement of worn-out joints and blood vessels, for example.

The whole apparatus of science is brought to bear on the diagnostic and therapeutic work of the modern physician. Computerized X rays, radioactive scanning techniques, and automated biochemical investigations all help in diagnosis. In treatment microsurgery, joint replacement and kidney transplants are now commonplace, and new drugs are continually being developed to help in the battle against infection, pain, and allergy.

In the large teaching hospitals and research institutes, medical research workers continue the search for new understandings and methods to help physicians treat the sick. Modern electron microscopes allow researchers to visualize particles and structures within cells, to analyze their contents, and to identify even single elements such as pollutants from the environment. Scanning methods and multiple trace recordings provide new insights into the workings of the brain. Transplant surgery of the heart is now emerging from the experimental stage.

The future

The future of mankind is as unanswerable a question as the one with which we began, but some problems face us still and our future depends on their solution. The world's population and the world's food supply are not always in balance, and distribution problems lead to the scandals of starvation and waste still coexisting on this planet. Space for living is not always wisely used, and squalor and overcrowding in towns and lack of services in rural areas still exist widely in the world. Our social systems do not always produce contentment or allow for the aspirations of the people, and our technology does not always respect the environment in which we have to live. But perhaps most important of all is that on our shrinking world we must achieve a cultural and social understanding between peoples so that conflicts among races, religions, and nations will fade and die forever.

Perhaps only through a realization of the unity of humankind, through the study of the human animal, can this respect for each other be made a reality.

Man has progressed from merely sheltering in caves to making weatherproof dwellings and building cities, so that people can now live almost anywhere on earth. Combined with a detailed knowledge of the workings of the human body and medical science based on it, this technology has effectively accelerated human development in terms of adaptability, and, properly used, should ensure continued survival.

Body systems

The human body is made up of over 10 million million cells. Most are smaller than a pinpoint, yet each is a living entity, receiving nourishment from, and ejecting waste into, the fluid in which the cell is bathed. Hundreds of millions of cells die every minute, but many millions more are being born as cells divide and multiply.

Under a low-powered microscope, a typical cell may look like a blob of jelly. Higher magnification reveals that it includes some strange and complex structures. Between them, these support and repair the cell and help it reproduce.

Most cells contain a clearly demarcated control center called a nucleus, which is embedded in the jellylike cytoplasm that makes up most of the rest of the cell. The major constituent of the nucleus is the complex of protein and DNA called chromatin. When a cell divides, chromatin forms into threadlike chromosomes, each of which contains genes, the hereditary factors determining the characteristics of the new cells produced by cell division. The nucleus also includes at least one nucleolus—a granular unit rich in ribonucleic acid (RNA) that helps to manufacture protein molecules according to "instructions" given by the DNA. The nuclear envelope around the nucleus and its nucleoli is a thin membrane serving as a sieve that regulates the flow of nutrients and wastes both in and out of the nucleus.

Extending from the nuclear membrane through the cytoplasm are paired membranes pleated like a half-closed concertina and called the endoplasmic reticulum. These membranes help to regulate the flow of chemicals. The outside surfaces of the endoplasmic reticulum in many cells are covered with tiny granular structures called ribosomes, where ribonucleic acid builds amino acids into protein, both for the cell itself and also for other uses.

Cytoplasm also contains a variety of tiny specialized structures, including Golgi bodies, mitochondria, lysosomes, and centrioles. Golgi bodies consist of groups of flattened parallel sacs derived from the endoplasmic reticulum. Their function seems to be to take in newly made protein and add carbohydrate to produce mucoprotein (the main constituent of mucus). Lysosomes are sacs containing enzymes that digest large molecules so that the products can be oxidized. Mitochondria resemble minute hollow sausages (some cells have thousands of them). These are the power plants of the cell, for here its respiration occurs, and its energy is stored as a chemical compound, adenosine triphosphate (ATP). Centrioles appear like cylindrical bundles of tiny rods or fibrils. They play a part in cell division.

Cytoplasm also contains many other structures, some with functions yet to be discovered.

The whole cell is surrounded by a plasma membrane made up of fat molecules sandwiched between two protein layers. Small molecules pass in and out of this cell wall by diffusion; larger molecules, such as those of glucose, may be brought inside by specialized receptor molecules that lie within the membrane.

The human body is a complex combination of systems—circulatory, lymphatic, digestive, urinary, nervous, endocrine, and reproductive—supported by the skeleton and musculature, which also give the body its shape. The whole body is enclosed within skin.

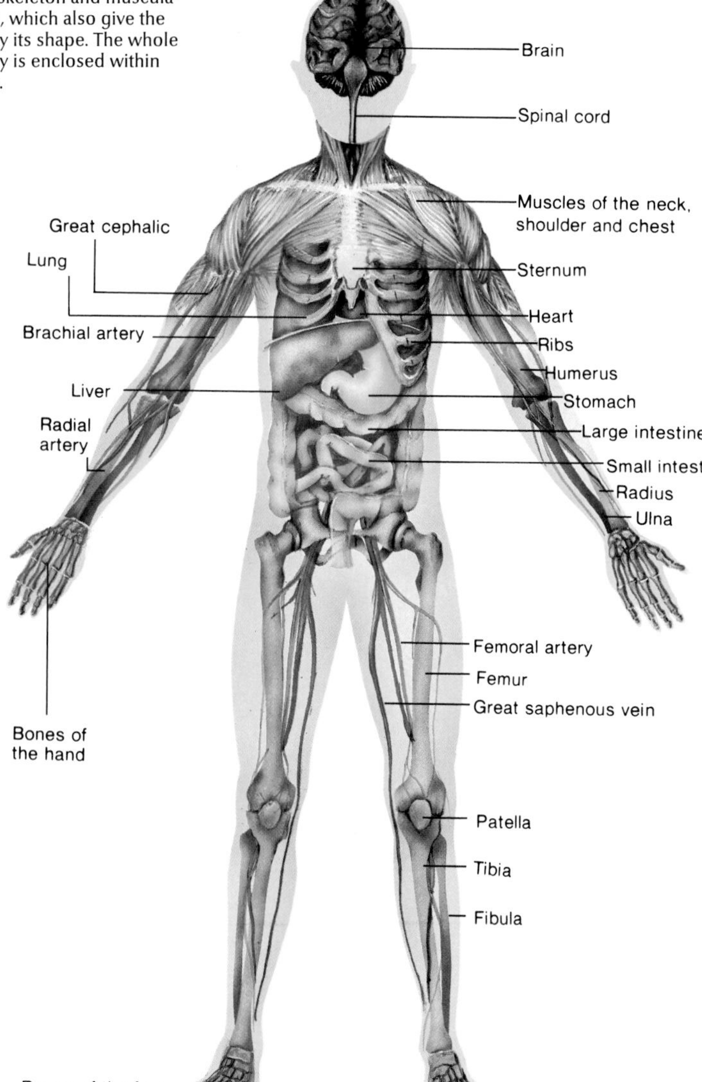

Tissues and organs

By no means are all cells identical. Their form reflects their function, and cells may be specialized in many ways. For instance, neurons (nerve cells) act like minute cables, conveying messages. Long, slim muscle cells contract. And cells lining much of the respiratory system have projecting whiplike threads that help to move mucus.

Similar cells performing a similar task form a mass of tissue. Examples are muscular tissue;

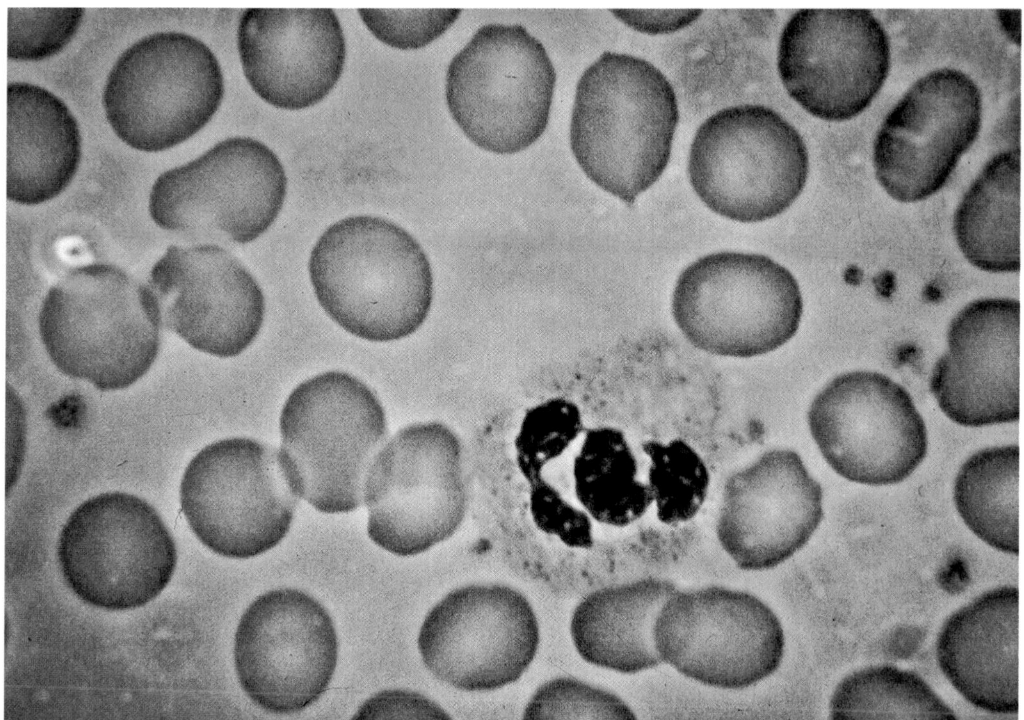

Cells occur in many forms, which reflect their function. Blood cells, for example, include erythrocytes—atypical cells without nuclei (here shown as the globules)—and more typical leukocytes, in which the nucleus is large and lobular (the darker, more fragmented object).

A typical cell contains many microscopic structures within its cytoplasm and nucleus. Most are so small that they can only be observed with the aid of an electron microscope.

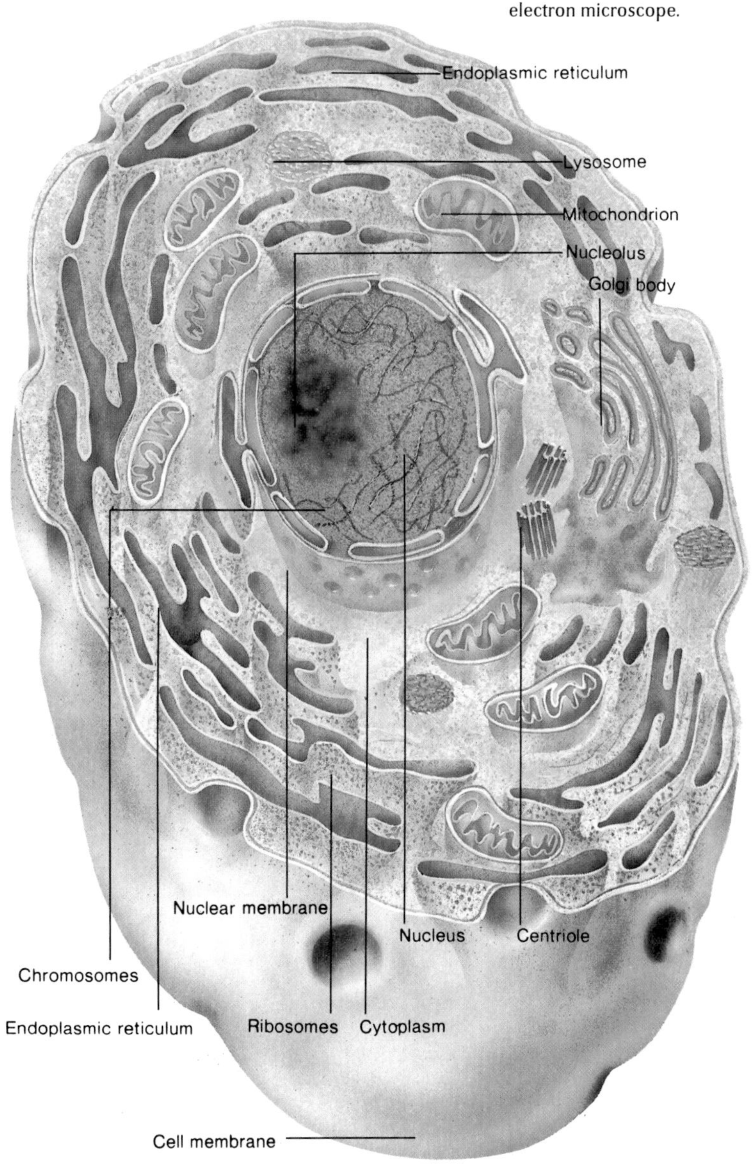

nerve tissue in the brain; the epithelial tissue of the skin and of internal body linings; connective tissue, which serves to support or pack other types of tissue or body organs (themselves made of specialized tissues); and skeletal tissue, which supplies the body's framework.

Different tissues grouped together for a common purpose form an organ, such as the stomach, heart, or lung. Cooperating groups of organs, in turn, build up body systems.

Body systems

The human body is built up of nearly a dozen major interrelated systems, each designed for a special function. The skeleton provides a strong framework. Muscles are the engines of the body. Bones (with tendons, ligaments, and fibrous sheaths linking joints and muscles) provide the system for translating muscular contractions into bodily movements. The fuel and oxygen that keep muscles working travel through thousands of miles of tubing in the circulatory system, which in turn depends upon the respiratory system to supply the blood with oxygen, and the digestive system, where food is broken down into nutrients that can be used as fuel. The urinary system gets rid of processed body wastes. The endocrine system and the nervous system control bodily activities. And the senses, extensions of the nervous system, keep us aware of our surroundings. All these interlocking systems are contained neatly by the skin.

Though many body systems parallel systems in a complex machine, the body is no ordinary mechanism. Its lymphatic and circulatory systems can prevent or minimize damage and replace worn components. The reproductive system enables human beings to reproduce themselves. And no machine has yet learned how to think.

The skeleton is the framework around which the body is built.

The skeleton

The human skeleton comprises more than 200 strong, bony rods, blocks and plates buffered by cartilage and linked by joints. Between them, different bones provide internal scaffolding, muscle-operated levers, and shields protecting vital organs. Bones also contain marrow, which manufactures blood. Furthermore, despite a popular misconception, bone is a living substance and, like the brain, needs nourishment.

Bone types and structures

Some anatomists classify bone into four types: long, short, flat, and irregular. Long bones form the levers of the limbs. Short bones, as in the wrist and ankle, provide strong, compact structures. Flat bones, such as those of the skull and shoulder blades, protect other structures or provide broad surfaces for muscle anchorage. Irregular bones, such as the bones of the spine, are those too peculiarly shaped to be grouped with any of the rest.

There are two main types of bony tissue. The hard, solid, heavy walls are made of dense tissue called compact bone. Inside is a mesh of spongy, or cancellous, bone. The two combined give bones their strength and relative lightness. Bone's hardness comes from layers of crystals of compounds of calcium, phosphorus, and other elements. Bone's resilience depends upon pliable threads of the fibrous protein collagen, which has high tensile strength and forms a network within which the hard crystals are laid down. Strength, hardness, and limited flexibility combine to help bone resist forces that would otherwise crush or bend it.

If you cut through a typical long bone you find first a thin covering of tough tissue, the periosteum. Then comes the hard compact bone built up of so-called Haversian systems: concentric rings with central canals carrying the blood vessels that supply oxygen and nutrients to the bone. Beyond the compact bone, a network of spongy bone occupies the bone's interior and its bulging ends. The inside of the shaft and spaces between the "struts" of spongy bone, however, are filled with pulpy marrow, of connective tissue, blood vessels, and red blood cells. As long bones mature, fatty yellow marrow takes the place of red.

The ends of long bones are covered with cartilage, a dense, flexible connective tissue that is a precursor of bone in children and serves to protect bones from friction against other bones and from damage from jarring within the joints.

Bones link together to form the skeleton, which is symmetrical about a vertical, central plane. The illustration shows the skeleton seen from the front on one side, and from the back on the other. Bones in the center of the body have been shown cut in half.

Axial skeleton

The axial skeleton of skull, vertebrae, and ribs provides the body's structural core, supporting the appendicular skeleton of limb bones and providing the frame for the internal organs.

The skull's 22 bones include 8 interlocking cranial bones, forming a dome that holds and shields the brain, and 14 facial bones, forming the basis of the face and jaws: a rigid maxilla (upper jaw) and hinged mandible (lower jaw). Air-filled cavities, called sinuses, lighten certain facial bones, and bony basins support and protect the eyes. The nasal cavity and mouth provide openings for the respiratory and digestive systems. The skull rests on the topmost of the 33 or so short, strong irregular bones called vertebrae. (Their numbers vary slightly in some individuals.) These and the fibrous disks between them form the spine. This flexible, weight-bearing column with a double bend supports the upper body's weight; bony arches at the backs of vertebrae sheathe the fragile spinal cord. From top to bottom, the spine's five sets of vertebrae comprise typically: 7 cervical (neck) vertebrae; 12 thoracic vertebrae at the back of the chest; 5 lumbar (lower back) vertebrae; 5 fused vertebrae forming the sacrum; and the 4 fused vertebrae of the coccyx, a vestigial tail.

The ribcage consists of 12 pairs of flat, curved bones projecting forward from the thoracic vertebrae. Pairs 1-7, the true ribs, meet the sternum, or breastbone, at the front of the chest. Pairs 11-12, the floating ribs, stop short. Ribs and breastbone protect the heart and lungs inside the chest cavity and work with the diaphragm during breathing.

Appendicular skeleton

Limb bones are anchored to the axial skeleton by frameworks known as girdles. The pectoral or shoulder girdle has two clavicles (collarbones), which help muscles hold the shoulders back, and two scapulae (shoulder blades), which lie at the back of the chest. A humerus (upper arm bone) fits into a socket in each scapula. Each forearm has two bones (radius and ulna) that are articulated so they can twist, allowing hand rotation. Each hand has 27 bones comprising carpals (wrist bones), metacarpals (palm bones), and phalanges (fingers). The pelvic or hip girdle has two sets of three bones (ilium, ischium, and pubis) that flank and join the sacrum and, with it, form a bony, pelvic basin. This pelvis supports and protects internal organs, and each side of it has an acetabulum, a cup-shaped cavity, serving as a socket for a femur (thighbone). Below the femur are two other leg bones, the tibia (shinbone) and fibula. The tarsals, metatarsals, and phalanges form the bones of the back of the foot, the forefoot, and the toes, respectively.

Joints, ligaments, and tendons

Bones can transmit body weight and help muscles move limbs and other parts of the body only because they are linked at joints—that is, where bone meets bone. Different types of joints serve different purposes. At fibrous joints, like those between the cranial bones, fibrous tissue knits bones almost rigidly together. At cartilaginous joints, like those between the vertebrae, however, springy cartilage buffers bone ends, and between these lies a fibrocartilage pad. Much greater movement occurs at synovial, or movable, joints, such as those of the ankle, elbow, and shoulder. Some are gliding joints, others are pivot, hinge, or ball-and-socket joints. Many are superbly designed to combat friction and the stress induced by sudden jolting. In each synovial joint, opposing bone ends are capped by cartilage and separated by a cavity walled by ligaments—bands of flexible tissue that give the joint stability and strength. The inner lining of the joint capsule surrounding the cavity consists of smooth, slippery synovial membrane producing syrupy synovial fluid that lubricates joint surfaces. Active movement of many joints would be impossible without tendons—the strong, tough, plaited fibers forming the cords that attach bone or cartilage to muscle.

Teeth and nails

Tooth enamel resembles bone in that it is made of mineral crystals in a mesh of protein, but enamel has a higher mineral content than bone and so is even harder. Tooth enamel, however, is not part of the skeleton: with the substance of toenails and fingernails, enamel forms the nearest human equivalent to an insect's exoskeleton.

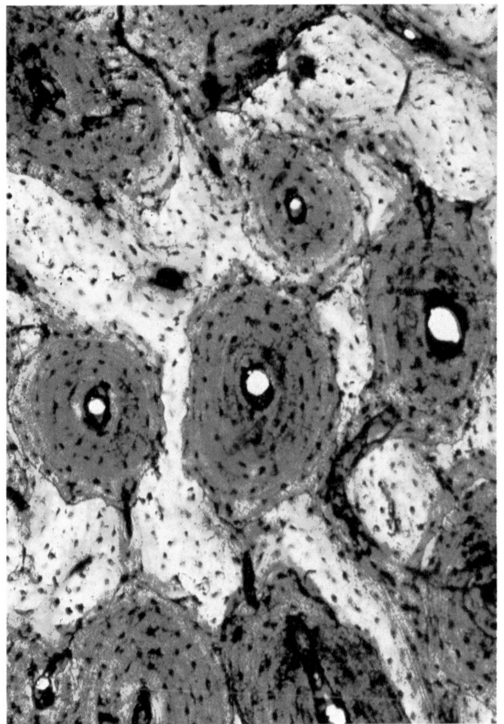

Compact bone, which forms the outer part of bones and gives them their strength, is made up of many columns—shown here in cross-section—of cells called osteoblasts, arranged concentrically around central Haversian canals.

The hip joint consists of a moving bone, the femur, attached to a group of fixed bones, known collectively as the pelvic girdle. Ligaments and muscles hold the femur in place and make it move. The head of the femur and the socket (acetabulum) into which it fits are lined with cartilage. Synovial fluid, produced by the enveloping synovial membrane, allows these two surfaces to move against each other without friction. The femur is a typical long bone, with a thick layer of compact bone around its shaft, and with spongy bone inside. The latter allows bones to be both strong and relatively light; it also contains a rich supply of blood vessels and the blood-forming tissue called marrow (not shown). The shafts of long bones contain yellow marrow, which is also a store of fat cells. Red marrow is found in the head of the femur, as well as in the flat bones of the body—among them, the bones of the pelvic girdle.

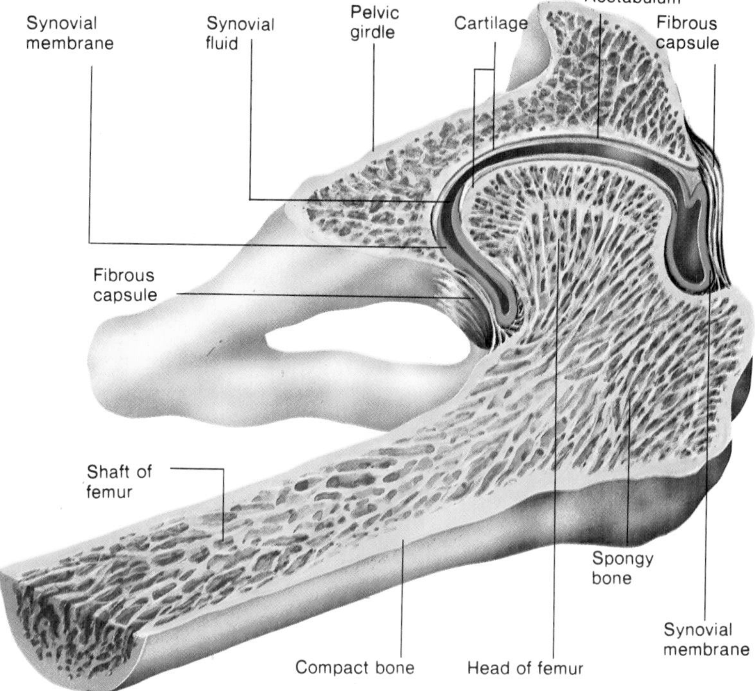

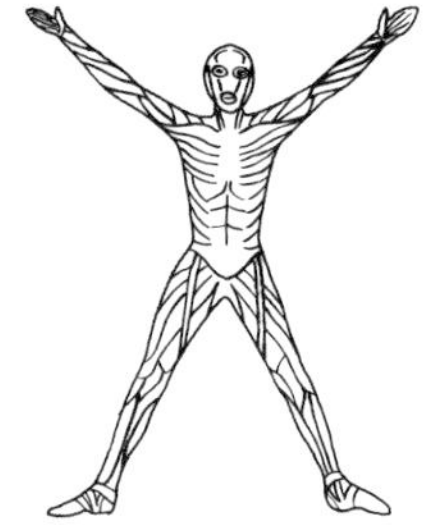

Muscles hold and move the skeleton and give the body its shape.

Muscles

Muscle makes up nearly half the body weight of an adult. More than 600 muscles cover the skeleton and give the body bulk and form. But their main task is to move limbs, push food through the gut, make the heart beat, and control blood flow around the body.

A typical skeletal or voluntary muscle comprises thousands or millions of fibers whose coordinated contractions cause the whole muscle to contract. The energy for muscular contraction comes from chemical reactions involving fuel and oxygen brought to the muscles through a rich supply of blood vessels. Besides mechanical energy, muscle action produces heat and chemical wastes, which leave through capillaries leading to veins that carry spent blood from the muscle.

There are three main types of muscle: skeletal, smooth, and cardiac.

Muscles involved with movement are arranged symmetrically—like the bones to which they are attached—about a vertical, central plane. In addition to the surface muscles shown, there are many "deep" muscles, which play equally important roles.

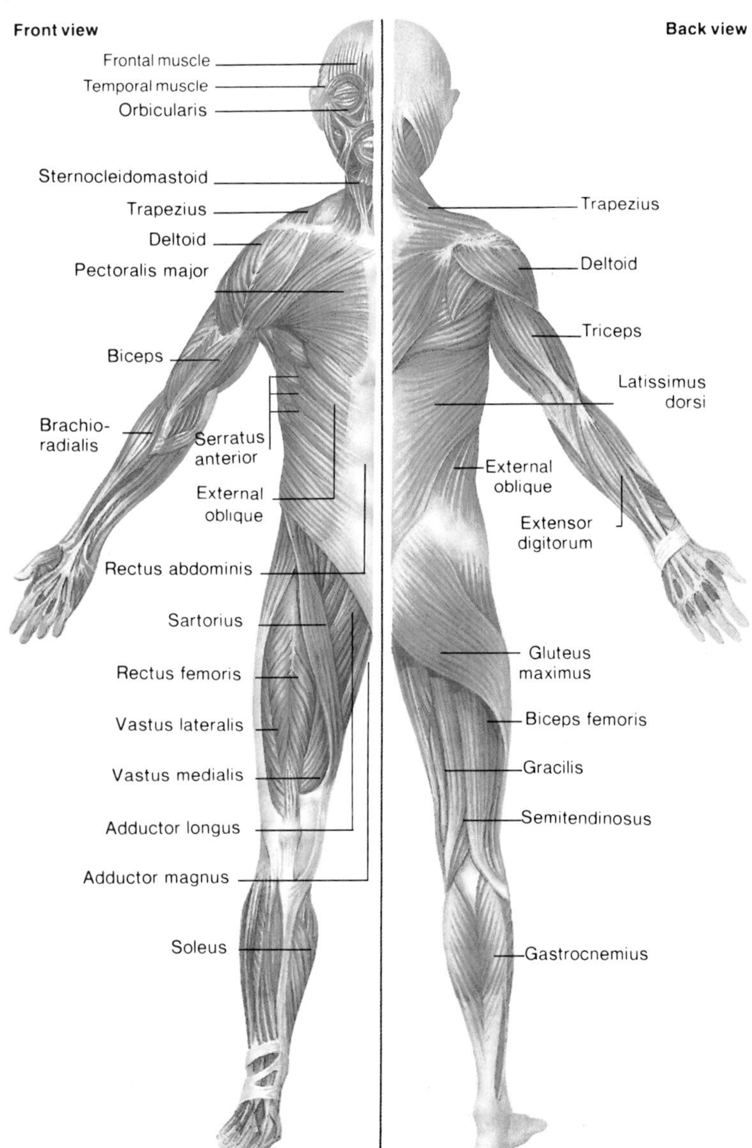

Skeletal muscle

Skeletal muscles are joined to bones and make them move. Groups of skeletal muscles operate the arms, legs, torso, neck, and face. They range in size from tiny muscles rotating the eye to the large, powerful thigh muscles. Each skeletal muscle consists of long, slim muscle fibers from less than .25 inch (a few millimeters) to more than 1 inch long, in bundles bound together by connective tissue. Each fiber has a number of nuclei. Fiber bundles are organized according to the tasks they must perform. Thus, parallel bundles capable of strong contractions form the muscle felt at the side of the neck. And the deltoid muscle—the topmost muscle on the outside of the arm—has short fiber bundles arranged like the barbs of a feather that produce limited but powerful movements.

The basic units of each fiber are thick, dark filaments and thin pale ones. Seen under the microscope, these give skeletal muscle a striped appearance so that it is also called striped or striated muscle. Because we can usually move skeletal muscles at will, they are also known as voluntary muscles, although they are capable of involuntary reflex movements, too, as when a hand jerks away from a source of heat.

Skeletal muscle contracts when it is stimulated by an electrochemical signal from the central nervous system. This acts on nerve endings linked to the muscle fibers. How much a whole muscle contracts depends on how many of its fibers have been activated.

In order to work, a typical skeletal muscle needs to have both its ends connected to the skeleton—either directly or via tendons or fibrous sheets called aponeuroses. The fixed muscle end, closest to the body's center, is called the origin. The other end—called the insertion—is attached to the bone that actually moves.

Many muscles have names that indicate their function. For instance, flexors bend joints, extensors straighten them. Abductors pull a part of the body away from its central axis, adductors do the opposite. The to-and-fro action of a limb or jaw or eyeball depends upon pairs of muscles acting in opposition to each other. Muscles have to work in opposing pairs because each muscle acts in just one direction. It can pull or squeeze, but then simply relaxes, for muscles cannot push.

Skeletal muscles can be grouped in four main categories according to their general function: prime movers contract to cause active movement; antagonists act in opposition to prime movers; fixation muscles hold steady such parts as the shoulder blade to provide a base for movements involving other muscles; and synergists combine with prime movers to keep joints still.

Coordinated signals from the central nervous system ensure that opposing muscles do not contract simultaneously to cancel out one another. So when the triceps muscle of the upper arm contracts to straighten the arm, the opposing biceps muscle relaxes. The triceps is then acting as a prime mover and the biceps as the antagonist. But when the elbow is bent, the biceps contracts, the triceps relaxes, and their roles are reversed.

Powerful skeletal muscles moving long bones make these act as levers so that a short

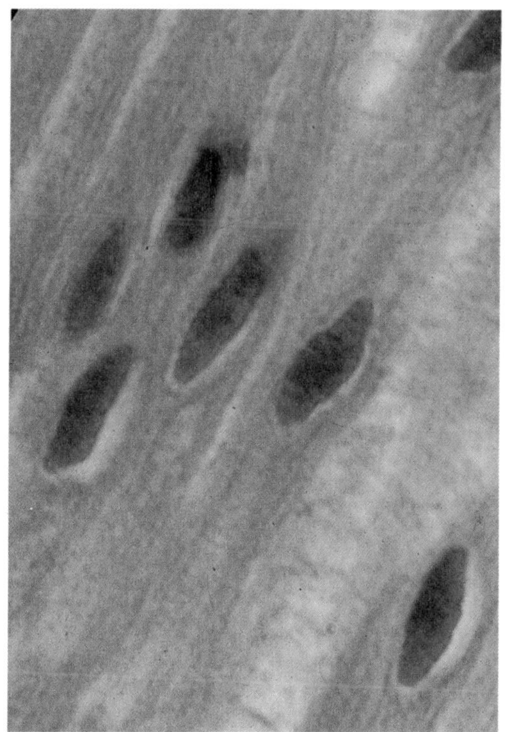

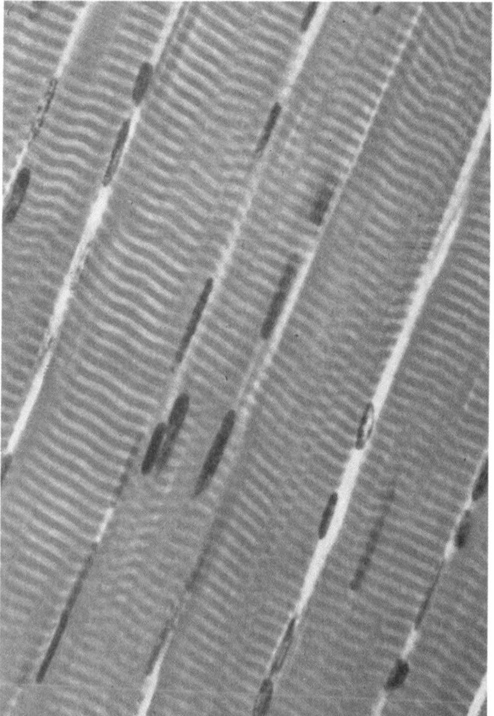

Smooth muscle *(far left)*—which consists of elongated cells, each with its own nucleus—is found in tissues such as the stomach and the intestines.

Skeletal muscles *(left)*, also called striped or voluntary muscles, are controlled directly by the motor nerves of the central nervous system, and are chiefly concerned with movement. They consist of long, thin, striped fibers, each with several nuclei.

muscle movement produces a large limb movement. For example, a muscle contraction of less than 3 inches (8 centimeters) moves the fingers through an arc that is 12 times greater, although the force involved is correspondingly diminished.

Smooth muscle

Smooth muscle occurs in the digestive tract, urinary tract, blood vessels, bronchial tree, and other internal structures. Unlike skeletal muscle, a fiber of smooth muscle lacks stripes and has one nucleus instead of many nuclei. Also, it contracts more slowly than a skeletal muscle fiber, tends to contract rhythmically, and is not under direct control of the brain. By contracting or relaxing, smooth muscle narrows or enlarges the diameter of blood vessels to control the blood flow passing through. Similarly, alternate contraction and relaxation of smooth muscle forming stomach and intestine walls drives food through the gut in the action called peristalsis. The rate at which smooth muscle contracts depends on hormones and the autonomic nervous system. Because we cannot normally control its action, smooth muscle is also called involuntary muscle.

Cardiac muscle

Cardiac muscle is striped like skeletal muscle, but contracts automatically like smooth muscle. Its fibers surround the ventricles—the heart's main pumping chambers—and contract rhythmically at intervals regulated by the sinoatrial node, the "pacemaker," and by the autonomic nervous system.

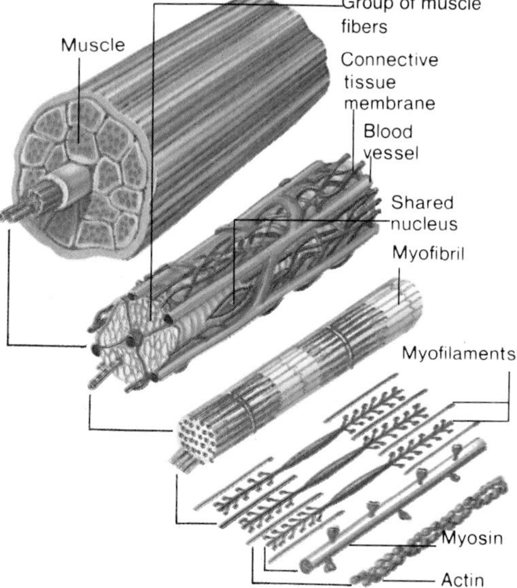

A striped muscle consists of muscle fibers with shared nuclei, enclosed in a connective tissue membrane through which the fibers receive their blood and nerve supply. The fibers are composed of myofibrils, which contract or relax as filaments of myosin and actin that they contain move against each other.

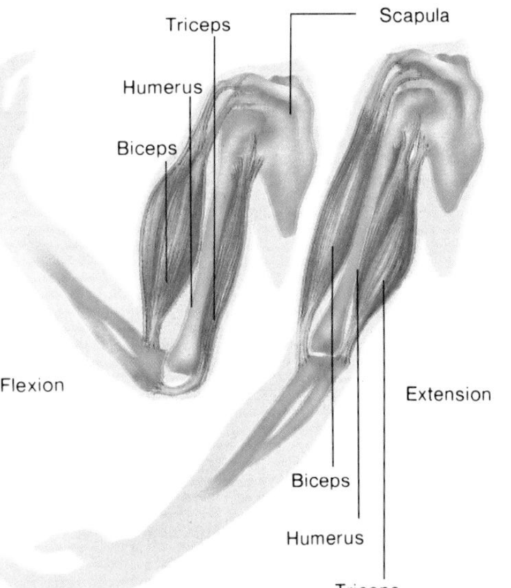

Muscles can only contract or relax, which enables them to pull or to be stretched. They cannot push. So to move bones at a joint, there must be opposing muscles or sets of muscles. In the arm, the biceps bends the elbow joint and is called the flexor. The triceps straightens the joint and is called the extensor.

The heart and circulation

The heart and the blood circulation are the major elements of the body's internal transportation system.

The heart and the blood vessels provide the body with a pump and a closed system of about 100,000 miles (160,000 kilometers) of tubing through which some 5 quarts (4.7 liters) of blood circulate continuously. In this way, blood reaches every living tissue, bringing oxygen and nutrients from lungs and digestive tract, respectively, and removing wastes to be disposed of by the lungs and kidneys.

The heart

Blood vessels extend to all areas of the body. Oxygenated blood is pumped through arteries to microscopic capillaries, where oxygen is released to the tissues. Veins return deoxygenated blood to the heart, where it is pumped to the lungs for reoxygenation.

The heart is a fist-sized bag of tough-walled cardiac muscle protectively encased by the thin, tough tissue of the pericardium, and shaped roughly like a pear. It lies in the chest cavity, slightly to the left of center.

The heart is an electrically-activated pump, contracting rhythmically to keep blood coursing through the arteries and veins. More precisely, it works as two connected pumps, separated by a muscular wall, the septum. Each side contains an upper and lower chamber called the atrium (or auricle) and the ventricle, respectively. The two thin-walled atria receive blood from the veins, and the two thick-walled ventricles pump this blood away through arteries. One-way valves control this blood flow through the heart.

The heart's pump action works in the following sequence. Oxygenated blood from the lungs fills the left atrium. This contracts, driving blood past the mitral valve into the left ventricle. Then this contracts, and the blood pressure inside it shuts the mitral valve, forcing blood out through the aortic valve (also called the semilunar valve) to that huge artery, the aorta, which supplies oxygenated blood to all parts of the body. Meanwhile, deoxygenated blood from body tissues fills the right atrium. It contracts, driving blood past the tricuspid valve into the right ventricle, which then contracts. The resulting pressure shuts the tricuspid valve and forces blood out via the pulmonary artery to the lungs, where it is reoxygenated.

Both valves of the heart relax and fill simultaneously, then contract and empty a fraction

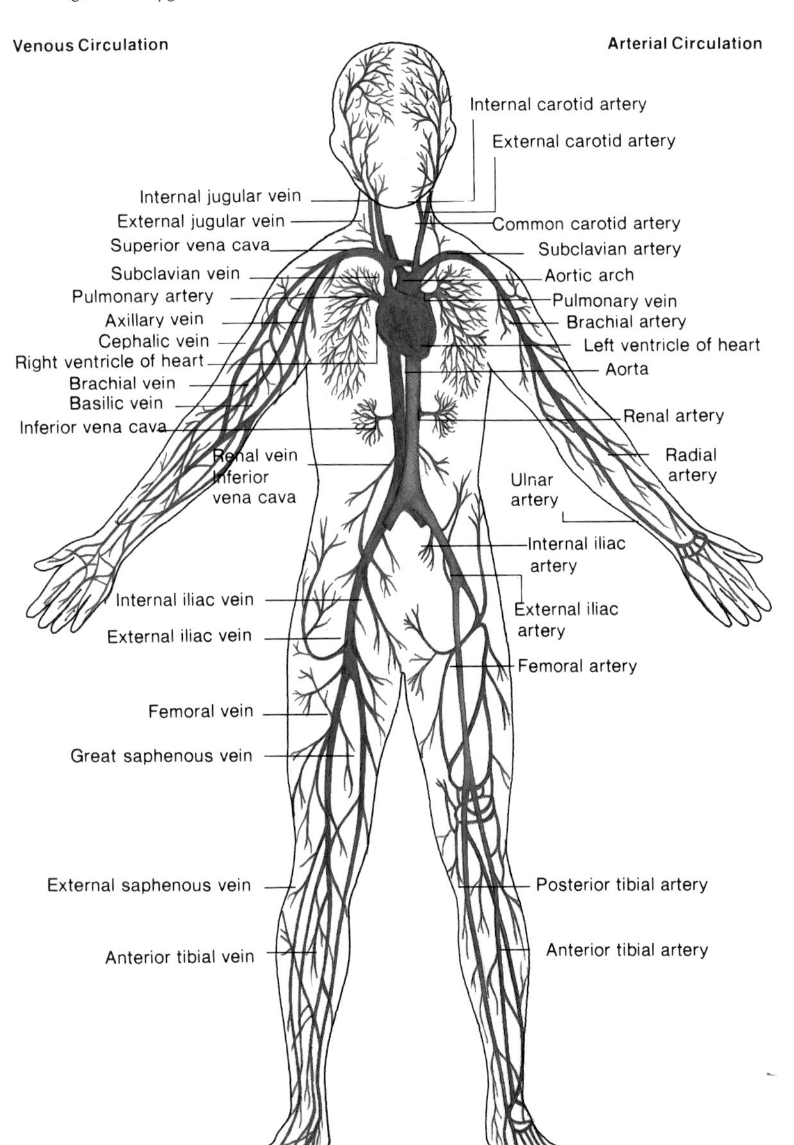

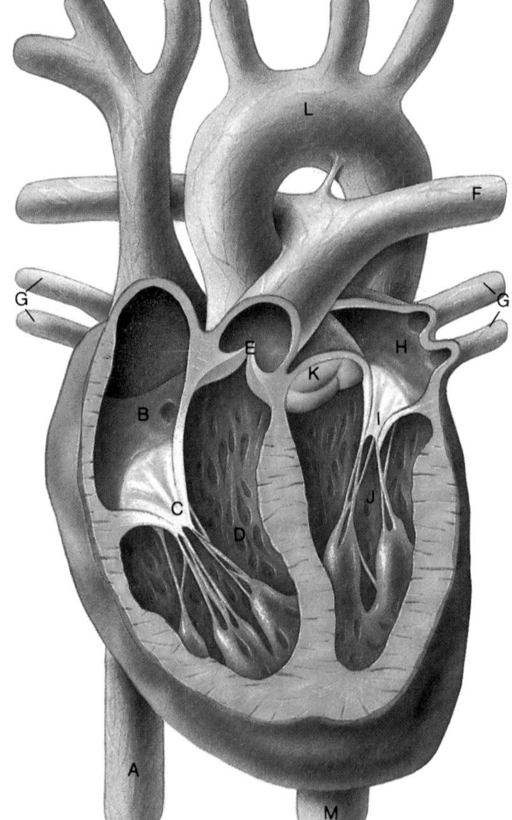

The heart accepts blood from the vena cava (A) into the right atrium (B), which pushes blood through the tricuspid valve (C) into the right ventricle (D). From here, it is forced through the pulmonary valve (E) to the pulmonary arteries (F) and the lungs. Blood returns through the pulmonary veins (G) into the left atrium (H), which pushes it past the mitral valve (I) into the left ventricle (J). This pumps blood through the aortic valve (K) into the aortic arch (L) and aorta (M).

of a second later. The brief phase of ventricular relaxation is called diastole, the contracting phase, systole. Each systole can be felt as a heartbeat. Each normal beat expels one-third of a pint (17 centiliters) of blood. In one day, an adult's heart may pump out altogether 3,475 gallons (13,637 liters). The heart beats about 70 times a minute in resting individuals, but the rate can double if activity demands a greatly increased oxygen supply.

Although cardiac muscle tends to contract rhythmically, coordination comes from the sinoatrial node (also known as the pacemaker), an area of special tissue in the wall of the right atrium. Impulses from this node control the rate of contraction of the heart muscles. The actual impulse for cardiac contraction is transferred from the atria to the ventricles by the atrioventricular node, located between the atria and ventricles.

Arteries and veins

Blood pumped out from the heart travels under pressure through large, strong-walled arteries. The aorta, the largest artery, lies deep inside the body, but you can feel blood pulsing through other arteries—such as the radial artery in the wrist and the carotid artery in the neck—as their elastic walls expand with each heartbeat.

Branching off from the main arteries are smaller arteries, which in turn branch into minute arterioles, about a tenth of a millimeter or less in diameter. These have a simpler structure than arteries, but have some smooth muscle and elastic tissue similar to the internal elastic lamina of the larger vessels. Arterioles expand or contract, allowing more or less blood to pass as the autonomic nervous system dictates changes in the tissues' need for blood.

Arterioles themselves give rise to even smaller tubes—capillaries, with walls just one cell thick. These microscopic tubules infiltrate all parts of the body, bringing blood to every living tissue.

When the tissues have absorbed oxygen and nutrients from the blood, and have given up waste products and carbon dioxide to it, blood begins its return journey to the heart. First it passes through venules—tubules made of endothelium with muscle fiber and connective tissue. These lead on to the larger, stronger veins. By now, the pressure pushing blood along is very weak, so many of the larger veins have valves to combat the effects of gravity. In the legs, contracting calf muscles provide extra pumps that squeeze the veins, thus driving blood on up toward the heart.

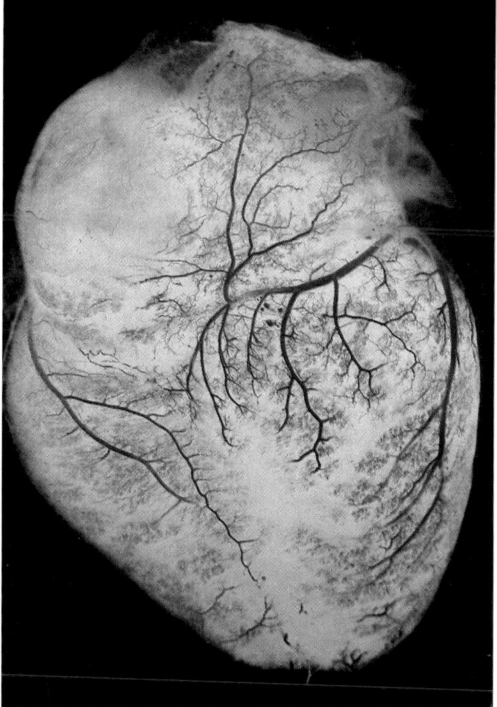

An X ray of the heart shows the coronary blood supply, which nourishes the muscles of the heart and without which the heart will cease to work.

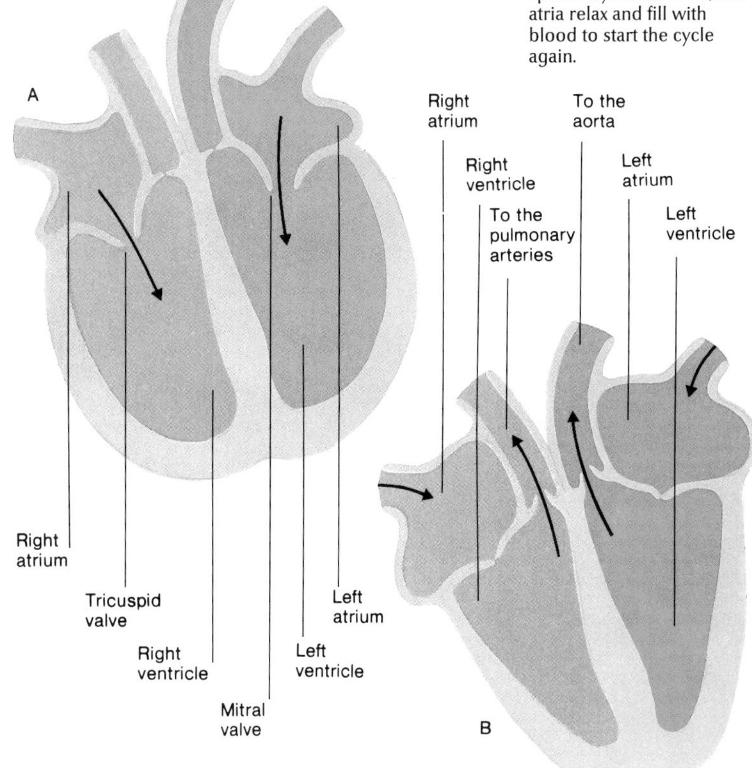

The heart is a strong muscular pump with four chambers: right atrium, right ventricle, left atrium, and left ventricle. The atria contract (A) to push blood into the ventricles as the latter relax. Then the right and left ventricles contract (B) to pump blood into the pulmonary arteries and the aorta, respectively. Meanwhile, the atria relax and fill with blood to start the cycle again.

Fact entries

Herophilus of Chalcedon (flourished about 300 B.C.), Greek medical teacher who worked at Alexandria in Egypt and was the first to distinguish clearly between arteries and veins. He also studied the nervous system and identified the nerve trunks as either sensory or motor branches.

Harvey, William (1578-1657), English physician who discovered the principles of circulation of the blood. Published in 1628, *An Anatomical Treatise on the Motion of the Heart and Blood in Animals* abolished old beliefs that had long hindered the development of physiology.

Malpighi, Marcello (1628-1694), Italian anatomist who discovered that capillaries take blood from the arteries to veins. He first saw them when he used a simple microscope to study blood vessels in a frog's lung. For most of his life he lived and worked in Bologna.

Barnard, Christiaan (1922-), South African surgeon who performed the first heart transplant operation on a human being. In 1967, he gave 55-year-old Louis Washkansky the heart of a 25-year-old woman. Such operations later became common, though Barnard did few.

Blood and lymph

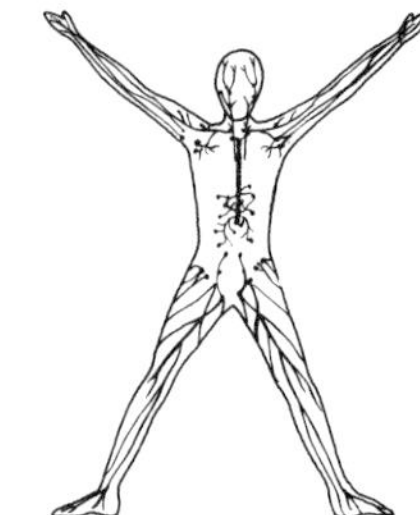

Lymphatic ducts drain body tissues, returning intracellular fluid to the circulatory system. Lymph nodes are found where ducts converge.

Coursing ceaselessly through arteries and veins, blood is vital for the life of every tissue in the body. This complex fluid contains the foods and fuel that provide energy and the materials for repairing damaged cells and building new ones. Blood also helps demolish and remove worn-out cells, other wastes, and harmful foreign bodies. It also takes heat from the body core to the extremities. And blood brings to wounds the materials that minimize blood loss and promote healing.

A man weighing about 155 pounds (70 kilograms) contains about 1.3 gallons (5 liters) of blood; a child half his weight has only half that quantity. Most blood is manufactured in bone marrow, although some components come from the lymphatic system. The four main ingredients of blood are plasma, red cells, white cells, and platelets.

Plasma

This pale yellow fluid accounts for 55 to 65 per cent of blood by volume, and it is in this that the blood cells are suspended. Plasma is 90 per cent water and 10 per cent dissolved substances, chiefly salts and proteins. Most salts are ionized and can diffuse out from capillaries into the surrounding tissues, but the proteins are too large to escape. The resulting difference of concentration inside and outside capillaries creates osmotic pressure, which helps maintain a healthy balance between the fluid in the capillaries and in the tissues.

Important plasma proteins are albumin, globulin, and fibrinogen. Albumin (a substance also found in egg white) helps maintain blood volume and pressure. Globulin contains various antibodies—each kind combining chemically with a specific kind of foreign body such as a bacterium or virus—which help to neutralize disease-inducing germs. Fibrinogen plays a crucial part in blood clotting. Plasma deprived of clotting factors forms the watery liquid known as serum, which often oozes from a minor injury to the skin.

The lymphatic system consists of small, thin-walled vessels containing lymph. These drain into larger ducts and ultimately into the large thoracic duct that runs near the aorta and the spine.

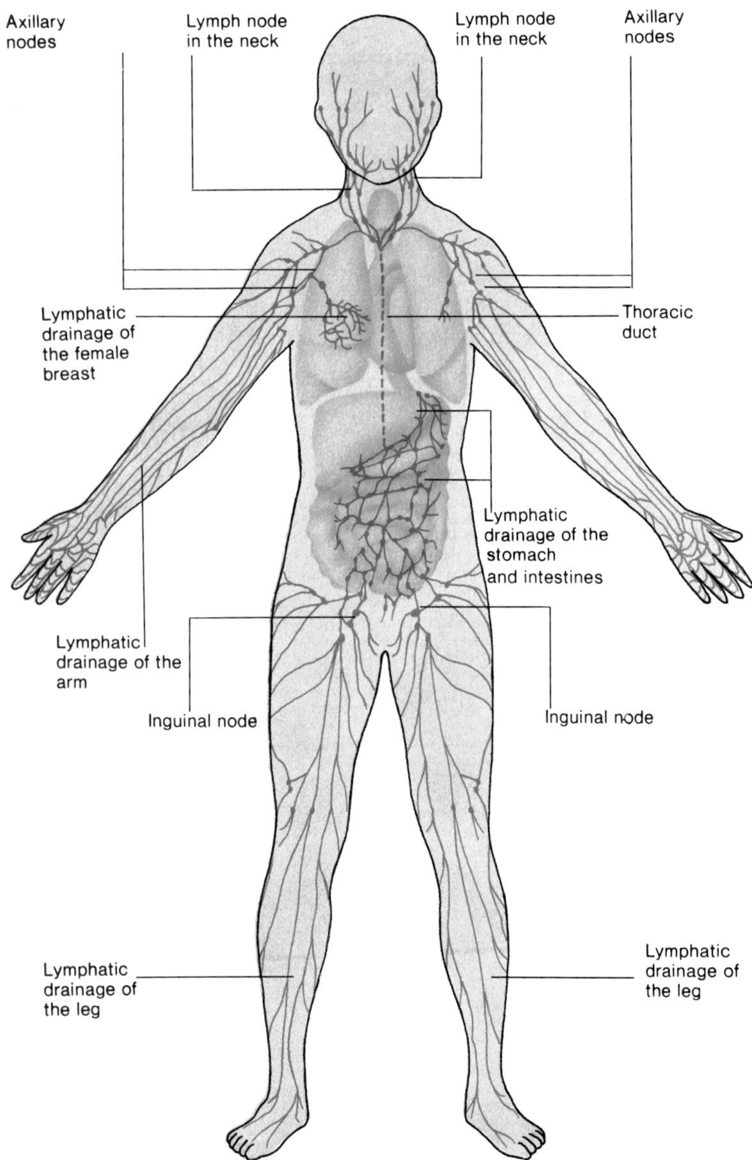

Red blood cells

These account for more than 99 per cent of the total volume of all blood cells. A mature red blood cell is a disk with concave sides, and is only 7 microns in diameter. Erythrocytes, as red cells are also known, perform the vital task of bringing oxygen from the lungs to tissues. They can do this because red cells contain the oxygen-attracting compound hemoglobin, which picks up oxygen molecules from the lungs. These oxygen molecules transform hemoglobin into oxyhemoglobin, a compound that colors the erythrocyte bright red. When erythrocytes surrender oxygen to tissues in exchange for carbon dioxide, blood becomes more purple in color, which explains the general color difference between bright red arterial blood and the duller-colored blood in veins.

Typically, a normal human body contains about 25 billion red blood cells; each microliter of blood contains from four to six million red blood cells. Bone marrow produces over 100 million every minute to make up for the millions destroyed. Each erythrocyte loses its nucleus before it leaves the marrow, then survives about 120 days before it is broken down in the spleen, liver, or blood vessels.

White blood cells

White blood cells, or leukocytes, are larger than red blood cells but far less plentiful—a mere 4,000 to 10,000 per microliter compared to 5 million red blood cells. White blood cells protect and scavenge, many of them moving actively to sites of danger. There are three main types of leukocyte: granulocytes, monocytes, and lymphocytes. These account, respectively, for 70 per cent, 10 per cent, and 20 per cent of all white blood cells. The first two come from bone marrow, the third comes from lymph glands.

Granulocytes—cells that have a granular appearance when stained and viewed under the miscroscope—include cells that swarm upon infected tissue and devour bacteria by a process called phagocytosis. Monocytes produce macrophages that settle primarily in the spleen and liver, where they engulf old red cells and

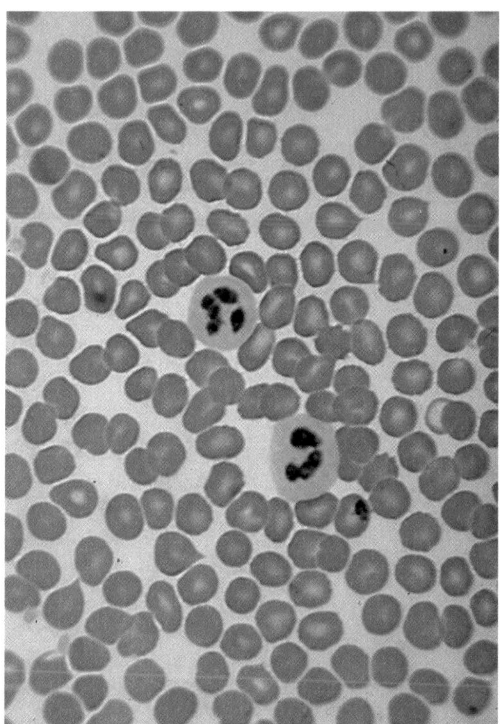

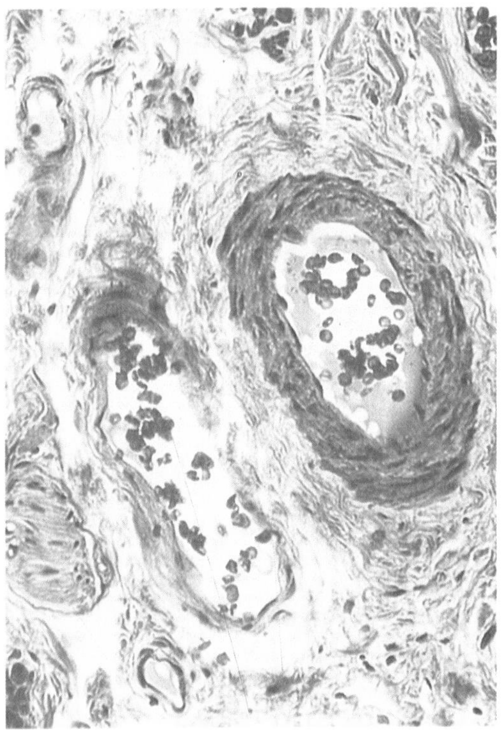

Blood consists principally of red cells in plasma. Microscopic examination of a blood sample *(far left)* also shows white cells (leukocytes) and the very small platelets.

Arteries and veins, shown in cross-section *(left)* appear quite different, although they are composed of similar tissues. Arteries are subject to greater blood pressure than veins and are much thicker, with more smooth muscle in their walls. This also enables them to control the blood flow by constricting or dilating in response to stimuli such as temperature or the presence of epinephrine in the blood.

foreign bodies. Lymphocytes are the core of the body's immune system: some kinds "remembering" specific types of foreign body and recognizing fresh invasions by them, others producing antibodies that coat these foreign bodies and make them easy prey for granulocytes and macrophages.

Platelets

These smallest blood particles, of which there are from 150,000 to 400,000 per microliter of blood, play a crucial part in clotting. They collect where an injured blood vessel is leaking blood, then stick together, thereby partly plugging the hole in the vessel wall. Platelets also react with clotting factors to convert the soluble fibrinogen in blood plasma into a mesh of fibrin threads, creating a net that traps other cells, to plug the gap completely.

Lymph and the lymphatic system

While blood circulates through arteries and veins, the blood-based fluid lymph flows through the lymphatic system.

Lymph is colorless, like plasma, but with little protein and no blood cells. Leaking from capillaries, lymph bathes the body's cells and drains into the lymphatic system, taking with it waste matter, dead cells, and bacteria. Tissues pressing on the smaller thin-walled tubes (the larger ones have one-way valves) drive lymph into two major ducts that drain ultimately into broad veins at the sides of the neck. On the way, lymph flows through lymph nodes that filter out wastes and produce bacteria-destroying lymphocytes and other defensive cells. During illness, node activity increases, producing enlarged lymph glands that can be felt in armpit, neck, and groin.

Besides the lymph nodes, the tonsils, adenoids, intestines, spleen, and the thymus gland all generate protective lymphocytes.

Composition of blood

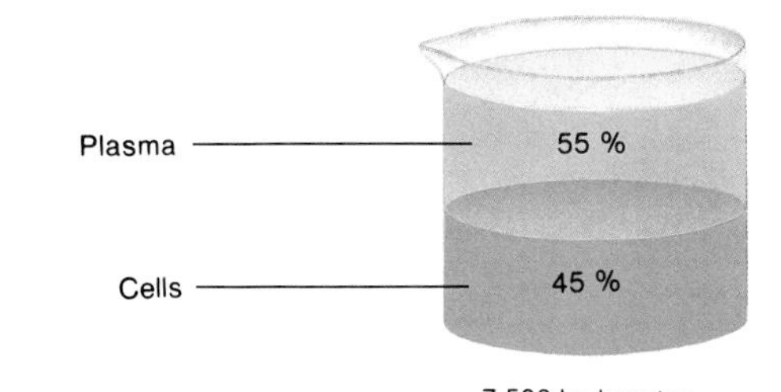

Blood contains plasma and cells. The latter constitute about 45 per cent of the total volume of blood.

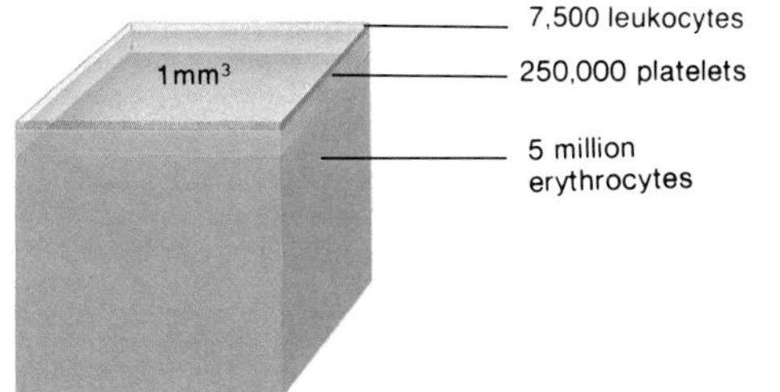

A cubic millimeter of blood contains about 5 million erythrocytes, about 7,500 white cells (leukocytes), and about 250,000 platelets.

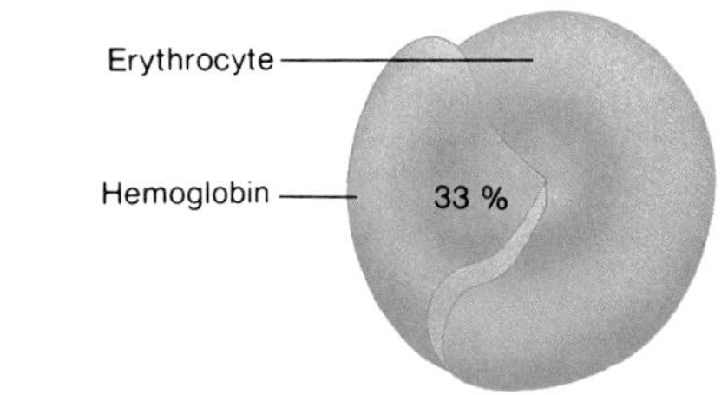

Erythrocytes are red because they contain the red pigment hemoglobin, which makes up about one-third of their weight.

Incidence of ABO blood types

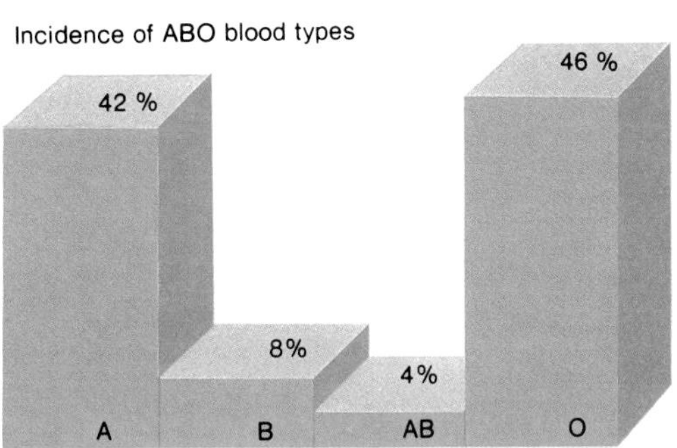

Blood types are most commonly classified according to the ABO and the Rhesus (Rh) systems. ABO classifies blood by the presence of A-proteins (A), B-proteins (B), both (AB) or neither (O). The presence or absence of the Rhesus factor is indicated by Rh+ or Rh−.

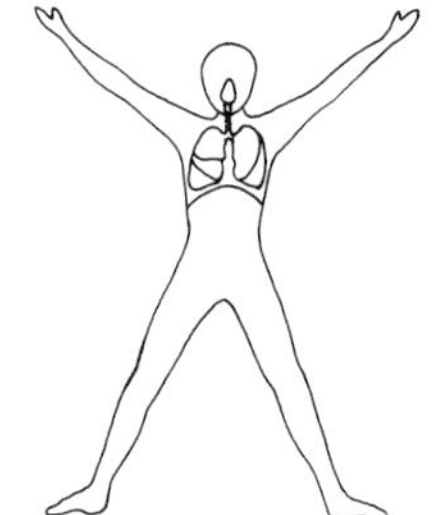

The lungs draw air into the body through the mouth and nose so that oxygen can be absorbed into the bloodstream.

Lungs and respiration

The air around us provides our body tissues with the oxygen they need for oxidizing nutrients derived from food to provide energy for the processes of living. Respiration is the process by which the body gets that oxygen and expels waste carbon dioxide. External respiration involves air flow in and out of lungs. From the lungs, blood supplies tissue cells with the oxygen they need for the energy-releasing chemical reactions collectively called internal respiration.

Parts of the respiratory system

Some tiny, primitive animals allow oxygen to reach all their cells by diffusing it in and out through openings in the body wall. A human's much larger body needs an active pump to supply oxygen to the lungs where the gas can be absorbed into the blood for transportation throughout the body. This system consists basically of two bellows (the lungs) that fill with air, then empty, as muscles make them open and close.

Seen from the outside, lungs appear as two roughly pyramidal spongy structures that almost fill the conical thoracic (chest) cavity, walled by ribs and backbone, with the diaphragm—a sheet of muscle—as the floor. The left lung is smaller than the right, to make room for the heart. The left lung is divided into two main lobes, the right into three; each lobe is subdivided into segments. Both lungs and the cavity in which they lie are lined by the pleura—a thin, smooth membrane that secretes a lubricating fluid that prevents friction between lungs and ribcage.

The lungs and passages supplying them with air form complex structures that parallel the trunk and branches of an inverted tree. This bronchial tree's internal surface provides an area for gaseous exchange more than 40 times larger than the body's surface.

The "tree trunk" is the windpipe or trachea—a wide, flexible tube stiffened by up to 20 broad bands of cartilage and roughly 4.5 inches (11 centimeters) in length. Some tracheal bands can be felt at the front of the throat. Inhaled air reaches the top of the trachea via the nasal cavity or mouth and the pharynx—all of which are lined with mucous membranes that warm the air and moisten it. From the pharynx, air passes through a slim aperture, the glottis. When swallowing, this is closed automatically by a flap (the epiglottis) that prevents food from entering the lungs. From the glottis, air flows down through the larynx (the voice box), the position of which can be identified by the tracheal cartilage called the Adam's apple, at the top of the tra-

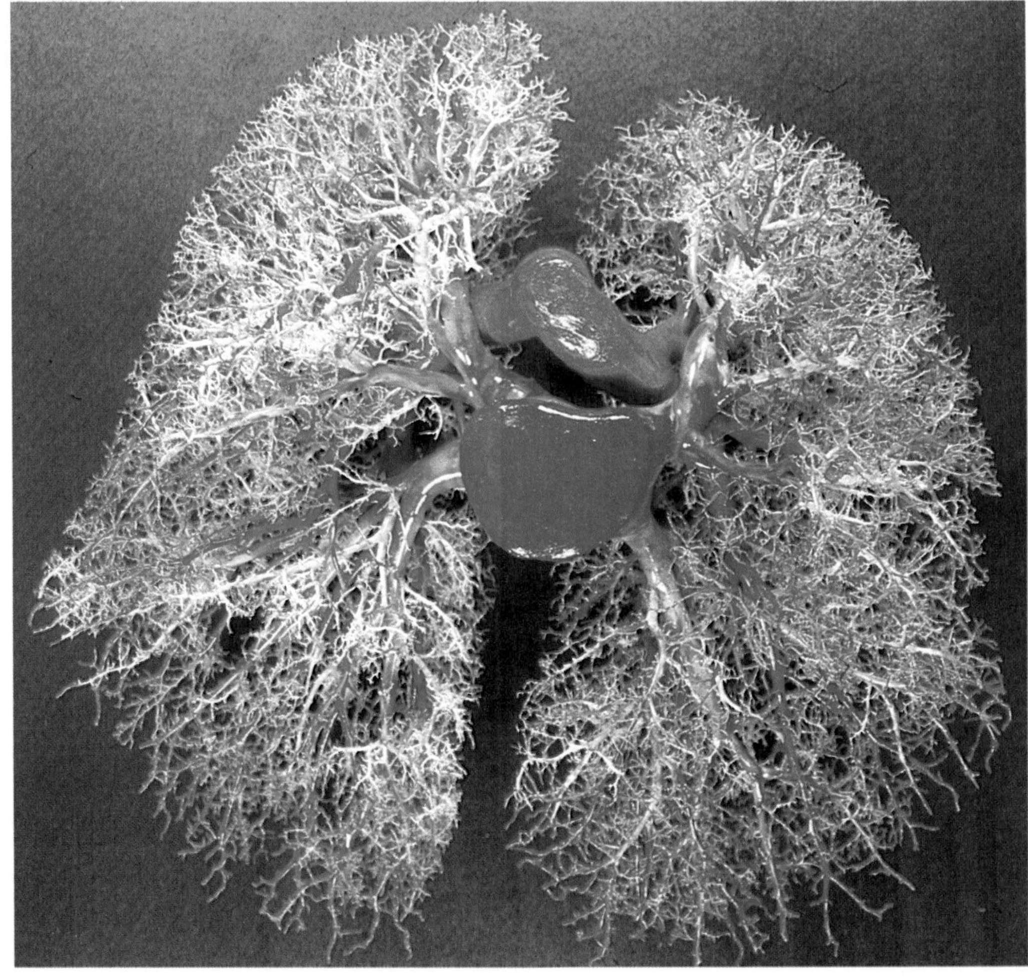

The respiratory system within the lungs—illustrated here by a model made from a resin cast—consists of a closely interlinked system of air passages, arteries, and veins. Deoxygenated blood, shown in blue, is pumped from the heart through a treelike arrangement of pulmonary arteries and arterioles until it flows through capillaries in and around the alveoli, which are the terminations of the bronchial "tree," shown in white. Oxygen is absorbed and carbon dioxide is released before the blood, now oxygenated and shown in red, returns through a similar arrangement of pulmonary veins to the heart. The model is seen from the front so the left side of the chest appears on the right. The heart lies in the left side of the chest, and to accommodate it, the two-lobed left lung is smaller than the three-lobed right lung.

chea below the chin. Changing the length and tension of the vocal cords—elastic bands of tissue stretched across the top of the larynx—changes vocal pitch.

At its lower end, the trachea forks into two hollow branches known as bronchi. Each supplies air to a different lung. In each lung, the bronchus divides into subbranches. The smallest subdivisions of a bronchus are bronchioles, less than one millimeter in diameter and walled by smooth muscle. The bronchial tree's outermost "twigs" are more than 250,000 tiny respiratory bronchioles about half a millimeter in diameter. Sprouting from these are some 6 million "leaves": tiny alveoli that resemble minute, clustered, air-filled bubbles. It is here that gaseous exchange takes place as you breathe in and out.

Breathing in, breathing out

When you breathe in, the muscles of the dome-shaped diaphragm contract. This pulls the dome down, thereby lowering the floor of the chest cavity. Meanwhile, the ribs' intercostal muscles contract, pulling the ribs up and out. These actions expand the chest cavity, creating a vacuum that causes air to flow into the lungs as they expand.

When you breathe out, the muscles of the diaphragm relax, and it rises in the chest cavity. The intercostal muscles also relax, and the elasticity of the chest wall causes the ribs to sink down and inwards, expelling air from the lungs. When breathing out forcefully, muscles of the abdomen contract to increase the pressure, which pushes the diaphragm upwards and forces air from the lungs.

At rest you may breathe in as little as .25 pint (57 centiliters) of air with each breath. During exercise, however, when the body's need for oxygen increases, each breath may draw in as much as 2 pints (4.5 liters).

Normally, about one-third of breathed-in air gets no farther than the bronchi or bronchioles. The rest fills alveoli. Oxygen molecules are absorbed by fluid lining each alveolus's thin wall, then pass to blood cells in a thin-walled capillary—part of a mesh that surrounds each alveolus and carries deoxygenated blood from the pulmonary artery. Oxygen molecules attach to the hemoglobin molecules of red blood cells. Meanwhile, carbon dioxide molecules, dissolved in the blood plasma, pass out from the capillaries into the alveolus. Expired air also contains water vapor from the moisture lining alveolar walls.

How fast we breathe depends on the carbon dioxide level in the bloodstream. The higher the level the more acid the blood. Cells in the brainstem and elsewhere monitor changes in the acid level and, as it rises, stimulate the breathing reflex.

Respiratory defenses

The body has various means of preventing and combating disease or injury in the delicate respiratory system. Mucous membranes warm and moisten inspired air to prevent it from chilling or drying the bronchioles and alveoli. Cough and sneeze reflexes expel food or other particles that find their way into the respiratory passages and the bronchial tree. Inside alveoli, cells called phagocytes swallow bacteria and dust, and tiny whiplike cilia projecting from the inner walls of the bronchial tree lash these foreign bodies up toward the trachea in blobs of mucus, which are coughed up as "phlegm."

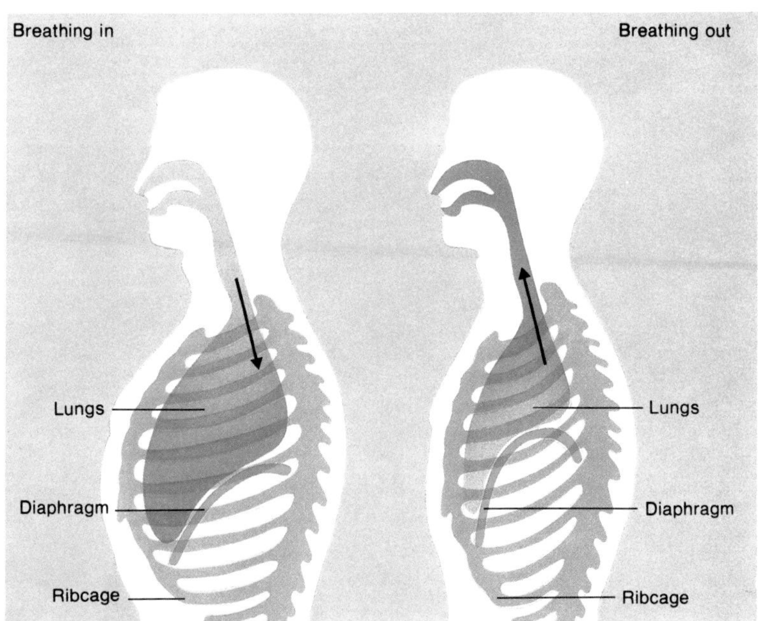

Breathing is accomplished by lowering the diaphragm and raising the ribcage, to expand the lungs and breathe in, then by relaxing the diaphragm and lowering the ribcage to breathe out.

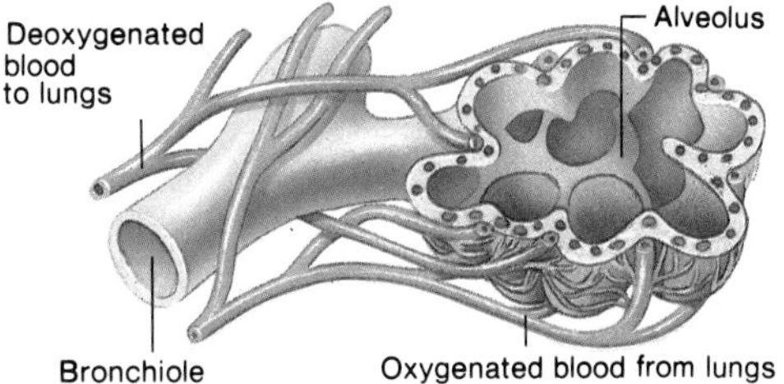

Alveoli, the extremities of the bronchial "tree," allow air to come into close contact with blood in capillaries, so that gas exchange can take place.

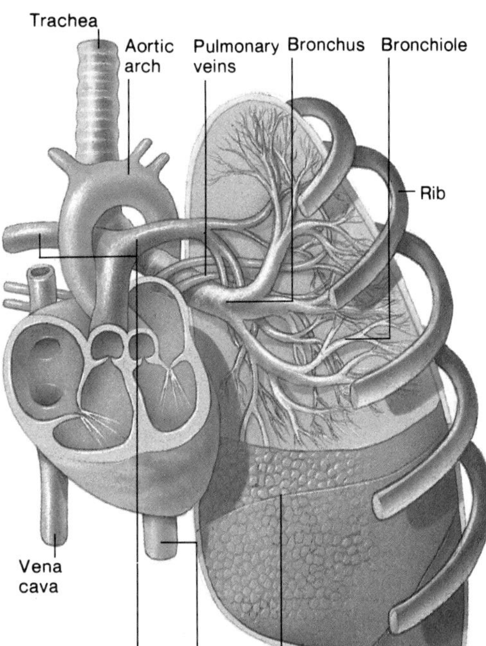

Lungs are composed of spongy tissue in which are thousands of tiny branches of veins, arteries, and bronchioles. Surrounding each lung is a thin membrane, the visceral pleura, which permits the lungs to move smoothly within the pleural cavity—the space occupied by the lungs in the chest.

Food and digestion

The digestive system consists of a long and convoluted tube, in which food is broken down physically and chemically so that the nutritional elements it contains can be absorbed.

The digestive system is a biological mechanism that dismantles foods into their chemical components—some destined to form muscle, bone, blood, skin, or other tissue; some producing energy to power the processes of life.

The main part of the digestive system is the gut, or alimentary canal, a convoluted muscular tube measuring about 30 feet (9 meters) if extended, with an opening at each end. One opening, the mouth, admits unprocessed food. The other opening, the anus, releases food wastes. Between these two lie specialized organs like the teeth, stomach, and pancreas. These break down proteins, fats, and carbohydrates into molecules small enough to filter from the gut into the blood supply. In this way, nutrients are absorbed into the body.

The process is principally one of chemical reactions speeded up by biological catalysts called enzymes. During digestion, starches and complex sugars break down into simple sugars. Fats become fatty acids and glycerol. Proteins break down into amino acids. But water, minerals, and vitamins enter body tissues undigested.

Inside the mouth

The first stages of digestion take place inside the mouth. Each mouthful of solid food is cut up and crushed by the teeth. An adult normally has 32 teeth of four kinds, designed for different purposes. Two sets of four somewhat chisel-shaped incisors at the front slice food with a scissorlike action. Four strong canines flanking the incisors have a pointed chewing surface and help to tear up large chunks of food into smaller pieces. Next come eight premolars, each with two cusps (pointed chewing surfaces) that crush food into still smaller pieces. The twelve molars at the back of the jaws are strong, broad-crowned teeth that grind food into small particles.

While teeth are masticating food, the tongue and cheek muscles push the food around so that all of it is subject to the chopping, grinding process. Reflex action ensures that the tongue itself does not get trapped between the teeth and bitten.

Meanwhile, saliva is entering the mouth cavity from three glands on each side of the face. These are the sublingual gland below the tongue, the submandibular gland below and behind the sublingual gland, and the parotid gland in front of and below the ear. Saliva is rich in ptyalin (salivary amylase), an enzyme that starts the conversion of starches into simple sugars. The lubricating, mixing action of

The digestive system begins with the lips, teeth, mouth, and tongue, which form a chamber in which food is moistened and crushed before it starts its passage through the stomach and intestines. Most absorption occurs in the long, narrow, "small" intestine.

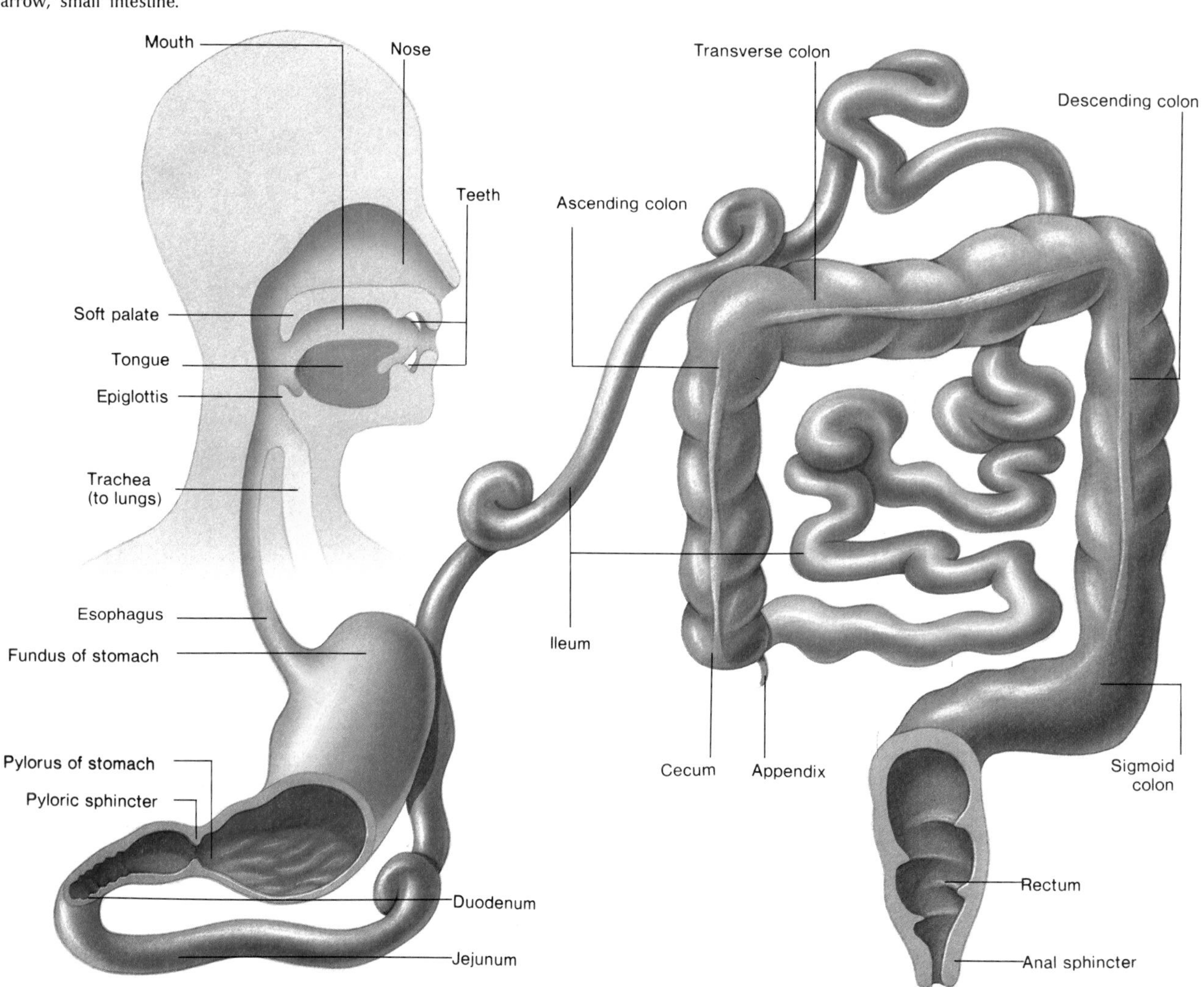

saliva helps to shape each mouthful of food into a ball (bolus) that can be swallowed easily and will not stick in the throat.

Swallowing involves coordinated reflexes that stop food from entering the nasal cavity or windpipe. As the tongue throws the bolus back into the pharynx, the soft palate automatically rises to protect the nasal cavity, and the epiglottis—a flap of cartilage and membrane—helps to shut the windpipe. Meanwhile, the top of the esophagus, or gullet, relaxes and receives the bolus, which now starts its journey through the gut.

Inside esophagus and stomach

The esophagus is a short length of tube between the lower pharynx (throat) and the stomach. Like other sections of the gut, its inner surface is lubricated by mucus. The tube's thin walls consist of both skeletal and smooth muscle, which contract in waves (peristalsis) that move down through the esophagus, each wave taking about ten seconds from top to bottom.

The lower end of the esophagus is usually kept closed by a ring of muscle called the cardiac sphincter and by external pressure. The sphincter opens to release food into the stomach, then shuts again, preventing food from escaping back up through the esophagus.

The stomach is an enlarged section of the gut shaped rather like a letter J and closed by sphincters at the top and bottom. Three muscle layers, each with fibers aligned in a different direction, form the stomach walls.

The stomach serves partly as a place to store swallowed food before this passes on into the small intestine. As eating fills the stomach, its elastic walls relax and allow it to expand.

The stomach also acts to mix the swallowed food. Its muscles contract in a coordinated fashion that sends waves sweeping through the stomach, churning up its contents. This mixes the food with gastric juices secreted by glands and cells in pits in the mucous lining of the stomach wall.

Each day, the stomach yields about 6 pints (3 liters) of secretions. Among these is the stomach's chief digestive enzyme, pepsin, which starts to break down proteins. Pepsin needs acid if it is to work, and the stomach obliges by manufacturing hydrochloric acid. This also helps to kill bacteria that might otherwise cause intestinal infections. Stomach acid is strong enough to burn skin, but the stomach's walls are protected by their mucous coating.

Food mixed with and partly broken down by gastric juices forms a homogeneous mixture known as chyme. From this mixture, water, glucose, salts, and alcohol can pass directly to the bloodstream.

Every minute, however, about one per cent of the stomach's contents spurts out through the pyloric sphincter, the stomach's lower opening, into the small intestine, where the last all-important stages of digestion and absorption occur.

The intestines

Below the stomach food passes into the con-

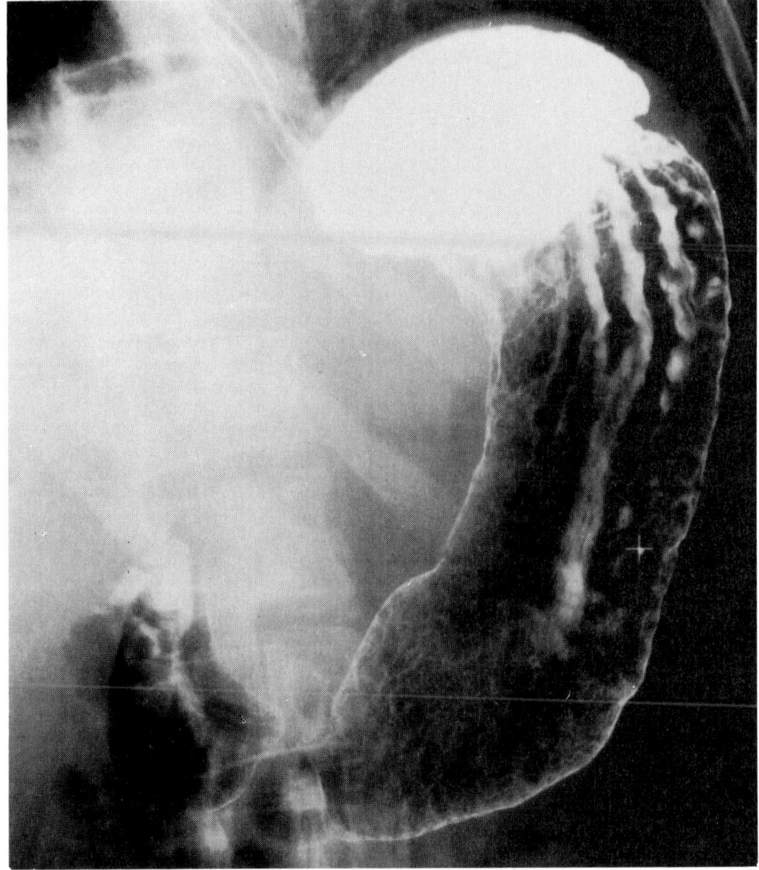

An X ray of the stomach taken after a radiopaque substance—called a "barium meal"—has been swallowed shows most of the barium in the fundus of the stomach. Some remains in the esophagus, however, and some is beginning to move through the rest of the stomach as a result of the stomach's muscular action.

Salivary Glands	Mouth	Convert
Salivary amylase	Saliva	Starch to maltose
Gastric Glands	Stomach	Convert
Pepsin	Gastric juices	Proteins to peptides
Pancreas and Liver	Duodenum	Convert
1 Amylase 2 Lipase 3 Trypsin	Pancreatic juice and bile	1 Starch to maltose 2 Fats to fatty acids and glycerol 3 Proteins and peptides to amino acids
Intestinal Glands	Ileum	Convert
1 Lactase 2 Lipase 3 Maltase 4 Peptidase 5 Sucrase	Intestinal juice (succus entericus)	1 Lactose to glucose 2 Fats to fatty acids and glycerol 3 Maltose to glucose 4 Peptides to amino acids 5 Sucrose to glucose

Digestion is accomplished by the actions of digestive juices, which are secreted by glands into different parts of the alimentary canal. The table shows some of the main glands and the enzymes they produce, in the left column; the part of the alimentary canal and the medium in which they act, in the center column; and their effect, in terms of the main chemicals they act on and produce, in the right column.

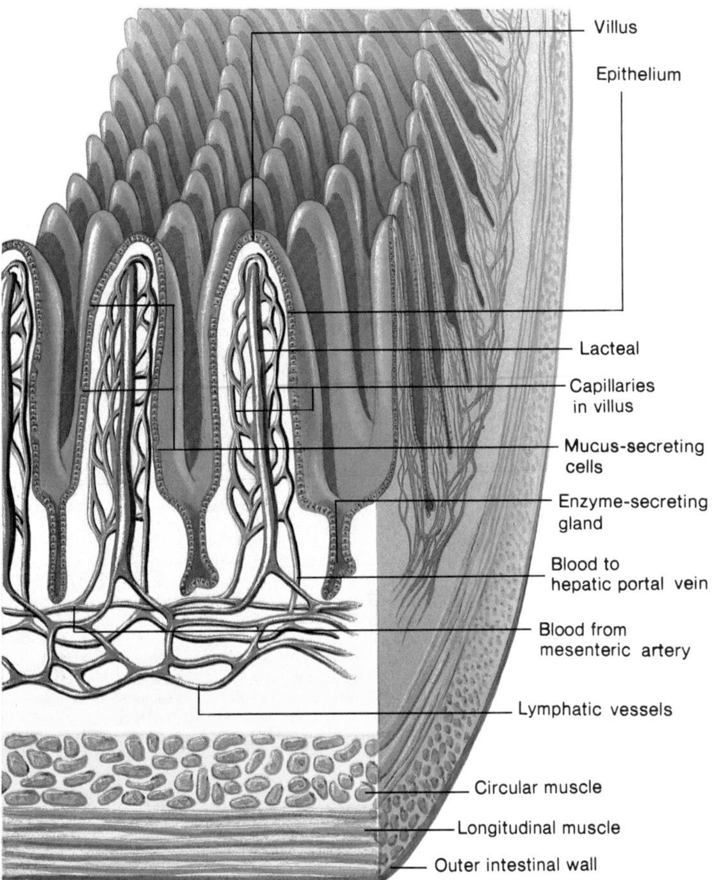

The ileum, where most absorption of nutrients occurs, is a narrow tube formed by layers of smooth (involuntary) muscle around numerous fingerlike villi projecting into the lumen of the tube. These villi give the ileum an enormous surface area and so maximize the quantity of dissolved nutrients that can be absorbed through the epithelial cells. Amino acids, glucose, and some fatty acids enter the blood capillaries and are carried through the hepatic portal vein to the liver. Other fats pass into the lymphatic system via the lacteals, and ultimately return to the circulation and reach the liver by this route. Digestive enzymes are produced by the enzyme-secreting cells at the base of the villi. Mucus-secreting cells on the villi help lubricate the ileum's contents.

voluted intestines: the long, narrow small intestine and the shorter, broader large intestine. The small intestine is supplied with juices that help complete the breakdown and absorption of most proteins, fats, and carbohydrates. The large intestine turns undigested wastes into feces for expulsion from the body.

The small intestine

This longest section of the gut forms closely-packed loops through which waves of muscular contraction force chyme—food mixed with gastric juices. Anatomists divide the small intestine into three sections: duodenum, jejunum, and ileum.

The duodenum, a curved, short length of tubing, leads from the stomach and receives ducts from the pancreas and liver. This makes the duodenum chemically very active, for digestive pancreatic juice flows in from the pancreas, while the liver yields bile, a digestive juice made up of salts and pigments produced by chemical breakdown. Much of the bile reaches the small intestine via a storage depot, the gall bladder. The flow of bile and pancreatic juice varies with hormone output that is stimulated by chyme arriving in the duodenum from the stomach.

The alkaline pancreatic juice and bile counteract gastric acid from the stomach and make the duodenum strongly alkaline, which helps to activate its digestive enzymes and neutralize digestive juices from the stomach. When duodenal ulcers form, this happens at the duodenum's upper, stomach end, where unneutralized acid chyme makes contact with the duodenum wall.

Inside the duodenum, carbohydrates, fats, and proteins are broken down. Bile salts and the churning action of the duodenal walls break large fat droplets into smaller ones. These offer a large surface area to be attacked by lipase—a fat-splitting enzyme that indirectly helps bile salts to create still smaller droplets called micelles. Meanwhile, the enzyme amylase is breaking down carbohydrates to simpler compounds, the sugars dextrose and maltose. The enzymes trypsin and chymotrypsin found in pancreatic juice break down proteins into their component amino acids.

From the duodenum, chemically dismembered particles of food continue through the jejunum—the first two-fifths of the remainder of the small intestine. The jejunum is a major transfer station where nutrients from digested food are absorbed into the bloodstream. This absorption is facilitated by the structure of the small intestine's inner surface, pocked with pits and lined with millions of tiny, fingerlike projections known as villi, each supplied with a network of capillaries around a central lymph channel. Some villi in their turn form bases for millions of even smaller microvilli. The mass of villi and microvilli produce a surface like fine velvet pile: its total area may exceed that of the complete body surface by five times. This enormous area permits the mass transfer of digested particles of food from the small intestine into the bloodstream. Digestion is carried out by glands at the bases of the villi, which release enzymes that complete the breakdown of fats, proteins, and carbohydrates into units small enough to be absorbed.

The ileum has an especially thick lining of villi that complete this stage of food absorption.

The large intestine

Shorter and less convoluted than the small intestine, but much broader, the large intestine, or colon, starts in the right lower abdomen with the cecum, a short blind passage leading downward. The human cecum is the vestigial equivalent of a relatively much larger structure found in such herbivorous mammals as rabbits, where it is important for cellulose digestion.

Another vestigial structure, the vermiform (worm-shaped) appendix is a slim tubular cul-de-sac about 3.5 inches (9 centimeters) long, projecting from the otherwise blind end of the cecum. Lined with lymphatic cells, the appendix has little known value to the body and can even prove a liability. Bacterial infection may inflame it, producing the condition called appendicitis. Inflammation can even cut off blood flow to the appendix, killing tissue and causing gangrene. Or an infected appendix may burst, spreading infection to surrounding organs. Appendicitis can thus cause peritonitis or inflammation of the peritoneum, the thin membrane lining the abdominal cavity. Swift, simple removal of an inflamed appendix usually prevents such complications and leaves the work of the intestines unimpaired.

By the time swallowed substances reach the large intestine, the work of digestion and absorption is almost complete. What remains is mainly indigestible roughage, salts, dead cells from the lining of the gut, bile pigments, and water. All these enter the large intestine where the ileum joins it just above the cecum.

Peristalsis pushes undigested debris upward through the ascending colon, then horizontally through the transverse colon, which lies across the upper abdomen. Then comes a sharp change of direction, with the descending colon, which plunges down in the left side of the abdomen. Lastly, the load of waste material travels through a sharp bend, the sigmoid flexure, down through the rectum, a straight, short length of tube, and out through the anus—a hole closed and opened by a ring of muscle, the anal sphincter.

Considerable changes happen to the wastes during their passage through the colon. Bacteria feed on these wastes and help convert them into feces. The bacteria also produce valuable vitamins and enzymes that help digest some fibrous vegetable matter. These useful products pass through the colon wall into the body, together with much water—the colon is the principal site of water reabsorption—and some salts.

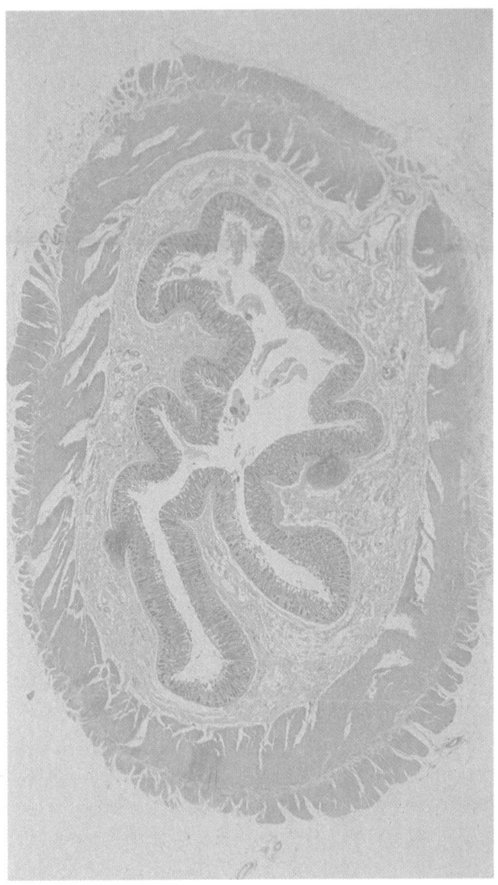

The colon, like the ileum, has—beneath its outer covering—a layer of longitudinal smooth muscle and, inside this, a layer of circular smooth muscle. These act together to move digested food from the cecum, into which food comes from the ileum, to the rectum, from which it is expelled as feces through the anus. Between the layer of circular muscle and the lumen is the mucous membrane. In contrast to the small intestine, the colon has no villi. The epithelium contains mucus-secreting cells and numerous absorptive cells, through which salts, other materials, and water are reabsorbed.

Food Categories and common sources	Vitamins and daily requirements	Needed for	Minerals and trace elements	Needed for
Proteins Eggs, fish, meat, milk products, nuts, potatoes, pulses, whole cereals	Vitamin A 0.75mg	Skin; mucous membranes; night vision	Calcium	Bones; teeth; muscles; nerves; blood clotting
	Vitamin B_1 1.5mg	Nerves; heart muscle; general metabolism	Chlorine (as chloride)	Body fluids
Carbohydrates Cereals, fruit, potatoes, sugar	Vitamin B_2 1.5mg	Skin; mucous membranes; general metabolism	Iodine (as iodide)	Thyroid hormones
	Vitamin B_6 2mg	General body functions; amino acid metabolism	Iron	Hemoglobin and myoglobin formation
Fats Animal fat, milk products, nuts, oil	Vitamin B_{12} 0.01mg	Nerve cells; red blood cells	Phosphorus (as phosphate)	Bones; teeth; cell membranes; metabolism
	Nicotinic acid 20mg	Skin; cell metabolism	Potassium	Body fluids; nerve and muscle action
Vitamins Eggs, fish, fresh fruit and vegetables, meat, milk products, nuts, whole cereals, yeast	Folic acid 0.2 mg	Nerve cell metabolism; red blood cells	Sodium	Body fluids; nerve and muscle action
	Vitamin C 40mg	Growth and repair of tissues	Cobalt	Vitamin B_{12} (cyanocobalamin) action
Minerals Cereals, eggs, fish, fruit, meat, milk products, nuts, salt, vegetables, yeast	Vitamin D 0.01mg	Bone formation; calcium and phosphorus absorption	Copper	Blood formation; enzyme function
	Vitamin E 30mg	Cell membranes and general metabolism	Magnesium	Nerve and muscle action; enzyme function
Liquids Water, milk, other drinks, fruit, vegetables	Vitamin K not known	Blood clotting	Manganese	Cell metabolism; fat production
	Pantothenic acid 2mg	Fat metabolism; cell enzyme functions	Zinc	Enzyme function

Food consists principally of proteins, carbohydrates, fats, and liquids, which in turn provide the essential vitamins and minerals that the body requires. The digestive tract also needs a proportion of indigestible matter, called roughage, which is usually provided in adequate quantities by a varied diet. This table lists the most common sources of the different kinds of food, indicates the importance of the major vitamins, and the average adult daily requirements of them (expressed in milligrams—1 ounce equals 28,350 milligrams), and lists the main minerals and trace elements.

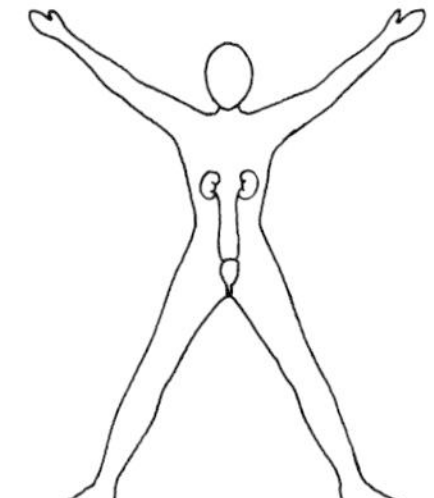

The urinary system consists of the kidneys, the ureters, the bladder, and the urethra.

The urinary system

Without an efficient disposal system, poisonous wastes would collect in body tissues. In fact, several body systems provide exits for unwanted by-products of the processes of living. Lungs remove carbon dioxide and some water and heat. The skin gives off heat and water with some salts and urea, a product of protein breakdown. The digestive tract expels feces containing indigestible food, some salts, bile pigments, and water. But most excretion—removal of the products of metabolism—involves the kidneys, ureters, bladder, and urethra, which combine to form the urinary system.

The kidneys

The kidneys filter blood brought by the renal arteries and removed by the renal veins. Filtration occurs in the renal cortex. Waste products collect in the renal pelvis and drain through the ureters to the bladder.

Kidneys ceaselessly filter substances from blood. They reabsorb some of these, with reabsorbed fluids, but principally, the kidneys act to concentrate chemical wastes and dispose of these as urine. Moreover, kidneys vary the amounts of salts and water they excrete, helping to maintain a healthy salt and water balance.

Kidneys work astonishingly hard. Each minute they process about 2.75 pints (1.3 liters) of blood—one-quarter of the amount pumped out by the heart in this time. All blood travels through the kidneys nearly 20 times every hour. Fifteen times a day they purify the body's entire fluid contents—handling a total of about 50 gallons (190 liters). Most of the fluid is reabsorbed, but approximately one-thousandth of the total volume passes out of the body as urine.

Remarkably enough, if one kidney is diseased or damaged, the other usually copes adequately.

From the outside, kidneys resemble a pair of purplish-brown beans the size of a man's fist. Each weighs about 5 ounces (140 grams). They lie on either side of the backbone, their concave sides facing inward. Cut open, a kidney reveals two major areas: a pale outer layer called the cortex, and a dark inner mass, the medulla. The cortex is made mostly of blood filtration units—venal corpuscles and tubules. The medulla contains tubules (loops of Henle) that collect the dilute filtrate and reabsorb most of the water, and the collecting ducts for the final concentrated filtrate that becomes urine. Blood for filtration flows into a kidney from the renal artery, which divides and subdivides into tiny branches. Treated blood leaves the kidney through a network of small veins that feed into the large renal vein.

How the blood is filtered

About a million blood filtration units, or nephrons, are packed into each kidney. Each nephron is a coiled tubule with a loop, and measures 1—2.5 inches (2.5—6 centimeters). The head of the nephron is in the cortex; it leads ultimately to a collecting duct that passes down through the medulla before opening into a large collecting area in the renal pelvis at the kidney's core. Each nephron's outer end (in the cortex) forms a double-walled cup known as a Bowman's capsule. This envelops a bulging knot of capillaries called a glomerulus. Blood driven through the glomerulus forces small molecules out through the capillary walls into the Bowman's capsule. Blood cells and protein molecules too large to pass through the filter remain in the capillaries. Filtration can occur at great speed because each kidney's glomeruli have an overall area of approximately a quarter of the total surface area of the body. The resulting filtrate includes water and dissolved sugar, salts, and urea.

In this way, the nephron removes impurities from blood, but leaves the latter too concentrated. So water and other valuable substances are returned to the blood as the filtrate trickles through the nephron's convoluted tubule, around a hairpin turn (the loop of Henle), and up again toward the cortex. Throughout this journey, salts, sugars, and even some urea filter out of the tubule and back into nearby capillaries.

By the time the fluid has passed through all

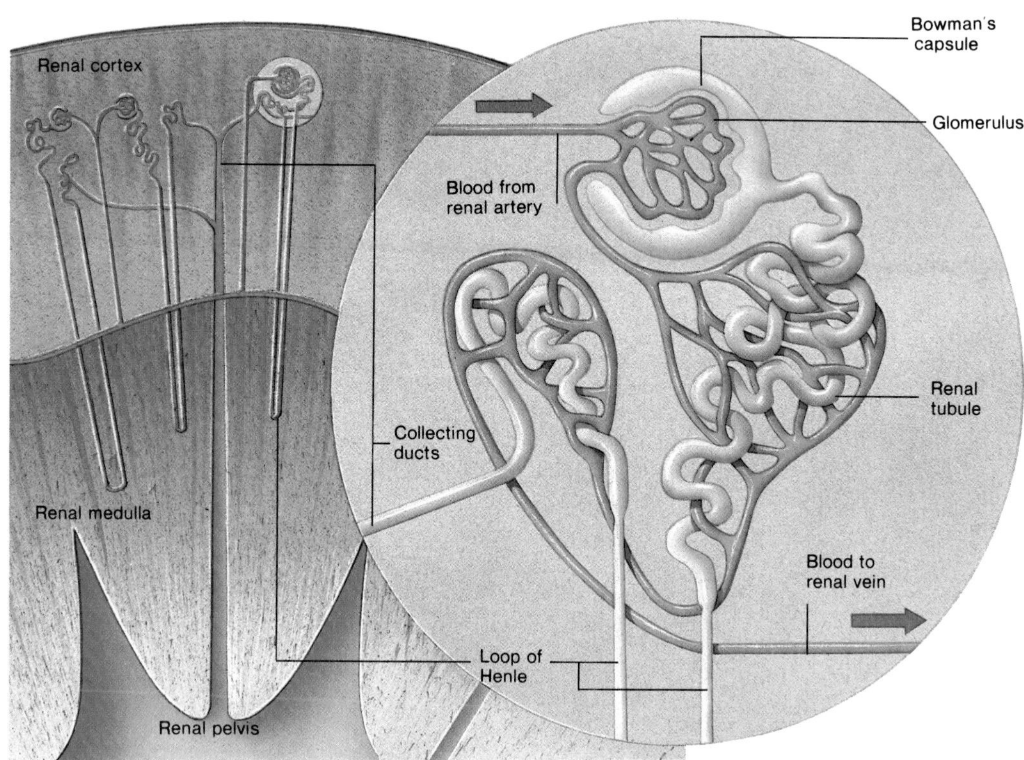

Filtration occurs as blood from the renal artery enters the knot of capillaries called the glomerulus. Salts, glucose, and nitrogenous waste filter into the surrounding Bowman's capsule. As this filtrate passes through the renal tubule and the loop of Henle, which extends into the renal medulla before returning to the renal cortex, many of the dissolved substances are reabsorbed. The concentrated filtrate passes from the renal tubule to collecting ducts that drain into the renal pelvis. The filtrate passes from there through the ureters to the bladder.

the nephron tubule and on to a collecting tube and then into the hilum, the kidney's main collecting area in the renal pelvis, it has been converted into urine, a concentrated urea solution with some salts and other wastes, which must be removed from the body.

Ureters, bladder, and urethra

From the kidneys, drops of urine continuously run down through two narrow, muscular tubes called ureters, each about 10 inches (25 centimeters) long. The urine collects in a muscular storage bag, the bladder. The rate at which urine leaves the kidneys depends on the amount of water in the body. If the body is dehydrated, the kidneys release no more than a cupful of concentrated urine daily. If the body is abundantly supplied with water, daily output can rise to more than 5.25 gallons (20 liters) of very dilute urine. Urine normally leaves each kidney at a rate of about one drop a minute. Contracting smooth muscles in the ureter's wall squeeze the urine down into the bladder, which is walled by thick layers of smooth muscle, with a ring of skeletal muscle—the external urethral sphincter—around the narrow outlet at its base.

Emptying the bladder involves a spinal reflex action that makes the bladder contract, and a consciously directed order from the brain relaxing the external sphincter. Children gain bladder control only when they are old enough to learn to master both muscular actions. However, even adults cannot retain urine when the bladder is overly full.

During urination, also known as micturition, urine from the bladder leaves the body through a duct called a urethra. This is longer in men than in women because it passes through the prostate gland and the penis.

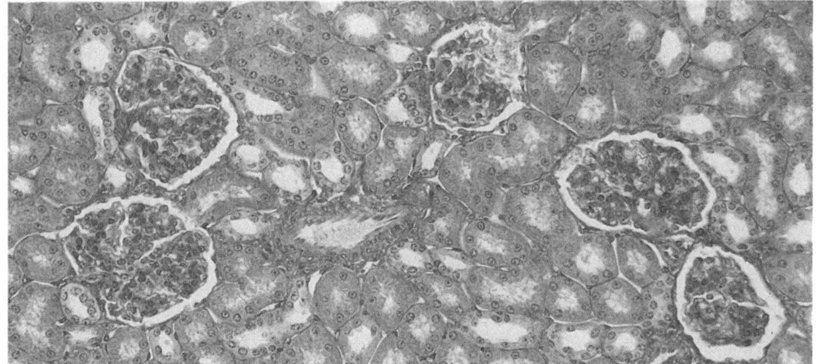

Renal corpuscles, comprising a glomerulus enveloped by a Bowman's capsule, lie in the renal cortex, surrounded by other corpuscles, renal tubules, collecting ducts, and some connective tissue containing blood, lymph vessels, and nerves.

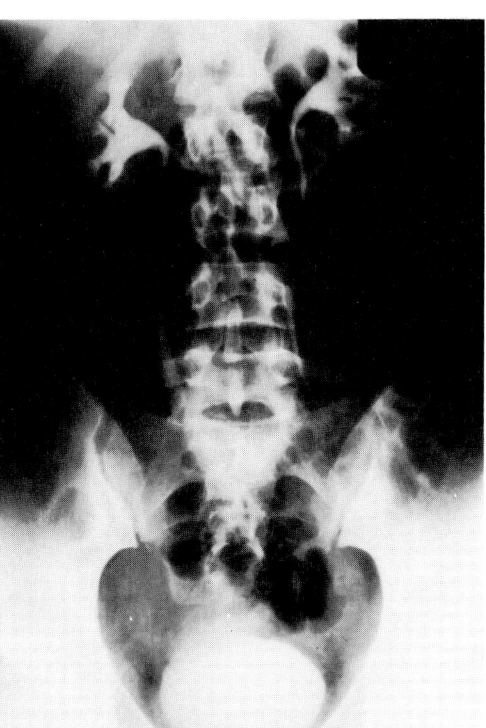

An X ray of the abdomen taken when a radiopaque substance is introduced into the urinary tract shows each renal pelvis, at the top of the photograph, on either side of the spinal column; the two ureters; and the bladder, at the bottom, situated within the bones of the pelvic girdle.

Metabolism

Every year each person eats many times the body's weight in food, yet his or her own weight is little changed. The explanation for this apparent miracle lies largely in metabolism, a complex of chemical life processes whose name comes from the Greek *metabole,* meaning "conversion."

Catabolism and anabolism

Metabolic processes bring about two major kinds of change: catabolism (the breaking down of organic compounds derived from food) and anabolism (the synthesis or building up of complex compounds from simple ones, also derived from food).

Catabolism releases energy by breaking down digested fats and carbohydrates. The breakdown products serve as fuels combining with oxygen from air for oxidation, a gradual "burning" process, which releases energy for cell-building and the activities of cells and muscles. Anabolism uses energy to manufacture proteins, fats, and certain carbohydrates. Meanwhile, old and damaged cells are being broken down and removed. The whole metabolic process is carefully controlled by subtle feedback systems.

Metabolism describes all chemical and physical changes that occur within a living organism, but more specifically refers to the changes that occur to food after it has been digested. Three principal products of digestion—amino acids, glucose, and fatty acids—take part in both anabolic reactions, when they are converted into body proteins, glycogen, or body fat, and catabolic reactions, when they are broken down through complex biochemical pathways to carbon dioxide, water, waste products, and energy.

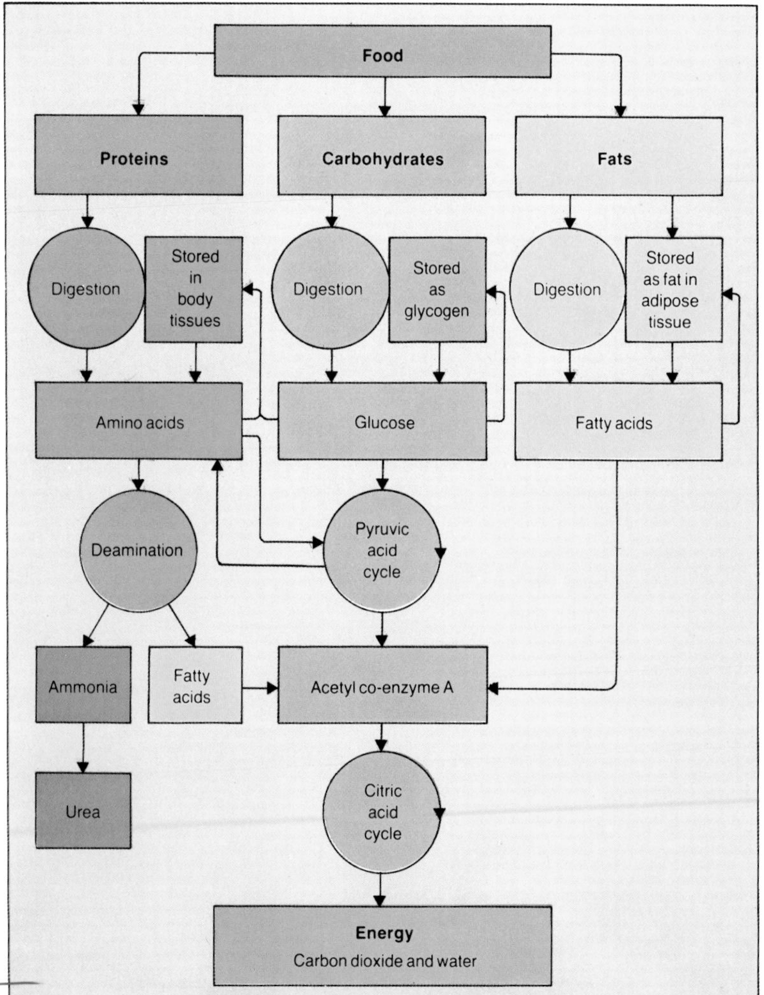

Metabolism maintains life by processes that largely balance the body's food input with its output of heat, mechanical energy, and processed body waste, to which is added waste from undigested roughage.

Enzymes in action

Metabolism involves complex chains of chemical reactions that would be impossible at body temperatures without help from the giant protein molecules called enzymes—biological catalysts that speed up chemical reactions between other substances without themselves undergoing metabolic change.

Specific enzymes operate on specific types of molecule (called the substrate), inducing chemical changes in the substrate molecules, which then break free from the enzymes and so allow these to tackle further substrate molecules. This happens astonishingly fast. Even at freezing point, one molecule of the enzyme catalase can break down 40,000 molecules of hydrogen peroxide in just one second. Accordingly, most enzymes are needed, and occur, in only tiny quantities.

Metabolism involves many kinds of enzyme—most acting on only one kind of substrate, in special conditions of acidity or alkalinity, in the presence of auxiliary activators called coenzymes.

Different enzymes cooperate in systems geared to the step-by-step breakdown or building-up of compounds. The major carbohydrate breakdown mechanism, glycolysis, occurs mainly in muscle, where the sugar glucose or the animal starch glycogen break down via intermediate compounds to pyruvic acid. This then enters the Krebs, or citric acid cycle—a complicated series of enzyme-controlled reactions that break down pyruvic acid in the presence of oxygen to yield carbon dioxide and ATP (adenosine triphosphate)—a source of energy that can be used for internal cell activity or for the external work of muscular contraction. Step-by-step release of energy involving oxidation may yield 673 kilocalories from just one gram molecule of glucose.

Oxygen required for energy release comes usually from air breathed in by the lungs. But the heart cannot always deliver enough oxygen to muscles. If energy demand exceeds oxygen supply, muscles can go on working for a time by anaerobic (oxygenless) metabolism. But this soon uses up all high-energy phosphate stores, and the resulting oxygen debt produces much lactic acid waste that prevents cells from working properly and causes muscular fatigue.

Catabolism breaks down most compounds to acetyl coenzyme A, a product that can be oxidized, or used as building blocks for making many complicated compounds. Almost all the fats and carbohydrates that the body needs can be built up like this, with help from different enzymes cooperating to form special metabolic pathways. In fact, most of the amino acid ingredients of proteins can be synthesized inside the body. Minerals and vitamins (except vitamin D) cannot be synthesized.

Metabolic facts and figures

The body releases about four kilocalories of

energy per gram of carbohydrates or protein catabolized, and nine kilocalories of energy per gram of fat.

The amount of energy released by the body in a given time is called its metabolic rate. This can be measured from the amount of oxygen consumed or carbon dioxide given off. A man's basal metabolic rate—energy output at rest per hour per unit surface area—is about 40 kilocalories per square yard of skin, compared with 32 for a woman. Sedentary male office workers expend about 2,520 kilocalories, about 400 more than women. A man performing heavy manual work may use as many as 3,600 kilocalories a day.

While the kilocalories content of food eaten matches the kilocalories of energy expended, body weight remains unchanged. If energy input exceeds output, the body may store the surplus energy as fat and put on weight. But if energy output exceeds input, the body first burns up its reservoir of fat and then starts to break down proteins as a source of energy, in time producing the muscle wastage and weight loss seen in malnutrition.

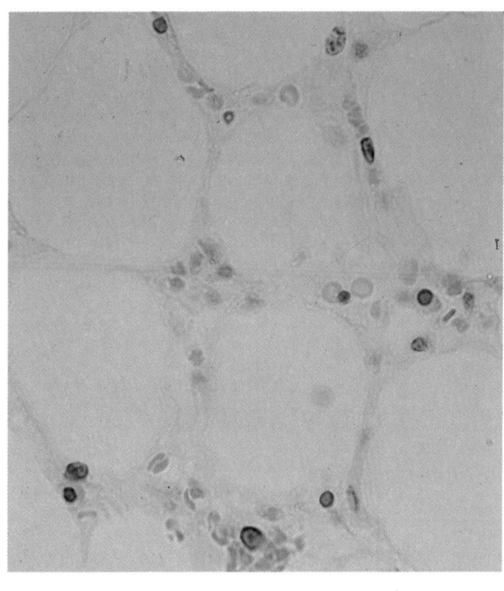

Fat cells store fat in adipose tissue. They have a nucleus and cytoplasm in which fat globules form. Large fat globules occupy a very much greater volume than the cytoplasm that surrounds them.

The liver's role

Besides producing the digestive fluid bile, the liver helps to process the carbohydrate and amino acid products of digestion brought by the hepatic portal vein from the digestive tract. It converts surplus glucose into the animal starch glycogen, storing it for reconversion and releasing it as glucose in later time of need. If the liver's glycogen stores are already full, liver cells begin transforming any extra glucose into fat, which travels around the body and collects just below the skin in adipose tissue cells in the abdomen and other places.

The liver also converts potentially poisonous nitrogenous wastes derived from protein into toxic urea, which is released into the bloodstream and excreted harmlessly by the kidneys.

Other valuable liver functions include storing vitamins, notably B_{12} which is needed in manufacturing red blood cells, and minerals, including iron, which is required for hemoglobin. Lastly, the liver makes a range of blood proteins.

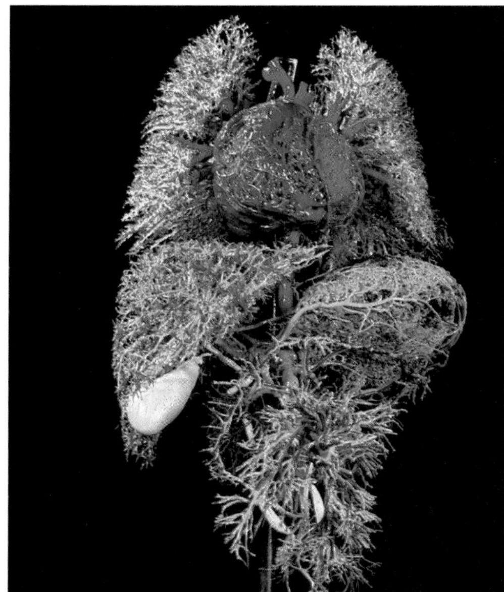

The blood supply to the thorax and abdomen is shown in a resin cast of the blood vessels. The liver is the triangular organ below the heart and lungs and above and left of the digestive system.

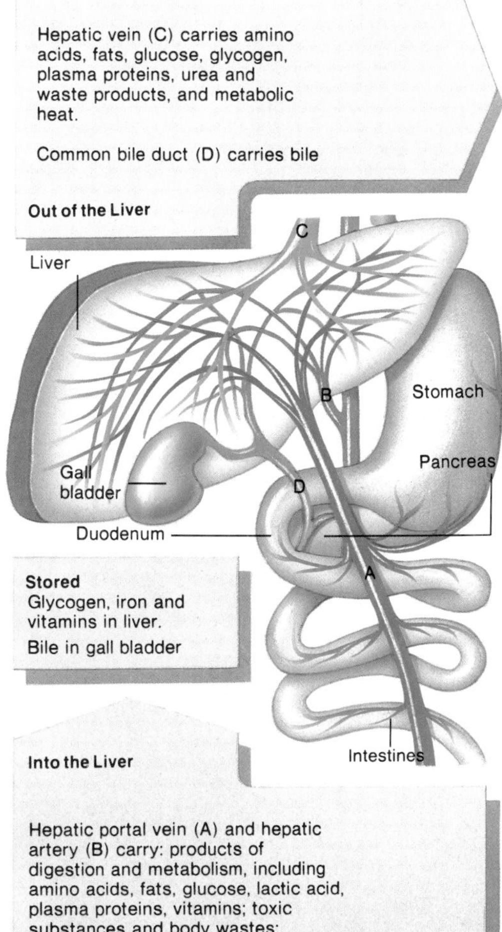

The hepatic portal system carries the products of digestion from the stomach and intestines through the hepatic portal vein (A). Oxygen arrives in arterial blood, supplied by the hepatic artery (B). The products of hepatic metabolism leave through the hepatic vein (C). Bile, containing pigment from the breakdown of blood cells, as well as bile salts, cholesterol, and urea, is produced in the liver and is stored in the gall bladder. From there, it reaches the duodenum through the common bile duct (D).

The nervous system

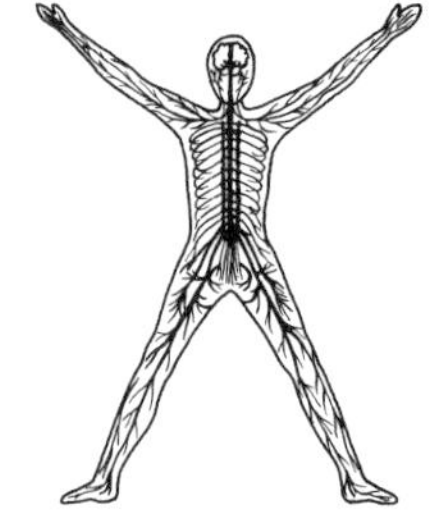

The nervous system centers on the brain and spinal cord.

All body systems would be immobilized without the nervous system, which receives and correlates information from inside and outside the body and reacts by sending signals to appropriate muscles and glands so that these produce coordinated responses. The body's nerve network has been likened to a telephone system, with the billions of elongated, interconnected cells called neurons serving as its wires.

Neurons form two great associated groups: the central and peripheral nervous systems.

The nervous system has three main parts. Central: the brain, cranial nerves, and spinal cord. Peripheral: sensory and motor nerves leading to and from the spinal cord. Autonomic: the sympathetic trunk and branches, and parasympathetic fibers.

Neurons and nerves

Neurons, or nerve cells, form the active units of the nervous system, although they are heavily outnumbered by glial ("glue") cells that help to supply the neurons with nourishment, support, and insulation. Neurons may be grouped broadly in three ways according to the jobs they do: sensory neurons (afferents) bring signals to the central nervous system from sensory receptors; motor neurons (effectors, or efferents) send signals out to muscles and glands; and interneurons (also called association neurons) serve as intermediaries.

Nerve cells are uniquely structured to communicate with one another. A typical neuron has three structural elements: a compact body, many short, branching "threads" called dendrites, and one very long "thread" called an axon. Dendrites receive signals from nearby neurons, and the axon hands them to another neuron muscle or gland. Naked dendrites and cell bodies color the gray matter of the brain and spinal cord; white matter consists of axons sheathed by a white, fatty, insulating substance known as myelin. Bundles of myelin-coated axons make up nerve fibers.

Unlike the electrical signals passed along a telephone wire, nervous signals travel by an electrochemical relay system. Inactive neurons tend to contain more potassium than sodium ions, while outside their cell membranes are more sodium than potassium ions. When a nearby neuron is stimulated, chemicals called neurotransmitters burst from sacs in knobs at its axon ends, leap the gap—or synapse—to the inactive neuron, and fill receptor sites in its cell membranes. This makes the cell lose some potassium ions and take in some sodium ions so that the cell's electrical charge is changed at the affected site. That charge flows through the cell at up to 220 miles (354 kilometers) per hour, which is very fast (but slower than an electrical impulse).

While excitatory neurotransmitters make neurons fire off signals, inhibitory ones tend to block them. A single brain cell may receive thousands of simultaneous signals. How it reacts depends largely on how many "fire" and "don't fire" signals it receives. Individual spinal and peripheral neurons act like brain cells, processing and responding to the information reaching them.

Right cerebral hemisphere
Left cerebral hemisphere
Cerebellum
Brainstem
Spinal cord
Facial (7th cranial) nerve
Vagus (10th cranial) nerve
8 cervical nerves
Musculocutaneous nerve
Brachial plexus
Median nerve
12 thoracic nerves
Radial nerve
Ulnar nerve
5 lumbar nerves
Nerves in spinal canal (cauda equina)
5 sacral nerves
Sacral plexus
Pudendal nerve
Femoral nerve
Autonomic nervous system
Sciatic nerve
Cardiac plexus
Posterior cutaneous nerve of the thigh
Gastric plexus
Common peroneal nerve
Mesenteric plexus
Sympathetic trunk
Tibial nerve
Pelvic plexus

Central nervous system

The command center of the body consists of the spinal cord and a swollen and highly differentiated outgrowth of it, the brain.

The spinal cord forms a cylinder of nervous tissue some 16-20 inches (40-50 centimeters) long in an adult, extending from the brain stem down through the bony arches of the vertebrae. The cord bulges at the points where nerves branch off to the arms and legs. It is buffered by three membranes called meninges that continue upward to enclose the brain. Beneath the meninges, both brain and spinal cord are bathed by cerebrospinal fluid, which acts partly as a shock absorber, as well as serving to bring nourishment to the nervous tissue and protect it from infection.

If you slice through the column of the cord you notice an outer layer of white matter—myelinated afferent and efferent nerve fibers, respectively, which transmit signals up and down the cord. Inside this layer is gray matter, the arrangement of which resembles butterfly's wings in cross section. The "upper" wings, pointing toward the back of the body, contain afferent neurons that receive signals from outside the cord. The "lower" wings, pointing toward the front of the body, contain efferents, controlling muscles and glands.

Peripheral nervous system

Nerves originating in or linked with the central nervous system branch out through the body. This outer, or peripheral nervous system, has two overlapping components: the somatic ("of the body") and autonomic ("self-regulating") systems.

Somatic motor nerves supply striated (skeletal) muscle. Somatic sensory nerves supply sensory receptors in skin, tongue, nostrils, eyes, joints, and muscles.

Twelve pairs of cranial nerves arising from the brain supply ears, eyes, nose, facial skin and muscles, the tongue, jaw and neck muscles, and various internal organs. Thirty-one pairs of spinal nerves sprout from the spinal cord, supplying limbs and trunk. Sensory nerve fibers enter from the back, motor nerve fibers leave from the front, both passing in or out through gaps between vertebrae. Although there are approximately as many gaps as spinal nerves, the spinal cord ends high above the bottom of the spine, so the nerves of the lowest nerve roots must travel some distance inside the spine before they reach their exit holes.

Autonomic nervous system

Part of the peripheral nervous system works automatically, controlling the smooth muscle of internal organs and some glandular secretions. It normally functions outside conscious, willed control.

The autonomic nervous system has sympathetic and parasympathetic divisions, which operate to counteract each other—the sympathetic system generally having an excitatory effect, the parasympathetic system the reverse.

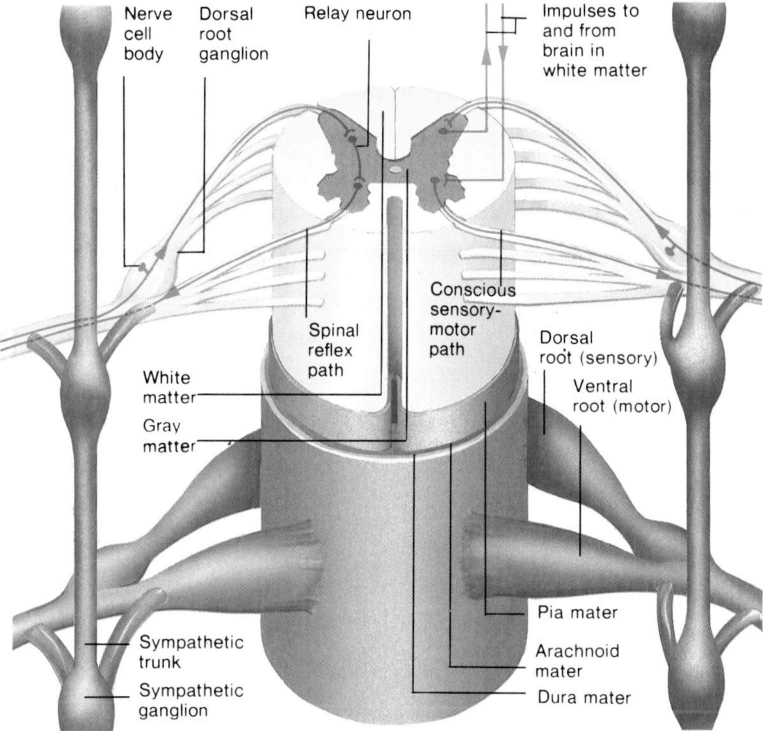

Spinal sensory and motor pathways may or may not pass through the brain. In a spinal reflex *(left)*, a sensory signal enters by the dorsal root and synapses with motor fibers within the spinal cord. These then stimulate muscular action through the ventral motor root. In a conscious action *(right)*, the signal travels to and from the brain.

The sympathetic system releases chemical neurotransmitters to stimulate heart, lungs, and other organs. Nerves of the sympathetic system form two cords parallel with the spinal cord and linked to it along its length, but not at its ends. Pealike swellings in both of these cords, called ganglia, contain nerve-cell bodies.

The parasympathetic system, arising from both ends of the spinal cord, releases neurotransmitters that act mostly on the same organs as those affected by the sympathetic system, but in ways that slow them down. Under stress, the sympathetic system dominates; at rest, the parasympathetic system takes control.

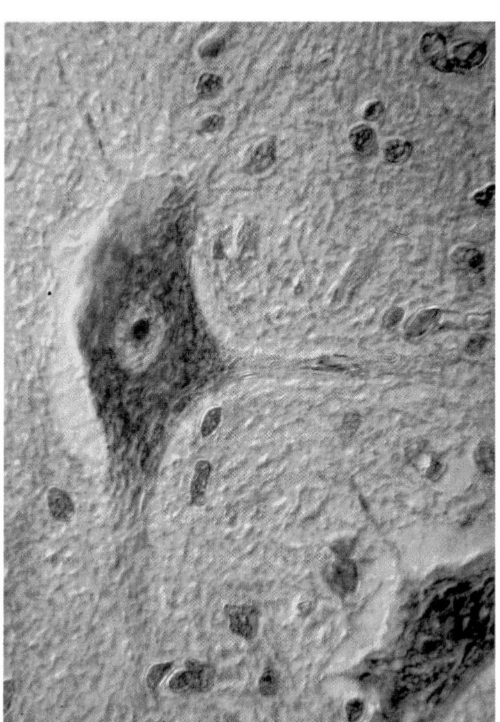

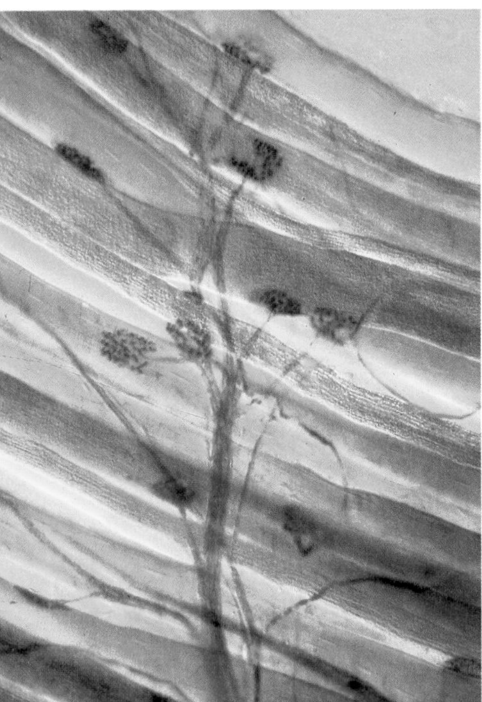

A spinal neuron *(far left)* consists of a cell body, with a nucleus, several threadlike dendrites linking with other neurons, and a longer fiber that carries the nervous impulse. In a motor neuron, this long fiber is covered by a fatty sheath and ends in a motor end plate.

Motor end plates *(left)*, shown here at the same magnification as the spinal neuron *(far left)*, attach to and stimulate individual muscle fibers.

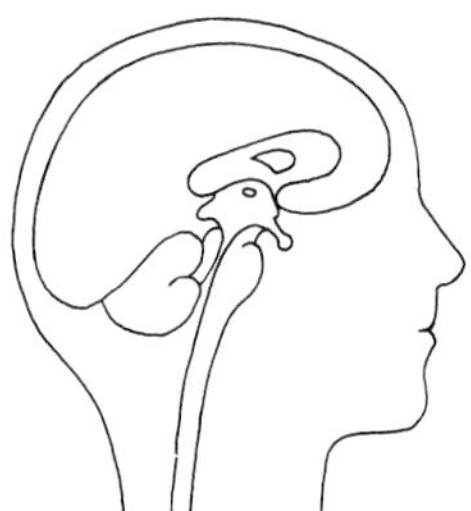

The brain is an outgrowth of the top of the spinal cord, enclosed and protected by the bony cranium of the skull.

The brain

The brain is shaped like a wrinkled walnut kernel, is about the size of a large grapefruit and appears as insubstantial as a moist, soft cheese. Two-fifths of it consist of no more than supporting glial cells. Yet it contains from 10 to 100 billion neurons with complex interlinking sensory, motor, and association pathways. Signals selectively transmitted through these routes enable us to eat, walk, lift loads, thread a needle, speak, love, hate, dream, think, remember, and make decisions. Computers may calculate faster than the human brain, but cannot match the versatility of this most amazing of all the body's mechanisms.

The brain has several major parts; each has its own shape and function, and all contribute to the amazing total of human mental capabilities. The principal areas of the brain are the brain stem, the cerebellum, and the inner and outer forebrain, which form the cerebral hemispheres or cerebrum.

Brain stem

This 3-inch (7.5-centimeter) long mass of nervous tissue forms the upper, clublike end of the spinal cord. The brain's evolutionary core, or root—the brain stem—carries sensory and motor nerve tracts and houses neurons controlling basic body processes. The brain stem has three sections: from the bottom up, the medulla, pons, and midbrain.

Neurons in the medulla control the automatic actions of the heart and lungs, serve as relay stations for five cranial nerves, and as the grand pathway for hundreds of millions of sensory and motor nerves connecting brain and spinal cord. Most of these cross over in the medulla, so that the brain's left side controls the right side of the body and vice versa.

Above the medulla, the pons and midbrain serve as further relay stations. Running through all three is a thicket of neurons called the reticular formation, which receives signals from sense receptors and controls consciousness.

Cerebellum

The cerebellum, or "little brain," accounts for 11 per cent of the brain's total weight. Bulging from the back of the pons, it lies tucked beneath the rear of the much larger cerebral hemispheres. The cerebellum monitors information from muscles, tendons, joints, and the inner ear and acts to adjust and coordinate muscle movements on instructions from the cerebrum. Every action, from drinking a glass of water to walking or playing the piano, proceeds smoothly primarily because of the unobtrusive work done by the cerebellum, which acts like an automatic pilot.

The inner forebrain

Distinctive groups of clustered cells form special structures deep inside the brain above the brain stem and around the ventricles—cavities filled with cerebrospinal fluid. Innermost of these structures are the thalamus and hypothalamus. The thalamus, a large double structure, is a major sensory coordinator, processing information from ears, eyes, mouth, and skin as it passes to the higher centers of the brain. Below the thalamus, the tiny hypothalamus controls thirst, hunger, sweating, shivering, and other processes essential to life.

Four neuron clusters, collectively called

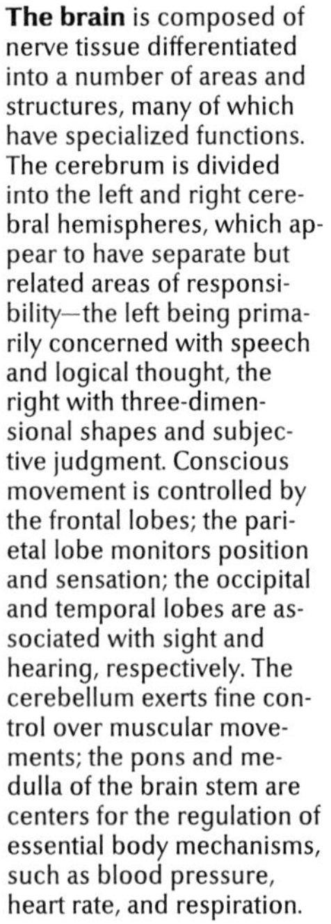

The brain is composed of nerve tissue differentiated into a number of areas and structures, many of which have specialized functions. The cerebrum is divided into the left and right cerebral hemispheres, which appear to have separate but related areas of responsibility—the left being primarily concerned with speech and logical thought, the right with three-dimensional shapes and subjective judgment. Conscious movement is controlled by the frontal lobes; the parietal lobe monitors position and sensation; the occipital and temporal lobes are associated with sight and hearing, respectively. The cerebellum exerts fine control over muscular movements; the pons and medulla of the brain stem are centers for the regulation of essential body mechanisms, such as blood pressure, heart rate, and respiration.

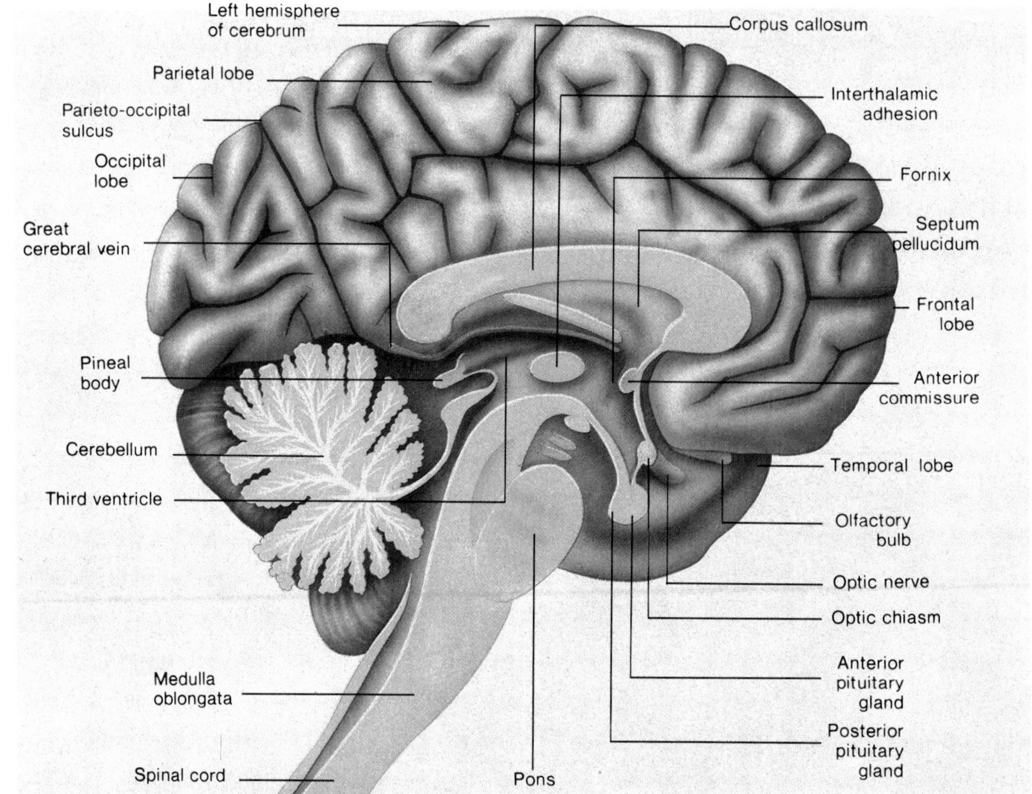

basal ganglia, crown the thalamus. Relaying information from cerebral hemispheres to brain stem and cerebellum, they help to regulate the body's movements. They also share a structure, the amygdaloid ("almondlike") body, with the so-called limbic system, a wishbonelike "mini-brain" encircling the brain stem and concerned with emotions and memory. The human limbic system resembles that of a primitive mammal, and, for this reason, it is sometimes called the "old" mammalian brain in contrast to the "new" brain, the cerebrum.

The outer forebrain

Seven-tenths of the cells of the entire nervous system lie in the cerebral hemispheres, the two large connected swellings at the front end of the forebrain. Deep wrinkles enormously enlarge the surface area of the cerebral cortex—the thin outer layer of gray matter that is, apparently, the seat of human intelligence. No other animal species has so much brain space allocated to this fragile layer. The human cerebral cortex contains about half a billion nerve cells with 620 miles (1,000 kilometers) of connecting fibers for every cubic half-inch.

Deep fissures in each convoluted hemisphere help to divide it into lobes, and special areas of cortex in different lobes deal with specific kinds of mental activity. Those areas receiving sensory input and dispatching motor signals are known as the sensory cortex and the motor cortex, also sometimes referred to collectively as the primary cortex. Primary cortex in the occipital lobes at the back of the brain receives signals from the eyes. Sensory strips of cortex down each side of the brain—where frontal and parietal lobes meet—receive input from the tongue, lips, face, head, hands, trunk, arms, legs, feet, and other areas. A strip of motor cortex running down the frontal lobe near the sensory strip triggers movement in specific muscles.

From primary cortex, signals flow to association cortex in the frontal, parietal, and temporal lobes. Here, received sensations may be associated with conceptual thought.

Prefrontal areas at the very front of the brain help to control personality and intellect. Speaking and understanding speech depend heavily on areas in three lobes of the left cerebral hemisphere. Visual recognition seems to reside in the right side of the brain.

Brain and mind

Most scientists believe that "mind" is just the product of the brain, not an independent entity, as some philosophers have held. Consciousness, perception, attention, memory, thought, judgment, emotion, personality, dreams, and hallucinations have all been shown to depend, at least partly, upon the function of some specific region of the brain. Yet much about the working of the brain remains mysterious. For instance, how do some mystics manage to achieve apparently voluntary control of automatic body mechanisms—for example, reducing their oxygen needs at times below the level normally needed for survival? How do techniques like hypnosis and autogenic training help certain people to cope with chronic pain? Study of mind and the brain remains one of the most challenging and—from a mechanistic point of view—most mysterious areas of investigation into the nature of the human animal.

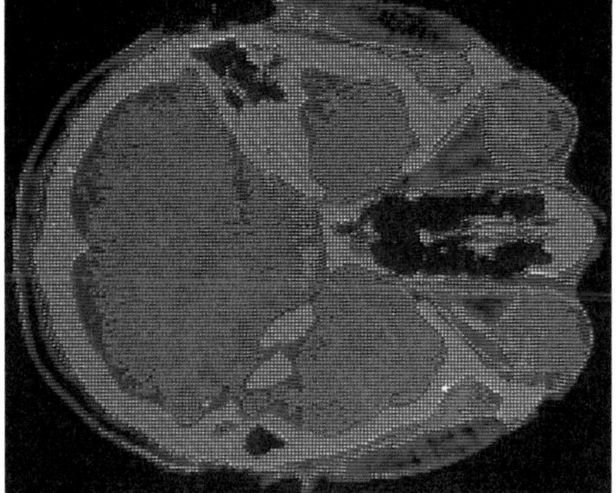

A cross section through the skull, made with a CAT (computerized axial tomography) scan, shows the horizontal relationship between the eyes, the nasal tissues, and the lower parts of the brain—the two temporal lobes and the cerebellum.

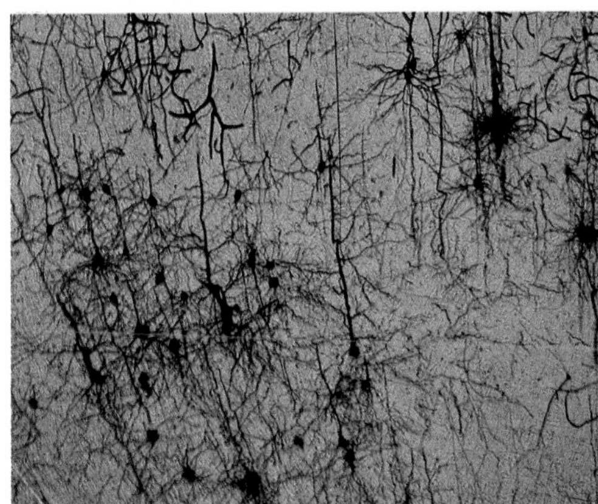

The cerebral cortex, the outer layer of the cerebrum, contains closely packed neurons with many interconnecting dendrites.

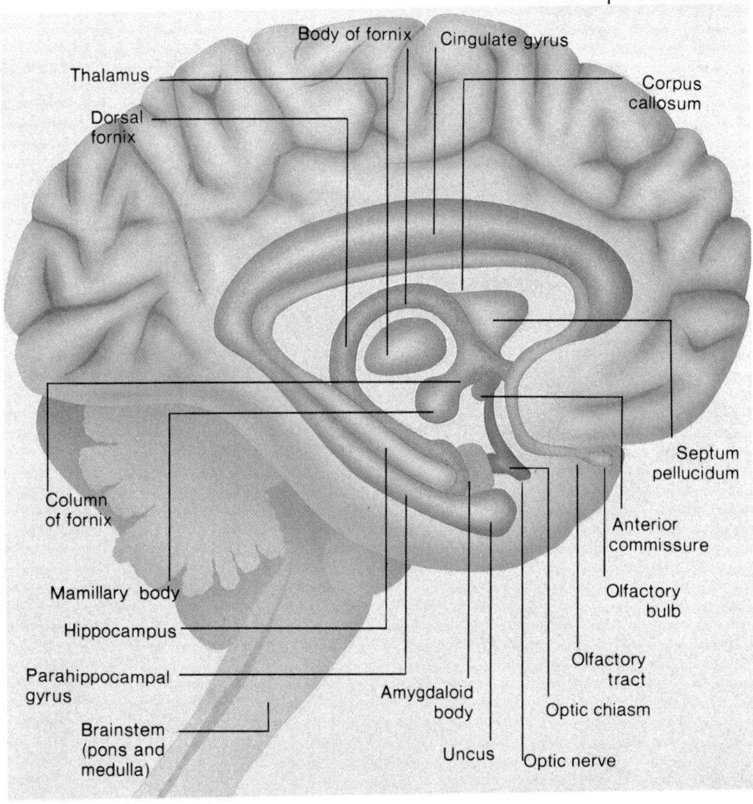

The limbic system forms two symmetrical loops, only one of which is illustrated, between the brain stem and the cerebral hemisphere. It is concerned principally with memory and emotion. The septum pellucidum is associated with pleasure, the amygdaloid body with aggression, the cingulate gyrus and hippocampus with memory. The thalamus and mamillary body appear to act as organizers. The fornix and anterior commissure link parts of the limbic system with each other and with other parts of the brain.

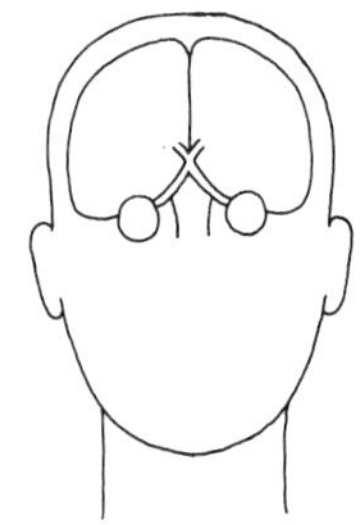

The eyes connect with the brain through the optic (2nd cranial) nerve. The visual pathways "cross over" at the optic chiasm.

The eye

Eyes tell us more about the world around us than any other of our senses. They inform us of the size, shape, position, and color of objects from pinpoints a few inches from our nose to stars billions of miles away in space. This is possible because each eyeball contains a nerve net (the retina) that is sensitive to light waves, which it converts electrochemically to signals that can be interpreted by the brain. These nerve nets are enclosed by two roughly spherical organs, the eyes, which can focus light, control the amount of light entering the eye, and move to follow a light source.

Eyelid and eyeballs

The delicate eyeballs are protected by the bones of the skull and by the two eyelids. Each eyelid has three main layers: skin; muscles that make it shut and open; and the tarsi, made of tough fibrous tissue. Blinking protects eyes from injury and allows tears to bathe the eyes. Tears, composed of a saline bactericidal fluid, come from each upper eyelid's lacrimal gland. The fluid drains away through a tear duct opening at each eyelid's inner corner into the nasal cavity.

Eyeballs are jelly-filled spheres set in fat, supplied with muscles, and shielded by the bony orbits of the skull. Six ocular muscles coordinate each eye's movements so that both eyes can follow moving objects together. The eyes' overlapping fields of view produce the binocular vision that enables us to judge depth and distance.

Light falling on the eye passes through the transparent cornea—the bulging, transparent front of the outer layer of the eyeball. The rest of the outer layer (the sclera, or "white" of the eye) is opaque to light and is covered with a layer of conjunctiva. Light rays then continue through a so-called anterior chamber filled with the watery fluid known as the aqueous humor. This fluid and the cornea refract incoming light and serve as the front lens of the eye.

Light refracted by this outer lens then enters the pupil—a hole surrounded by a muscular diaphragm, the iris. The pupil appears black because light is not reflected out from the interior of the eye. Pigmentation of the iris gives the eye its color. It contracts or dilates in response to the intensity of light, contracting in bright light to prevent too much light from entering the eye and dilating in dim light to allow as much light as possible to enter the eye. Light next passes through a flexible, transparent crystalline lens. Ligaments connect this lens to ciliary muscles that can make it shorten and bulge, or lengthen and grow slimmer, thereby altering its focal length to bring near or distant objects into finer focus.

Refracted further by this lens, light rays reach the eye's posterior chamber. This is filled with the jellylike vitreous humor. After passing through this fluid, light rays reach the retina—a layered network of nerve cells lining the inside of the back of the eyeball and separated from its outer, scleral layer by the chorion, or choroid, a layer of blood vessels that brings nourishment and removes waste products.

The eye lies in the orbit of the skull, held in place by the muscles that move it and cushioned by fat. The eyelids cover the conjunctiva and cornea, which together protect the interior. Light enters through the cornea, is refracted by this and the aqueous humor before passing through the iris to the lens, which focuses it on to the fovea. Rods and cones in the retina transmit impulses through the optic nerve to the brain.

The retina

The retina, or "net," covering the rear four-fifths of the eyeball's inner surface is a cup-shaped extension of the brain—linked to it by the second cranial, or optic, nerve. It seems to be back-to-front, for light rays must pass through the layers of nerve cells communicating with the optic nerve before they reach the retinal cells sensitive to light. Each retina has about 120 million rods and about 6 million cones. The long, thin structures known as rods are concentrated toward the rim of the retina. Rods are highly sensitive to low intensities of light but register only shades of gray. The six million cone photoreceptors are relatively short, thick cells that are most plentiful toward the back of the eye and concentrated especially at the fovea, a shallow retinal pit opposite the pupil. Cones work well only in good light but, between them, register green, red, and blue light, and so perceive the range of colors of the visible spectrum.

As light falls on both rods and cones, their light-sensitive pigments instantly decay and then re-form. This change sends electrochemical signals along the optic nerves to the brain, where the signals are interpreted as sight.

Inside the brain

We analyze and understand the images registered inside our eyes because each bit of the image travels in coded fashion from retina to visual cortex at the back of the brain. The journey through the fibers of the optic nerves is complicated. Nerves from each eye meet in the front of the brain at the optic chiasm. This is a partial crossing point where fibers from

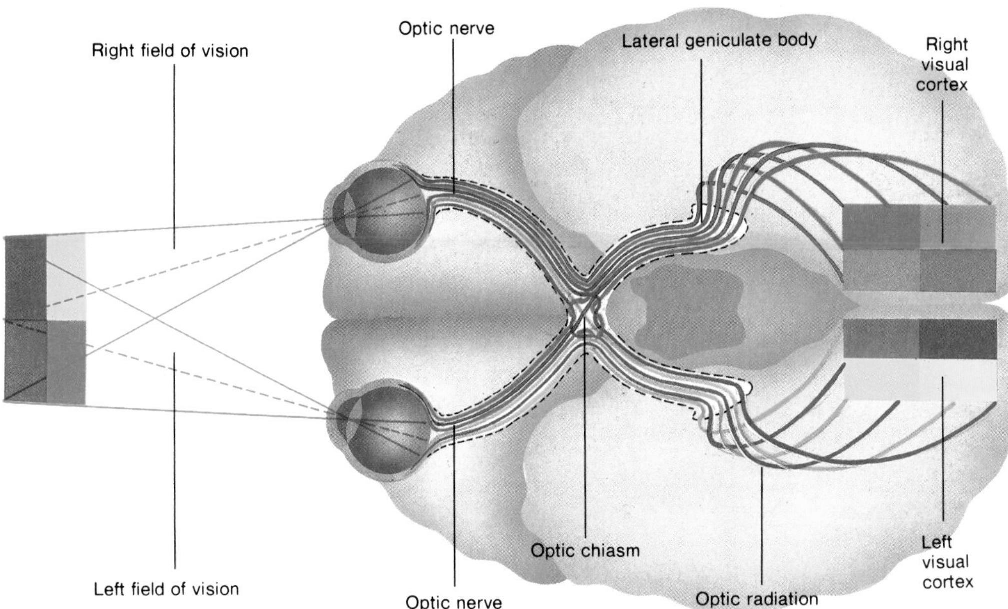

The visual pathways from each retina cross over at the optic chiasm. Nerve impulses from the left of each retina—the right of the visual field—travel in the optic tract to the left of the brain; impulses from the right travel to the right. The optic tracts continue to the lateral geniculate bodies, which coordinate visual information with information from other parts of the brain. Impulses continue to the visual cortex at the back of the cerebrum, where they are interpreted.

each eye's inner (nasal) side switch over to join the nerve-carrying fibers from the outer (temporal) side of the other eye. From the chiasm, both sets of nerve fibers—now known as optic tracts—continue through the brain. After passing the lateral geniculate bodies (relay stations in the thalamus), these nerve fibers fan out in the so-called optic radiation, ending at the primary visual cortex at the back inner edge of each cerebral hemisphere.

The partial crossing of fibers at the optic chiasm ensures that signals from the right side of each retina reach the right visual cortex while signals from the left side of each retina reach the left visual cortex.

Research suggests that, in addition to coordinating countless individual signals almost instantly, some specialization of visual perception may also occur. For example, different cell columns in the cortex may deal with signals from different regions in each retina. And three neighboring areas of cortex of some mammals (designated visual areas I, II, and III) have cells that are sensitive to different stimuli. The "simple" cells of visual area I react to bright lines and dark bars at special angles. Areas II and III have so-called complex and hypercomplex cells: the first register edges and movement; the second detect corners.

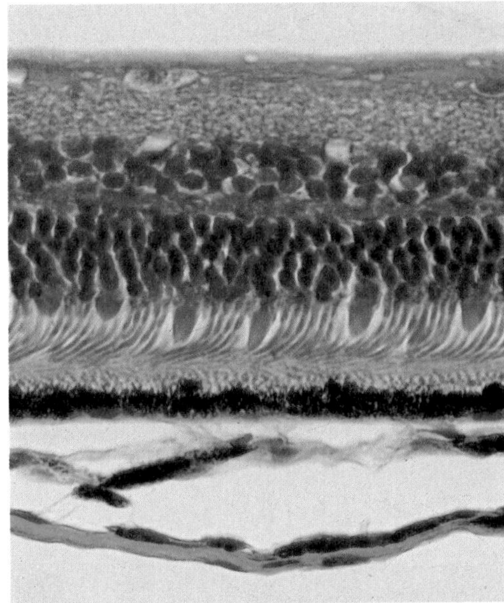

The retina (shown here in cross section) consists of several strata: from the top, there are nerve fibers to the optic nerve; several layers of ganglia and nuclei; rods and cones—the latter being the larger ovoid shapes among thin rods; and the pigmented layer.

The retina appears red when viewed through an ophthalmoscope. Blood vessels enter through the paler optic disk (blind spot).

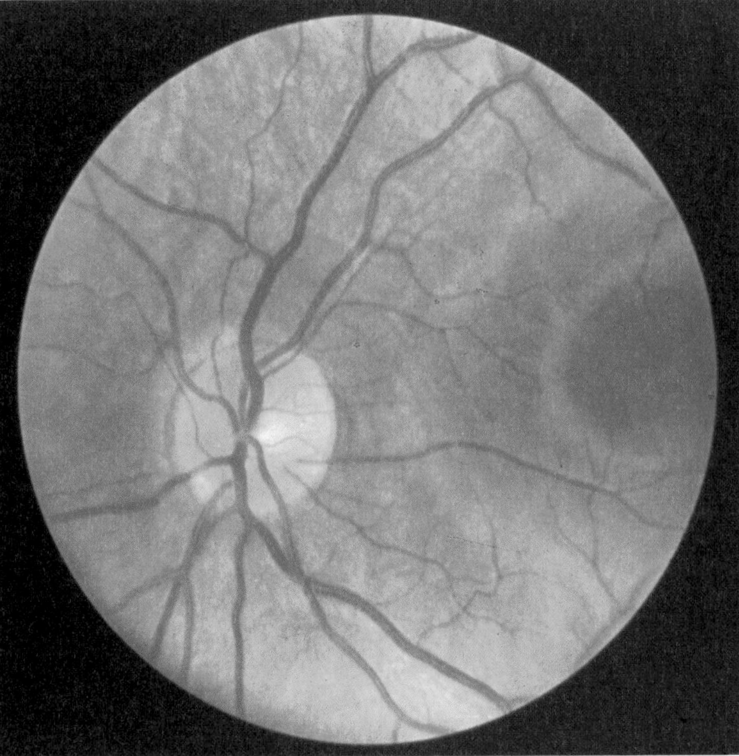

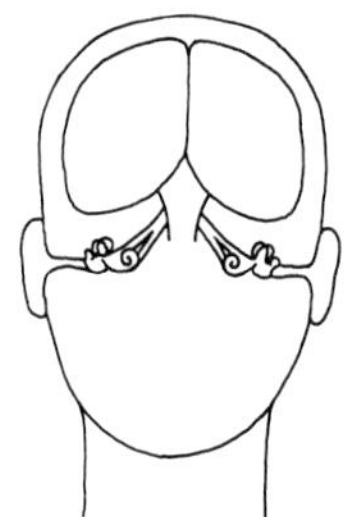

The ears are located at the sides of the head and are concerned with the senses of hearing and balance.

The ear

Ears convert pressure waves passing through the air into electrochemical signals that the brain registers as sounds. The ear itself has three main parts called the outer, middle, and inner ear.

Outer ear

The outer ear, also called the pinna, incorporates a flap of skin and cartilage connected to an opening in the head leading to a short cul-de-sac, the external auditory meatus, or canal. The auditory canal is a tunnel about 1 inch (2.5 centimeters) long. It contains a lining of wax and hairs that block invasive insects and bacteria, but let sound waves through to the middle ear.

Middle ear

The air-filled chamber contains structures that transmit sound vibrations from the outer to the inner ear. The middle ear roughly resembles a six-sided chamber joined to the nasal cavity and throat by the Eustachian tube, which opens during yawning or swallowing to equalize air pressure.

The eardrum, or tympanic membrane, which stretches across the outer entrance of the chamber, is a thin, delicate sheet of tissue that vibrates at the frequencies of the sound waves arriving from the outer ear. As it vibrates, it transmits vibrations to three tiny, connected bones (ossicles) that span the chamber. Among the body's smallest bones, these ossicles comprise the malleus (hammer), incus (anvil), and stapes (stirrup). The malleus and incus hang from the roof of the inner ear and are linked by synovial joints to each other and to the stapes. Ossicles pass on vibrations with diminished range of movement yet greatly increased pressure.

Inner ear: the cochlea

Different regions of the inner ear deal with sound and balance. Hearing depends upon the cochlea—a spiral tube resembling a snail's shell, filled with fluid and divided lengthwise by the basilar membrane into upper and lower chambers, separated from the middle ear by the oval and round windows, respectively.

It is in the cochlea that vibrations transmitted through the ossicles trigger signals in a nerve communicating with the brain. The stapes vibrates against the oval window, which in turn transmits pressure waves through the fluid of the upper chamber of the cochlea. The round window vibrates freely to equalize pressure between the cochlea and middle ear. Meanwhile, waves set up resonance in the basilar membrane and the attached organ of Corti—a tunnel flanked by hair cells that serve as auditory receptors. Disturbance of these

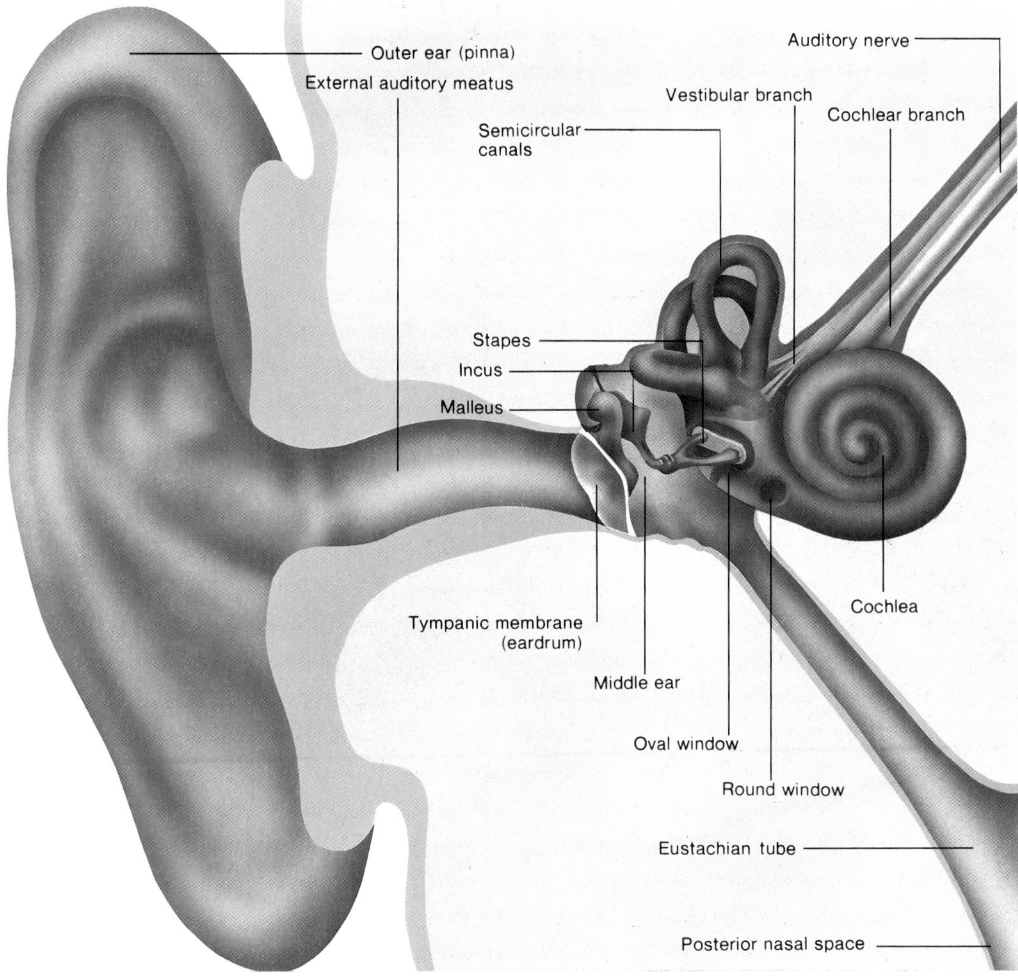

Each ear has three main parts: the external ear, the middle ear, and the inner ear. The external ear consists of the pinna and the external auditory meatus. The tympanic membrane forms the outer boundary of the middle ear. Sound waves cause it to vibrate, and these vibrations are transmitted by the three small ossicle bones—malleus, incus, and stapes—to the oval window of the inner ear. Vibrations are further transmitted from the oval window to the cochlea, which contains sensory cells that convert these vibrations into nervous impulses. These travel along the cochlear branch of the vestibulocochlear, or auditory, (8th cranial) nerve to the brain. The inner ear also contains the semicircular canals, or vestibular apparatus, which detect movement and posture and communicate with the brain through the vestibular branch of the auditory nerve.

cells stimulates fibers of the cochlear nerve. This forms part of the auditory nerve, which transmits signals to the "hearing centers" in the temporal lobes of the brain.

Whether we hear a sound as high or low in pitch depends on the part of the basilar membrane that resonates most strongly. Low-frequency pressure waves are detected where the membrane is broadest, and high-frequency waves have their effect near its narrow end.

Much as both eyes work together to help us judge depth and distance, so both ears help us to determine where a sound comes from. This auditory sense is much less well developed than the corresponding visual sense, however, and the ears themselves are less suited than the eyes to distance judgment and direction finding.

Age, internal injury, or disease may result in hearing loss in one ear or both ears, but there are also a number of ways that deafness can be overcome. Disease that prevents sound vibrations from passing through the middle ear is not sufficient alone to prevent hearing completely because some vibrations find their way to the cochlea by way of the skull bones. Hearing aids set in these bones make use of this. Aids fitted in the outer ear can often help to compensate for damage to the inner ear. And because some acoustic nerve fibers cross from one side of the brain to the other on their way to the tops of the temporal lobes, damage to one temporal lobe need not necessarily cause deafness in the ear on that side.

Inner ear: vestibular system

The inner ear's vestibular system helps us to keep our balance, even with closed eyes. The system consists of three semicircular tubes, called canals, at right angles to one another, and two sacs (the saccule and utricle), all filled with fluid and located near the cochlea. The canals broaden at one end into flask-shaped chambers (ampullae). Each chamber has a gelatinous capsule containing the hair cells of a receptor organ. The saccule and utricle contain gelatinous masses called static receptors, weighted with crystals called otoliths. When the head moves, fluid flows through the canals and sacs, disturbing the gelatinous masses and hairs, and generating signals in nerve endings near the hairs' roots.

Different head movements and positions stimulate different groups of nerve endings in the vestibular system. The superior semicircular canal registers nodding, the posterior canal detects tilting, and the lateral (or horizontal) canal responds to turning. Different positions of the head are registered by the saccule and utricle, because these cause different weight distributions of the otoliths, which affect nerve endings in these parts of the vestibular system.

From the vestibular system, signals pass through the vestibular nerve, which merges with the cochlear nerve to form the auditory nerve. From the vestibular nerve, many fibers pass directly to the cerebellum, where they assist limb, eye, and trunk coordination.

Balance is coordinated by signals from the vestibular apparatus.

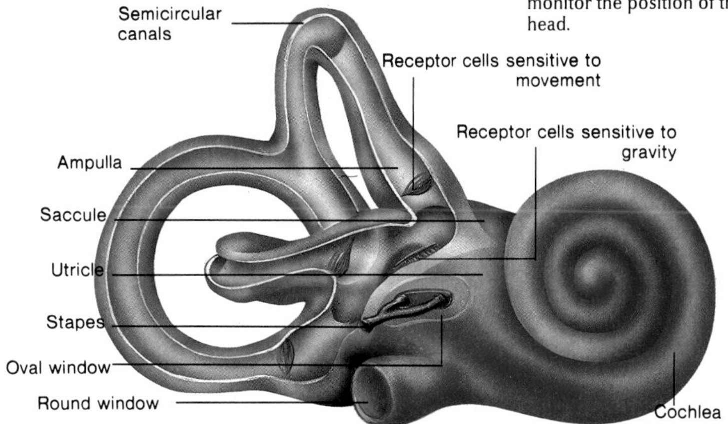

The semicircular canals, or vestibular apparatus, are oriented at right angles to each other. When the head moves, fluid flows and stimulates receptor cells in the ampullae. Other receptor cells sensitive to gravity monitor the position of the head.

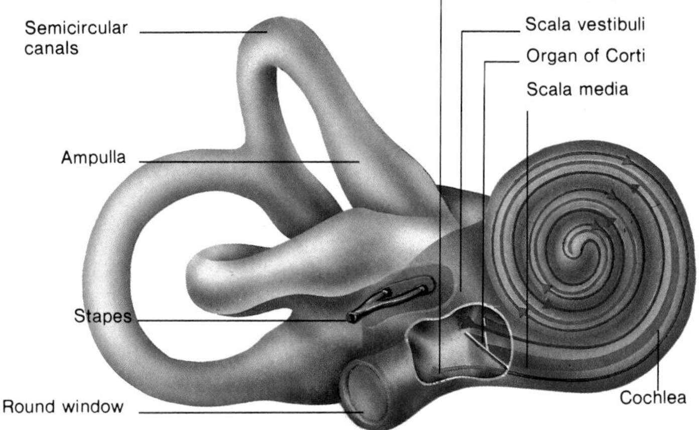

The cochlea carries vibrations from the oval window through the upper scala tympani, then the lower scala vestibuli to the round window. On the way, hair cells of the organ of Corti are stimulated and send signals to the brain, where they are interpreted as sound.

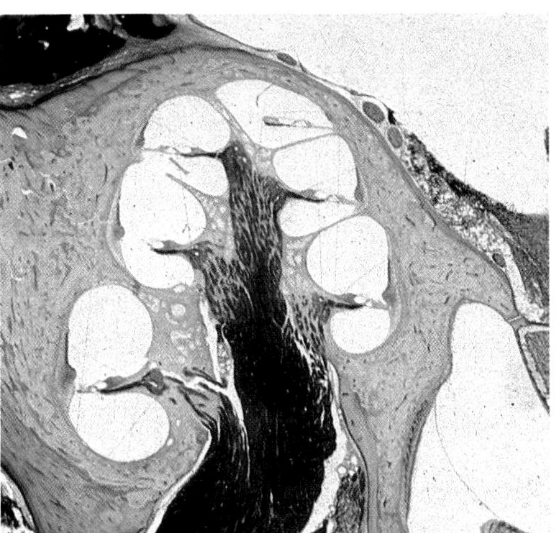

A cross section of the cochlea shows its three sections and the central cochlear nerve.

Smell and taste

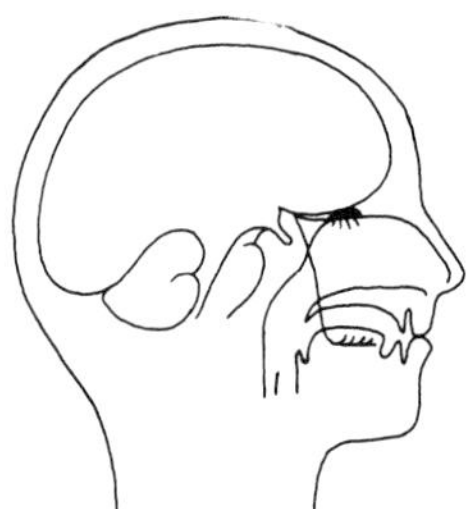

Smell and taste are the senses of the nose and tongue. Both are relayed by nerves from sensory cells in these organs to the brain.

Smell helps us to distinguish pleasant from unpleasant or dangerous substances at a distance; taste involves direct contact. But both are chemical senses that depend on foreign molecules touching sensory structures called receptor cells. In some ways, smell and taste may be the most primitive senses. Sometimes —for example in the discernment of some of the more subtle flavors—both work together more closely than most of us realize.

Smell

Smell is detected by sensory cells in two patches of olfactory epithelium, one in the roof of each nasal cavity, just below the cranium. Between them, the two patches occupy approximately one square inch (5 square centimeters), yet scientists calculate that they include millions of rodlike bodies projecting from the buried sensory cells. Each rod ends in filaments, or "hairs," the total area of which may exceed that of the skin surface.

These sensitive hairs, in common with the entire surface of each nasal cavity, are moistened by the mucous membrane that lines the nose. This membrane is kept warm by a rich supply of blood vessels and so warms and moistens air breathed in through the nostrils. Moisture plays a key role in the sense of smell, for chemical receptors can only detect substances that can be dissolved.

Probably only two per cent of breathed-in air passes close to the cell receptors. Yet these are so sensitive that a single molecule of some substances is enough to excite one receptor ending—for instance, the human olfactory system can sense less than one hundred millionth of a gram of musk. Furthermore, some people can distinguish as many as 10,000 different odors.

Exactly how smell works remains debatable. But the stereochemical theory of olfaction suggests that most odors are combinations of a few primary odors produced by distinctively shaped chemical molecules that fit into matching olfactory sites, like keys into locks. This suggests there may be different basic odors, in rather the same way as there are different basic tastes.

Smell and taste are detected by specialized sensory cells in the nose and tongue, respectively. In the nose, olfactory nerve fibers extend from the olfactory bulb beneath the forebrain into membranes lining the nasal cavity. Airborne chemicals dissolve in these membranes' mucous covering and stimulate nerve fibers that convey signals to the olfactory bulb and then along the olfactory (1st cranial) nerve to the brain. Taste buds in the tongue also respond to chemical stimuli. Those at the front of the tongue stimulate the lingual nerve, a branch of the maxillary nerve, which in turn is part of the trigeminal (5th cranial) nerve. Receptors at the back of the tongue stimulate the glossopharyngeal (9th cranial) nerve. The mouth and nose are sensitive to other stimuli apart from taste and smell and are correspondingly well-supplied by other sensory nerves.

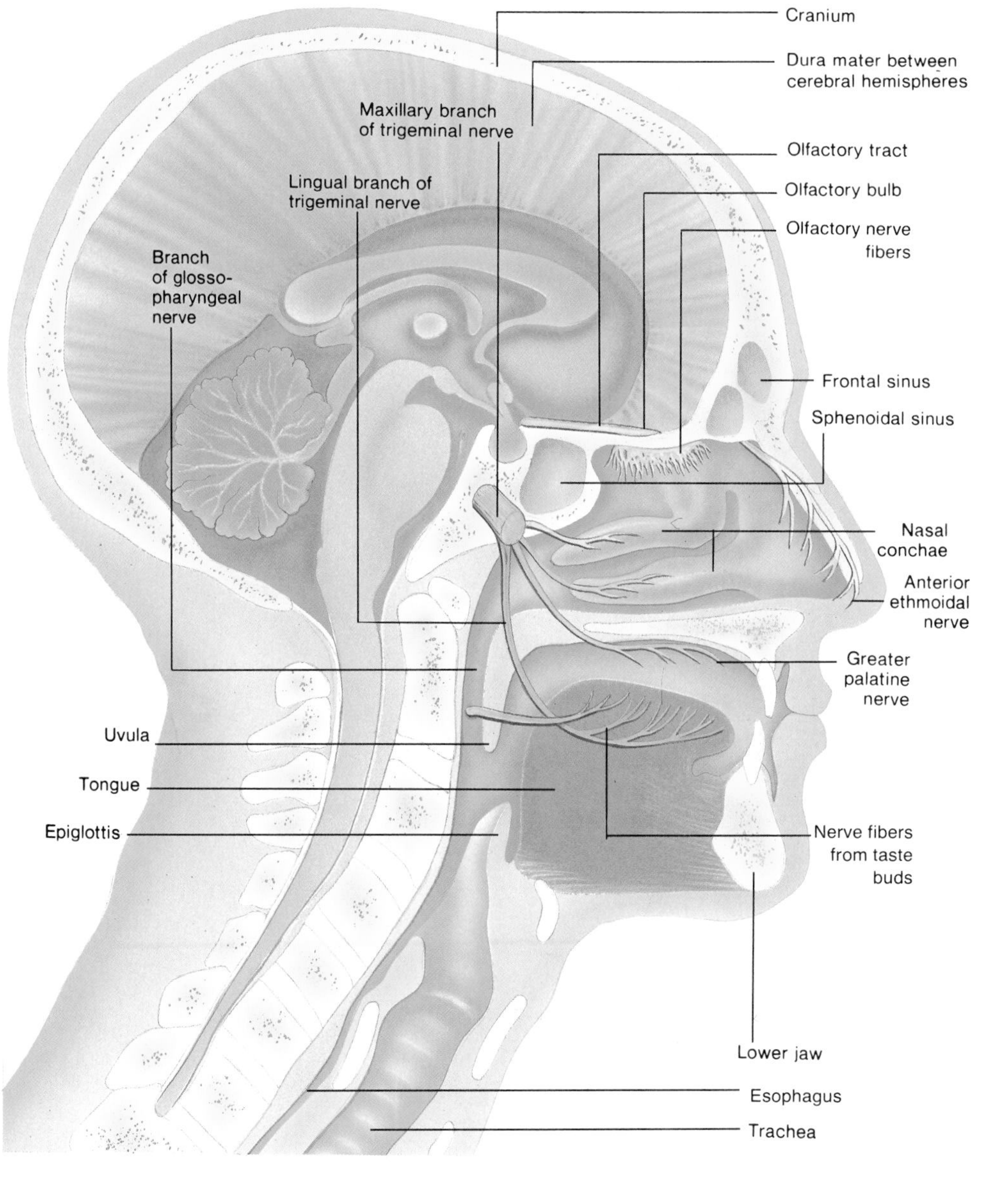

Cranium
Dura mater between cerebral hemispheres
Maxillary branch of trigeminal nerve
Lingual branch of trigeminal nerve
Olfactory tract
Olfactory bulb
Olfactory nerve fibers
Branch of glosso-pharyngeal nerve
Frontal sinus
Sphenoidal sinus
Nasal conchae
Anterior ethmoidal nerve
Greater palatine nerve
Uvula
Tongue
Epiglottis
Nerve fibers from taste buds
Lower jaw
Esophagus
Trachea

From the olfactory receptors, nerve signals travel to the two olfactory bulbs projecting from the brain, then on by complex routes to a diffuse olfactory region associated with the limbic system in the brain.

Taste

Compared with our sense of smell, our sense of taste seems poorly developed. Most taste-sensitive cells occur on the upper part of the tongue. A very few are found on the palate, lingual tonsils, and epiglottis. Groups of these receptors form each taste bud, and there can be many such buds on one papilla, or small projection on the tongue's upper surface, which feels rough because of the scores of papillae found there. Babies possess tens of thousands of taste buds, but numbers decrease with age: an adult normally has about 9,000.

Four types of taste buds, found in the papillae, enable us to distinguish between sweet, sour, salty, and bitter tastes. But the receptor cells that make up our taste buds do not have structural or functional differences that correspond to these tastes. The idea of the four categories of taste seems to be something that is learned. Taste categories may be only characteristics of taste; they tell us little about how the taste sense functions.

While olfactory signals pass through the olfactory lobes, taste signals travel through cranial nerves straight to the brain stem, then on to the brain's higher centers.

The taste of food

Taste and smell combine to help give many foods their flavors. This is apparent in the fact that flavors are difficult or impossible to distinguish when the mucous membranes are inflamed during an infection, such as a cold. The taste of food also depends upon its temperature: taste receptors are most highly sensitive to foods at temperatures of 85—105° F. (30—40° C).

In time, nerve cells adapt to prolonged exposure to certain tastes or odors so that these stimuli are no longer noticed. Furthermore, adaptation to one taste may also alter sensitivity to others. Thus, coffee tastes unusually bitter if you drink it after eating ice cream, while salt-adaption heightens sensitivity to bitter, sweet, and sour substances.

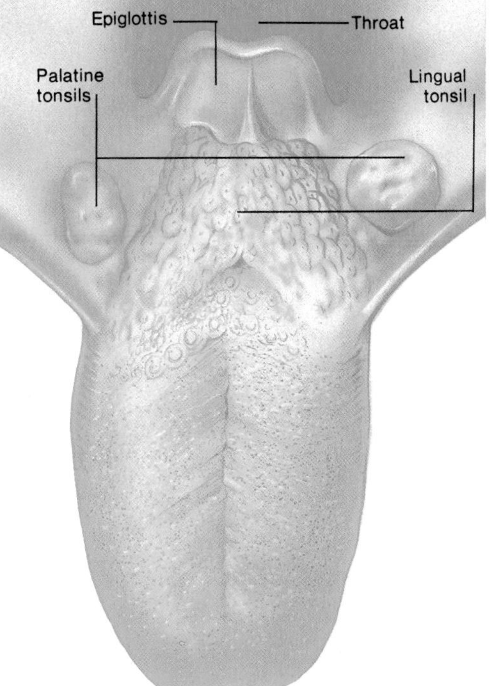

The tongue is a muscular organ projecting from the floor of the mouth. Its surface is covered with three types of papillae—rounded fungiform, pointed filiform, and columnar vallate papillae—and taste buds are found on many of these. Four types of taste buds, found in the papillae, enable us to distinguish between sweet, sour, salty, and bitter.

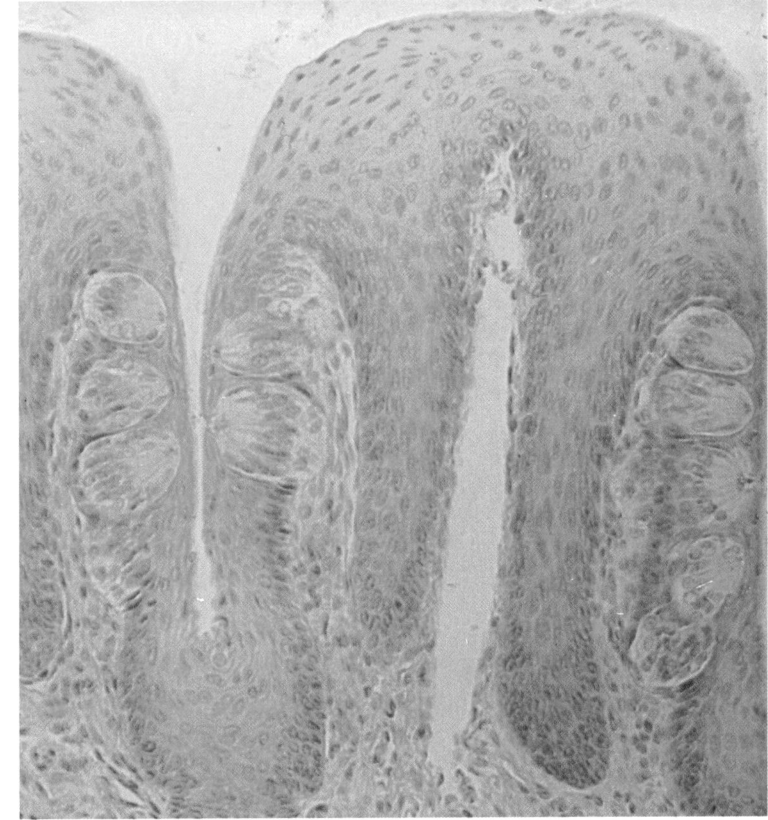

Taste buds on the sides of papillae respond to chemicals dissolved in saliva or other liquids in the mouth.

Fact entries

Tastes in man are of four types. Salty tastes are caused by the anions of inorganic salts such as the halogens chlorine and bromine, although a pure sensation of saltiness comes only from sodium chloride. Sour tastes come from the hydrogen ions in acids.

Sweet and bitter tastes tend to have organic origins. For instance, caffeine tastes bitter, sucrose tastes sweet. But sweet-tasting substances also include beryllium, a metal, and bitter-tasting substances include copper.

Taste in animals is similar, in that most vertebrates seem to share man's discrimination and sensitivity to tastes. Dogs, however, can taste sugars although not saccharin; and pigeons seem able to taste saccharin but not sugars. Chickens appear unable to detect either.

Even individual humans differ in their sensitivity. For example, 70 per cent of Caucasians can taste phenylthiocarbamide, a bitter-tasting chemical, but the other 30 per cent have not inherited the ability to do so.

The skin

Skin forms the body's largest organ. An adult's skin has a surface area of approximately 19 square feet (1.75 square meters) and weighs about 6 pounds (2.7 kilograms).

Skin provides the body with a tough, flexible barrier that protects against disease, injury, and loss of water from the moist internal tissues. It also helps control the body's temperature, excretes some wastes, and serves as a major sensory organ, registering pressure, pain, and temperature. An area of skin about the size of an adult thumbnail may contain about three million cells, 3 feet (90 centimeters) of blood vessels, 12 feet (3.7 meters) of nerves, and 100 sweat glands.

Skin has three layers of tissue: epidermis, dermis, and subcutaneous tissue.

Freckles are small patches of melanin pigment in the Malpighian layer of the epidermis. The same pigmentation causes the skin to darken in response to sunlight and is responsible for the dark skin of some people.

Epidermis

A slice cut through the epidermis would reveal subsidiary layers of cells, the lowest alive and multiplying, the topmost cells dead and flaking off.

Cells of the stratum basale, or Malpighian layer, resemble close-packed posts or columns. As they multiply they give rise to the "prickle" cells of the stratum spinosum, the layer just above, some five to ten cells deep. Next comes the stratum granulosum. There are no blood vessels here to bring nutrients or carry away wastes, so this layer's cells die off and accumulate granules of protein waste. Above these is a clear layer called the stratum lucidum, where granules have changed into the tough fibrous protein keratin—the substance nails and hair are made. The stratum corneum, or cornified layer, the topmost layer of the epidermis, consists of flat, dead, keratinized cells that are continuously flaking off.

The epidermis lacks blood vessels and has few nerves, but contains granules of the pigment melanin. This dark brown substance helps to determine the color of the skin. The skins of dark-skinned people contain much melanin. The freckles and suntans of pale-skinned people are also caused by melanin. Strong sunlight stimulates production of this pigment, which helps protect the skin from damage caused by overexposure to the sun's ultraviolet radiation. Ultraviolet light also has a beneficial effect, however, by acting on the skin to help the body synthesize vitamin D—an important factor in the healthy growth of bones.

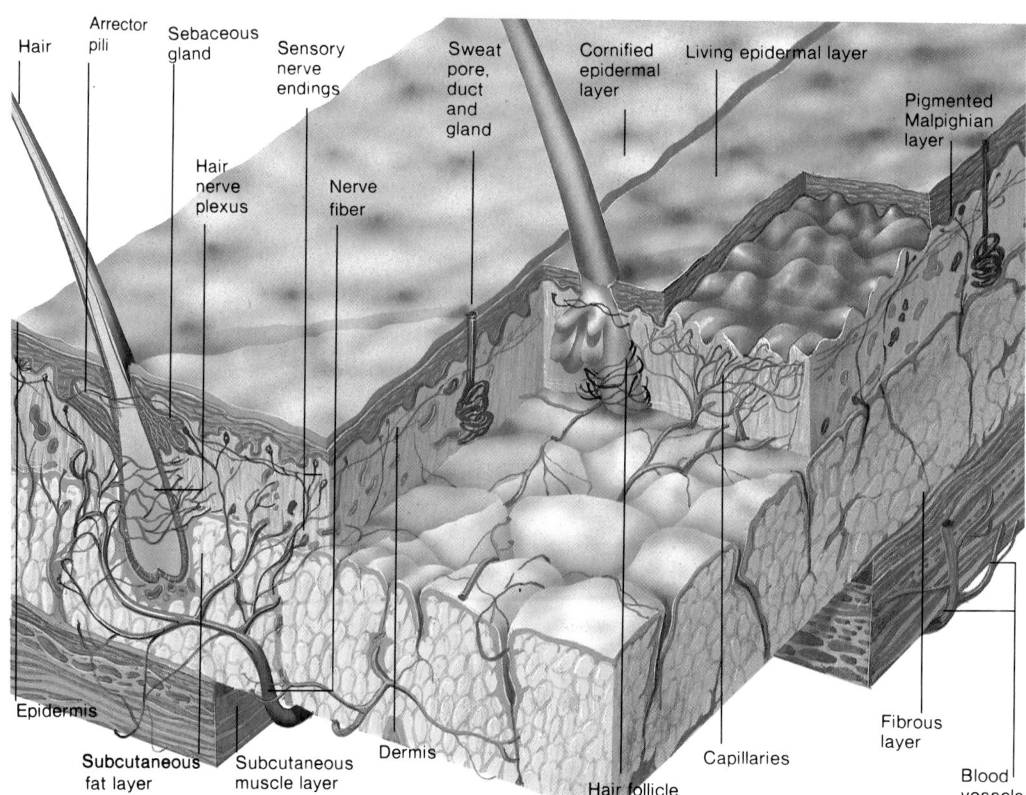

The skin has three principal layers—the epidermis, dermis, and a layer of subcutaneous tissue, composed of fat, a fibrous layer, and a layer of subcutaneous blood vessels and muscle. The epidermis itself has three main layers—the Malpighian generative layer, a layer of living cells, and an outer layer of dead "cornified" cells. The dermis contains numerous tiny blood capillaries, nerve endings, sweat and sebaceous glands, and lymph vessels. Hair follicles run through this layer. Associated with hair follicles are a blood supply, a sensory nerve supply, a muscle which can cause the hair to rise, and a sebaceous gland.

Dermis

This is a closely woven network of connective tissue, thinnest in the eyelids, thickest in the back, and everywhere far thicker than the epidermis. Tough protein fibers in the dermis give skin its tensile strength and bulk. The dermis also contains scattered blood vessels, lymph vessels, nerve endings, hair follicles, and glands connected with the epidermis.

Thousands of tiny projections called papillae jut up from the dermis and fit into tiny pits in the bottom of the epidermis. Papillae grouped in rows form the ridges on fingers, giving each individual a distinctive set of fingerprints. Each of these papillae has a rich supply of tiny capillaries—blood vessels bringing nourishment to growing skin, and regulating heat loss from the body. Little heat escapes from the skin when its capillaries constrict to block the flow of blood, but heat loss is substantial when capillaries expand and let blood pass through freely. Papillae also contain nerve endings sensitive to touch.

Subcutaneous tissue

This consists mainly of blood vessels, connective tissue, and cells that store fat. This tissue helps protect the body from blows and other injuries and also helps retain body heat.

Sensors in the skin

Hundreds of thousands of sensitive nerve endings are embedded in the skin, especially in such regions as the lips and finger pads. Between them, different kinds of sensor detect touch, pressure, heat, cold, and pain. Touch receptors are shaped like bulbs. Other nerve endings form a mesh embracing the roots of hairs: these sensors are activated when a hair bends. Free nerve endings, resembling branching twigs, may register pain as well as touch and pressure. But pain is felt by several kinds of nerve if these are subjected to intense pressure. All these sensors are mechanoreceptors: receptors that fire off signals to the central nervous system when deformed by touch or pressure. Besides these, the skin has two types of thermoreceptor, in the form of nerve endings sensitive to temperature change. One type senses cold, the other heat.

Glands in the skin

There are two important kinds of gland in skin: sebaceous glands and sweat glands.

Sebaceous glands open into hair follicles in the dermal layer of the skin. These glands secrete sebum, a fatty substance that lubricates the hairs and their surrounding skin. Sebum accumulating in a blocked gland may produce a soft, sebaceous cyst, which may appear alarming, but is benign.

Some 2.4 million sweat glands activated by the autonomic nervous system excrete water, salt, and the body wastes, lactic acid and urea. These escape through narrow ducts with openings forming the tiny holes called sweat pores. Certain sweat glands (called apocrine sweat glands), located in the temples, armpits, and the genital area, produce a thick secretion under emotional stress. Others (called eccrine sweat glands) are widespread in the skin and produce a dilute salt solution when the body temperature becomes uncomfortably high, either in response to external heat or to physical activity. This solution helps to cool the body as it evaporates.

A man marching through a hot desert may sweat 2.5 gallons (10 liters) of water in a day—half from his trunk, a quarter from the legs and thighs, and a quarter from the arms and head. Copious sweating causes salt loss and this may produce cramping in people who replace the water by drinking without also taking salt to restore its concentration in the blood.

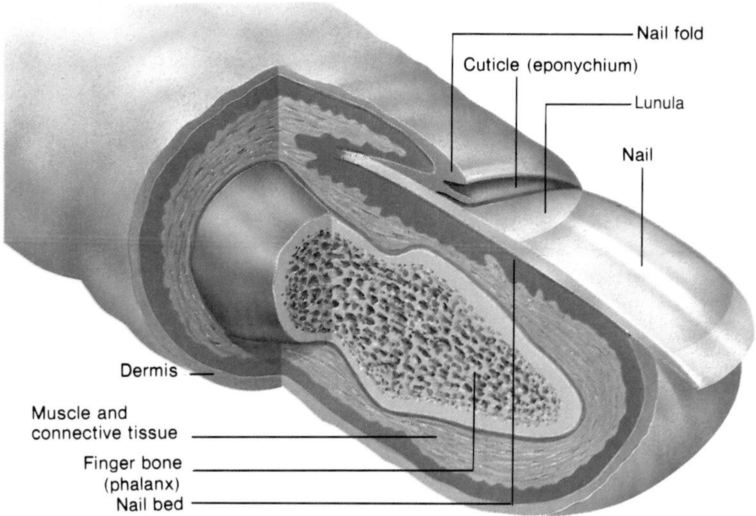

Nail is a specialized horny tissue that grows at the ends of the fingers and toes. The nail root is buried in a fold of skin. The body of the nail grows continually from this until it extends beyond the end of the finger or toe.

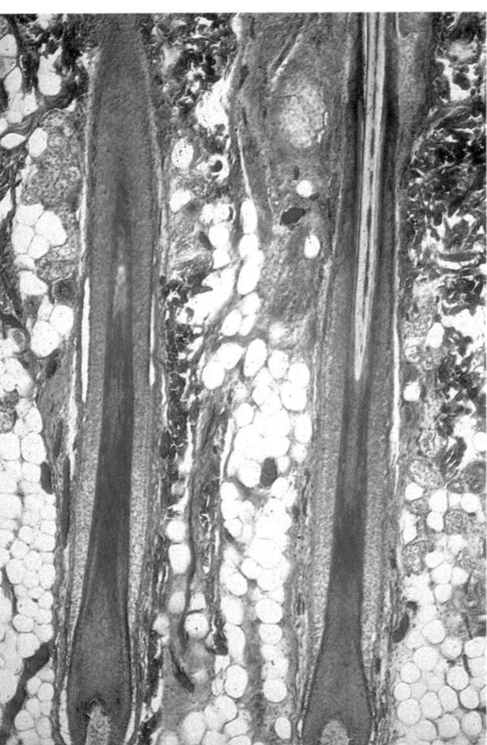

A cross section through skin shows two hairs in their follicles in the layer of subcutaneous fat just below the dermis.

The endocrine system

Endocrine glands are located in the head, neck, and abdomen.

The body's two main control mechanisms, which regulate all aspects of physical life, are the nervous system and the endocrine system. The endocrine system consists of eight principal ductless glands that release chemicals called hormones directly into the blood. These glands are the anterior pituitary; the posterior pituitary; the thyroid; the parathyroid; the islets of Langerhans in the pancreas; the adrenal cortex; the adrenal medulla; and the gonads—ovaries in a female, testes in a male.

Hormones at work

Hormones comprising several dozen different chemicals travel through the bloodstream and influence different kinds of "target" cells, modifying their activity in a variety of ways.

Each target cell has at least one type of receptor in its membrane, and each kind of receptor receives one type of hormone, which fits it rather as a key fits into a lock. For example, a hormone may cause the target cell to produce the messenger compound cyclic adenosine monophosphate, which affects such things as protein manufacture, energy storage, and even other hormone manufacture.

Endocrine glands and their hormones are shown below. The anterior pituitary influences the thyroid, adrenal medulla, and sex glands through thyroid-stimulating hormone (TSH), adrenocorticotropic hormone (ACTH), follicle-stimulating hormone (FSH), and luteinizing hormone (LH).

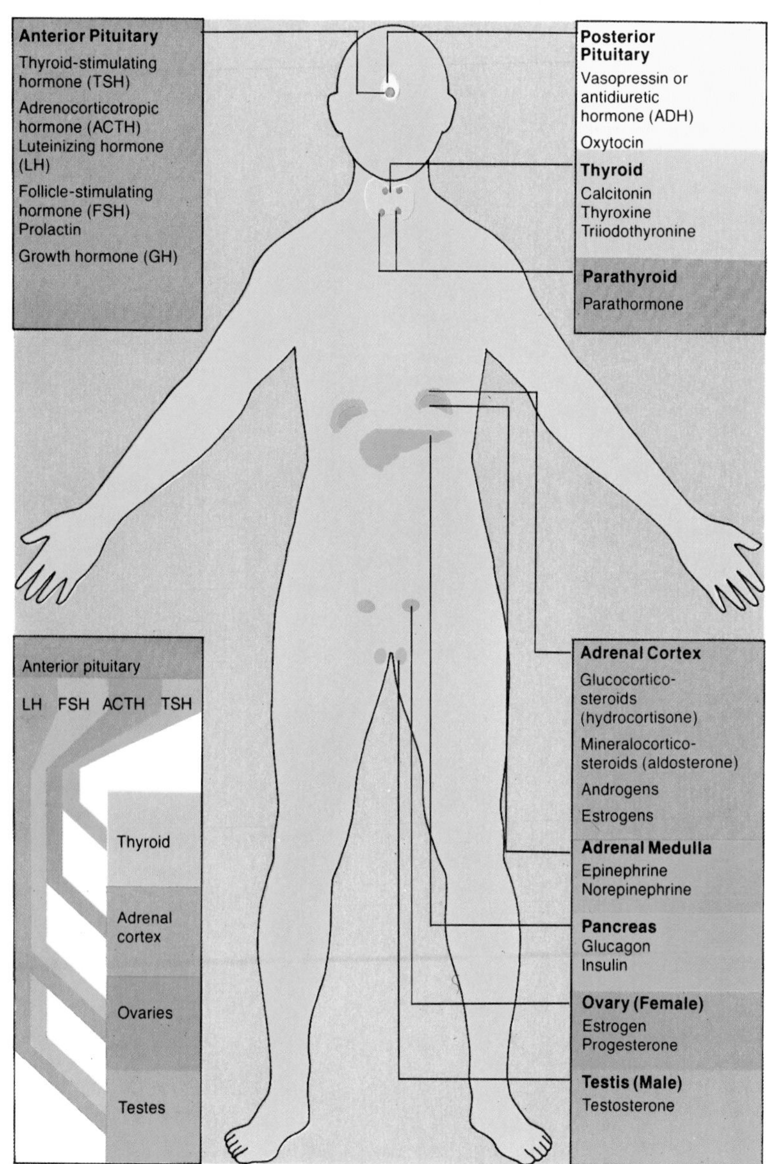

The action of endocrine glands

Endocrine glands are specialized chemical factories that produce hormones that perform a special task or group of tasks.

The thyroid and parathyroid glands lie in the front of the neck. The thyroid's main task is the control of energy metabolism by means of the hormones thyroxine and triiodothyronine. The thyroid uses almost all the iodine inside the body, principally to manufacture iodine-rich thyroxine, a hormone essential for growth and for regulating the body's basal metabolic rate. The thyroid gland also produces calcitonin, which encourages the deposition of calcium in bone, and so helps control blood calcium levels. The four parathyroid glands produce parathormone, which raises the calcium level in the blood, and helps control calcium metabolism.

The pancreas—a large gland opening into the small intestine—principally produces digestive enzymes, although its cell clumps called the islets of Langerhans produce the hormones insulin and glucagon, which regulate carbohydrate metabolism. Insulin stops the liver producing unwanted glucose, and prevents adipose tissue releasing glycerol and fatty acids. Glucagon counters the effects of insulin by boosting the release of glucose as this is required.

The adrenal glands, which lie one above each kidney, in fact each contain two glands. The outer part, the adrenal cortex, produces steroid hormones, including aldosterone and hydrocortisone. Aldosterone plays a major role in regulating salt balance in the body. Hydrocortisone is involved in metabolizing amino acids, fat, and glucose, and it helps to provide the raw materials and energy required for building and repairing tissues. As well as the testes and ovaries, the adrenal cortex synthesizes the male sex hormones (androgens) and the female sex hormones (estrogens), the balance of which in individuals of either sex determines secondary sexual characteristics.

The inner part of each adrenal gland, the adrenal medulla, produces epinephrine and norepinephrine—hormones that prepare the body for "fight or flight" in situations of stress—which between them increase heart rate, channel blood to muscles, and release glucose. These activities prepare the body for sudden action in an emergency, but also have an important role in active play.

The male testes and female ovaries yield testosterone and estrogen, respectively, which have fundamental effects on sexual development and reproductive activity.

The pituitary gland is the most important endocrine gland; among its functions is the control of other endocrine glands.

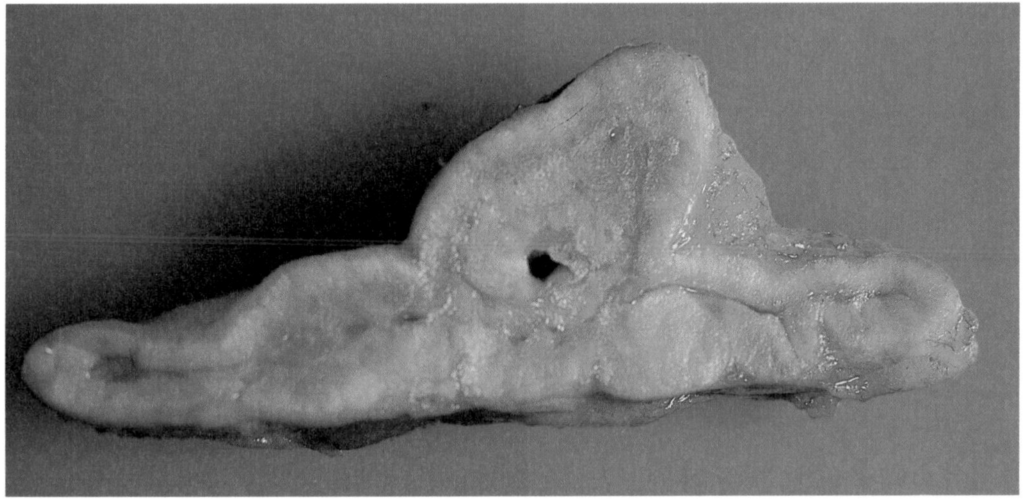

An adrenal gland is located on top of each kidney. The outer adrenal cortex, which produces one group of hormones, completely encloses the adrenal medulla, which produces different hormones.

Controlling the endocrine system

Too much or too little of any hormone may cause deformity, disease, or death. The pituitary gland and the hypothalamus of the brain control which hormones are released, in what quantity, and when.

The pituitary is a gland about the size of a pea, suspended in a bone cavity below the brain and above the nasal cavity. This tiny unit releases more than two dozen hormones that regulate the activity and hormone output of almost all the other endocrine glands.

The pituitary's anterior and posterior parts work separately. The anterior lobe (front part) releases trophic (nourishing) hormones, each of which triggers the production and release of a special hormone in a "target" gland. Thyrotropic, or thyroid-stimulating, hormone (TSH) stimulates the thyroid gland to produce thyroxine. Adrenocorticotropic hormone (ACTH) encourages hormone output from the cortex of each adrenal gland. Follicle stimulating hormone (FSH) and luteinizing hormone (LH) act upon the ovaries and testes. The anterior pituitary also produces growth hormone (GH), which indirectly affects cartilage in ways that are essential to growth and broadly influences metabolism. Changes in the anterior pituitary's output of gonadotropic hormones initiate sexual maturity.

The posterior lobe (rear part) of the pituitary stores and releases two hormones manufactured in the adjacent hypothalamus, a complex region of the brain located immediately above the pituitary and beneath the thalamus. Vasopressin, or antidiuretic hormone (ADH), controls urine output and so helps to maintain the water balance of the body. Oxytocin causes the uterus to contract during childbirth and stimulates the release of milk during nursing.

The pituitary gland knows when to liberate hormones stimulating target glands or muscles by a process called "feedback"—by means of which the controller is itself controlled. For example, when the thyroid gland releases thyroxine into the bloodstream, its presence inhibits the pituitary's production of TSH. This reduction in TSH results in a reduction in the thyroid's output of thyroxine. As this reduces, the pituitary responds by producing more TSH, so that overall, a balanced output of thyroxine is maintained.

This example illustrates the principle, but oversimplifies the mechanism of endocrine feedback. Endocrine feedback mechanisms depend to a great extent on the hypothalamus, chief coordinator of the endocrine and nervous systems. This part of the brain combines hormonal feedback information from the blood with nerve impulses received from brain centers, including those controlling body rhythms. The hypothalamus responds by sending amino acid chains—called peptides—to the pituitary, and it is primarily these that stimulate or inhibit pituitary hormone output. Thus, the peptide called thyrotropin-releasing hormone (TRH) stimulates manufacture of thyrotropin (thyrotropic hormone, or TSH) in the pituitary, and so indirectly affects the release of thyroxine from the thyroid gland; in this way, the central nervous system exerts control over the simplified feedback system described above.

Endocrine feedback between the thyroid and parathyroid glands controls calcium metabolism. Low blood calcium levels stimulate the parathyroid glands, causing them to release parathormone, which decreases the deposition of calcium in bone, decreases calcium excretion by the kidneys, and increases intestinal calcium absorption, thus raising blood calcium levels. This stimulates the thyroid to produce calcitonin, which has the reverse effect.

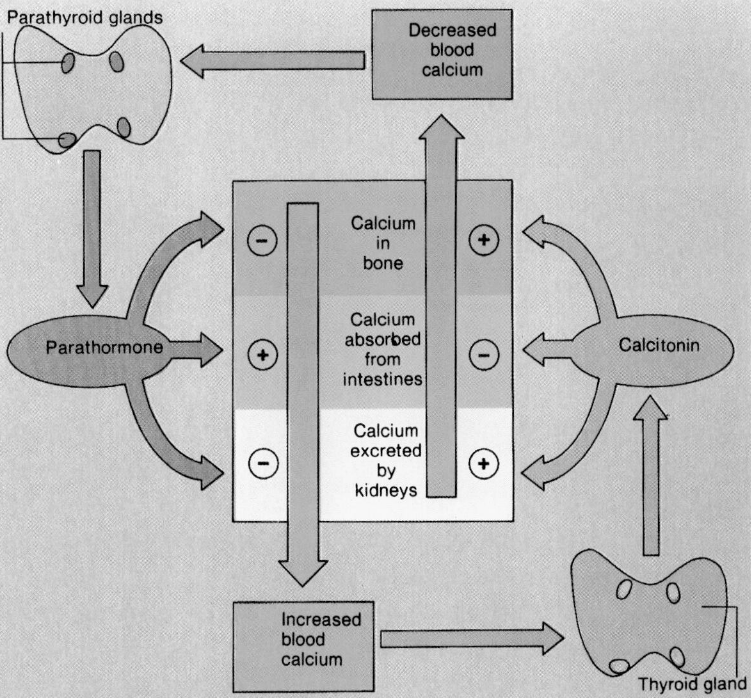

Sex and reproduction

Sex is probably surrounded by more interest and perhaps confusion than any other area of human activity. On a purely biological level, sex is the mechanism by which humans reproduce their young—a process that involves transferring a male reproductive cell (sperm) into the female reproductive tract, where it must join with a female reproductive cell (ovum) to produce a single fertilized egg (zygote). Over a period of nine months, this fertilized cell then develops within the female into a new individual.

Among humans, however, sex has also become a way of expressing profound emotions such as love and passion, a form of emotional expression unique to humans and which, in every age and culture, has been an integral part of human behavior.

Male and female reproductive systems

The male and female reproductive systems are perfectly designed for the job they have to do. The female system produces the ova and contains an organ, the uterus, or womb, in which the developing offspring is accommodated. The male system produces sperm and includes an organ, the penis, which deposits sperm within the female. Although both systems differ in structure, housing, and function, both develop from the same embryonic tissue and, in their adult forms, contain many counterpart or corresponding organs.

The female reproductive organs are housed inside the body within the pelvis. From the outside, all that can be seen are the external genitals, known collectively as the vulva. At the front, as if looking through a woman's open legs, is the mons veneris or mons pubis, a pad of fatty tissue that lies over the pubic bone and which from puberty onward is covered by pubic hair. Running down and back are two folds of skin, the labia majora, which surround two smaller folds, the labia minora. At their front, the labia minora form a hood under which lies the clitoris, a small, highly sensitive organ corresponding to the man's penis and similarly formed of erectile tissue. Below the clitoris lies the urethra, then below this, the vaginal opening. In women who have not had sexual intercourse, this opening is partly closed by the hymen, a thin membrane that is usually torn or ruptured the first time that a woman has coitus, although it may be stretched or torn earlier.

The vagina itself is a muscular passage about 4 inches (10 centimeters) long, which leads up from the vulva to the uterus. It is capable of great distention; during childbirth it distends greatly to allow a child to be born. A minute opening, the os uteri, forms the entrance to the cervix, or neck, of the uterus. Lined by a mucous membrane called the endometrium, the uterus is a small pear-shaped organ within which the growing fetus is sheltered.

From either side of the uterus, the Fallopian tubes reach back to the ovaries. These oval-shaped organs are the female gonads, or reproductive glands, equivalent to the male testes. The ovaries release a ripe ovum every month and also produce the female sex hormones progesterone and estrogen. These play a vital role in the female reproductive cycle and are also responsible for the development of such secondary sexual characteristics as breasts, fat, and body hair.

The male reproductive system lies both inside and outside the body and, unlike the female system, is linked to the urinary system. Visible organs are the penis and testes. The penis, whose size and shape may vary considerably, is normally flaccid. Behind and below the penis are the two testicles, or testes, the male gonads. These produce the sperm cells and the male sex hormone testosterone, responsible for such secondary sexual characteristics as facial hair and deep voice. The testes are flattened oval-shaped organs that lie inside the baglike scrotum. Within them, sperm cells are continually produced inside coiled seminiferous tubules. Once formed, the sperm cells are stored inside epididymides, two tubular organs adjacent to the testes.

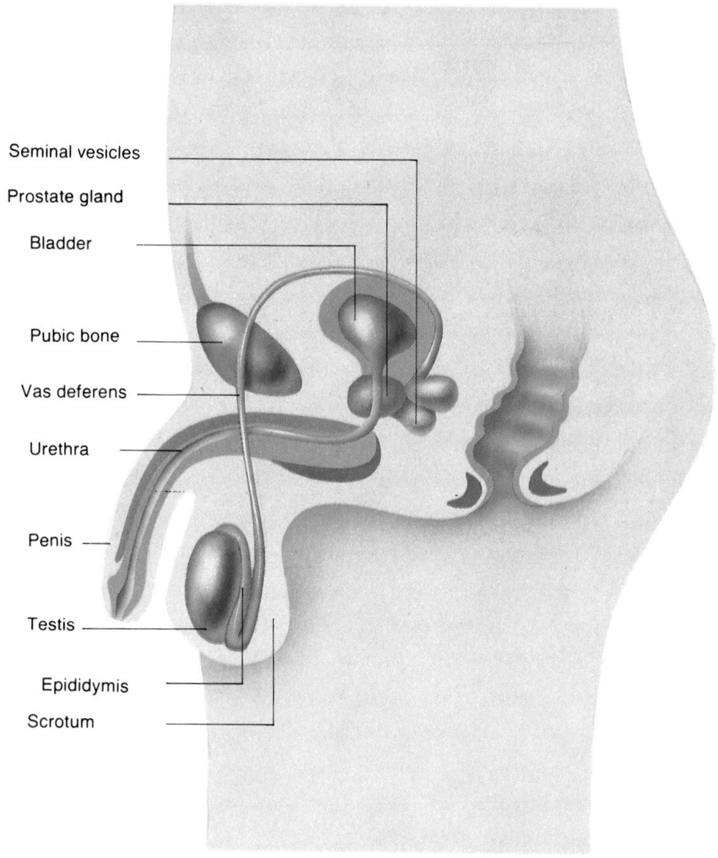

Male sex organs are shown in cross section, *above.* The male gametes—the sperm—are produced in the testes, which lie in the scrotum. They travel from the epididymis of the testis along the vas deferens to the seminal vesicles, which are located at the rear of the prostate gland. The spermatic ducts join with the urethra, the tube through which urine passes out from the bladder. The testes also produce the male sex hormone testosterone, which is secreted into the bloodstream and is responsible for initiating and maintaining male sexual characteristics.

Birth control

When reproduction is not the desired result of sex, some form of conscious regulation is required. This is commonly referred to as birth control. Although conception—the fertilization of an ovum by a sperm—is the natural result of sex, it does not necessarily happen every time two people have sexual intercourse. Because of her monthly reproductive, or menstrual, cycle, a woman is only able to conceive during a limited number of days each month, after ovulation and before the menstrual period. These days can be identified, although not always with certainty, by counting the days between menstrual periods and also by observing certain associated physical changes, such as small alterations in body temperature. The time before ovulation, when sexual intercourse will probably not lead to pregnancy, is called the "safe" period, and restricting sexual activity to these days is regarded by many as the most natural—and by some, as the only acceptable—form of birth control. The technique is sometimes referred to as the rhythm method of birth control.

Other methods of birth control range from using hormonal contraceptives, through physical or chemical barriers, to surgical sterilization. Hormonal methods, such as the oral contraceptive pill, work by preventing ovulation. Physical barriers, such as the condom or diaphragm, prevent sperm from reaching an ovum in the uterus. Chemical barriers—usually in the form of foam or gel—kill sperm before they reach the uterus. Another technique, involving an intrauterine device (IUD), seems to prevent the ovum from implanting in the lining of the uterus. Surgical sterilization involves cutting or tying off the tubes through which the sperm or the ovum must pass—the vas deferens in a man, the Fallopian tubes in a woman. In both cases, pregnancy is prevented because the partner operated on is made sterile.

Sexual activity

It is still not known exactly what determines sexual activity in humans. It would seem there are physiological rules that may be linked to changes within the body, such as changes in hormonal level that possibly interact with the central nervous system. But age, social, cultural, and psychological factors all play a part in determining human sexual behavior.

From various investigations into human sexual activity, such as the Kinsey Reports of the late 1940's and 1950's, the studies conducted over the last four decades by Masters and Johnson, and, more recently, surveys by Shere Hite, it is clear that individual requirements and practices vary enormously, ranging from those who live active sexual lives, whether with many partners or in a pair-bonding, to those who seem content to live with little or no sexual involvement.

Reproduction

Reproduction is a complex process, and for conception to occur a number of varying conditions must first be met. Some of the most

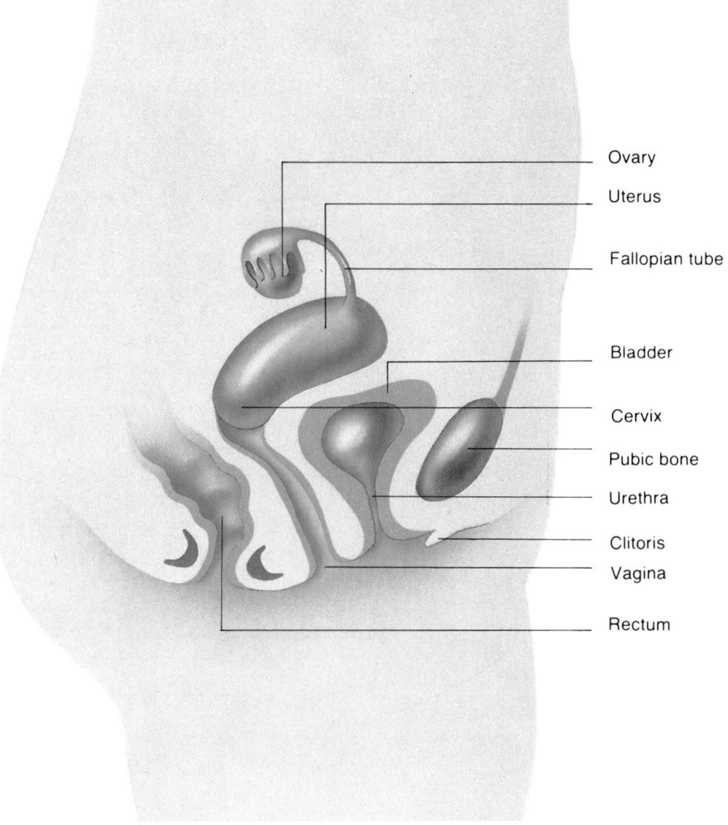

Female sex organs are shown in cross section. The vagina leads to the cervix of the uterus (the neck of the womb), and the uterus itself connects, by means of the Fallopian tubes, with the ovaries. These structures lie above and behind the uterus. During ovulation, at about the middle of the menstrual cycle, an egg is released from an ovary and travels down a Fallopian tube to the uterus. The ovaries also produce the female sex hormones progesterone and estrogen, which initiate and maintain female sexual characteristics.

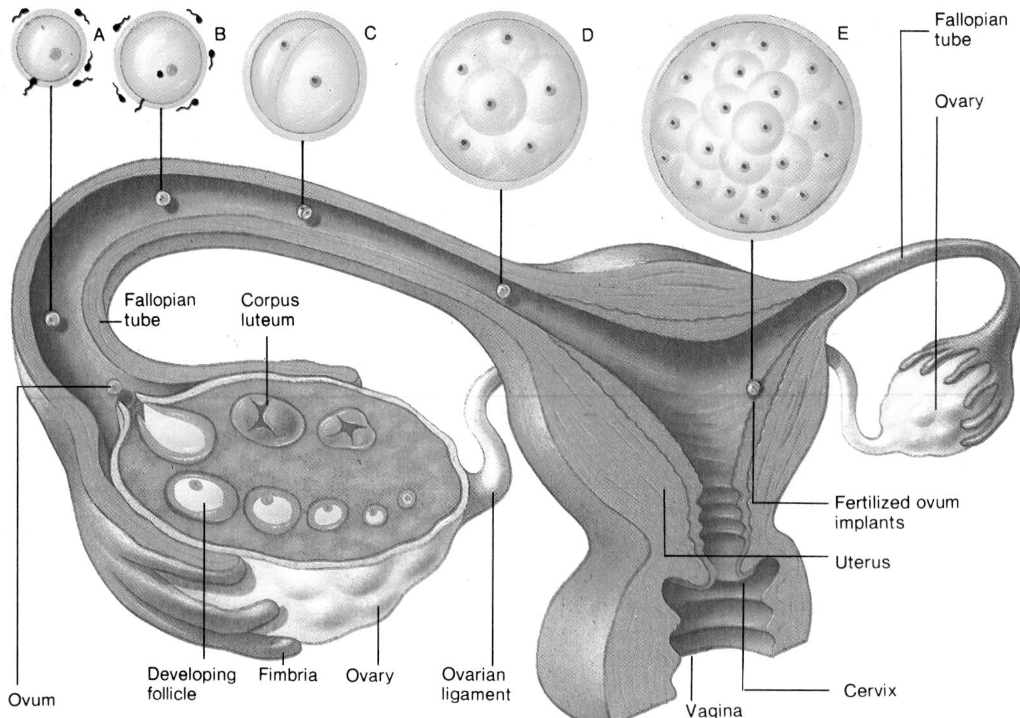

The female reproductive cycle depends on the menstrual cycle, which is based on monthly ovulation. During the menstrual cycle, the lining of the uterus thickens in preparation for the implantation of a fertilized ovum. If no ovum implants, the lining breaks down and is expelled as menstrual bleeding. An ovum, grown in a follicle of the ovary, is then released and is guided into the Fallopian tube by the tube's fingerlike fimbria. As it moves toward the uterus, it may encounter sperm (A), one of which may penetrate and fertilize it (B), causing cell division (C, D) to begin. After a few days, a fertilized ovum—now developed to the blastocyst stage (E)—reaches the uterus lining and implants there.

significant relate to the different sexual cycles of men and women.

Normally from puberty, a man is physically ready to reproduce at any time. From puberty, the male body continually manufactures sperm at a rate of some 200 million a day; at any one time there may be millions of mature sperm available in the seminal vesicles that can be released when a man ejaculates. By contrast, however, the ovaries produce a few thousand eggs, or ova, but only a few hundred of them are released during the female's lifetime. Normally, only one egg at a time is released during ovulation.

Female reproductive cycle

A woman is born with a full complement of immature ova contained within ovarian follicles. Some 2 million are present at birth, declining to about 300,000 by puberty. Every month, a woman's body undergoes a routine cycle of physical changes during which an ovum is released and the body prepares for gestation.

This cycle is known as the female sexual, reproductive, or menstrual cycle. It begins at puberty sometime between the ages of 10 and 16 when its onset is known as the menarche; the menstrual cycle repeats itself every 24 to 32 days in most women, unless an egg is fertilized. This cycle continues until the menopause, which usually occurs between the ages of 45 and 55 in most women.

The monthly cycle is affected by various hormones controlled by the hypothalamus. During the first phase—the follicular phase—the follicle-stimulating hormone (FSH) produced by the pituitary causes ovaries and ovarian follicles to enlarge; it also causes the ovaries to produce estrogen. One ovarian follicle outstrips the others in growth, ruptures and then, due to the action of luteinizing hormone (LH), releases the single egg. This is called ovulation and occurs midway through the cycle.

The mature ovum then enters the Fallopian tube and is propelled into the uterus. There, due to the action of estrogen and progesterone, the endometrium has become thickened and vascular in preparation for the arrival of a fertilized egg. If the egg is not fertilized by a sperm within about 12 hours, it dies.

During the second half of the cycle—the luteal phase—LH causes the follicular remains to form a bright yellow structure, the corpus luteum, and the endometrium continues to thicken. If a fertilized egg fails to arrive, the corpus luteum degenerates and the endometrial lining is shed together with blood, passing out of the body as menstrual flow. Menstruation lasts 3 to 7 days, then the entire cycle begins again.

Fertilization and implantation

Fertilization occurs high up in the Fallopian tube and as it can only happen if both male and female cells are present, intercourse and ovulation must occur within about 12 hours of each other.

When the man ejaculates, some 400 million sperm are deposited into the woman's vagina. Propelled by tail-like structures, the sperm make their way fairly rapidly up the vagina, through the cervix, and into the uterus. This takes less than an hour, but at least half the number die in the acidic conditions of the vagina; others die as the sperm continue to travel to the top of the uterus and into the Fallopian tube. Here, conditions are favorable for the few hundred sperm that remain and they can survive for up to 72 hours.

Fertilization occurs immediately if an ovum is already present. It is accomplished when one male sperm penetrates the surface of the ovum. The cell wall then becomes impenetrable to other sperm, and the nuclei of the two cells fuse together. Cell division begins almost at once, the ovum subdividing or segmenting, first into two and then doubling with each division until it becomes a rounded mass of cells—the morula. As the cells increase in number, they also differentiate to form the different cells that make up the human body. As the process continues, a fluid-filled cavity develops in the morula, now called the blastocyst; the outer layer forms a cellular wall—the trophoblast, which will form the placenta—while the remaining cells form a mass from which the fetus and amniotic sac will develop.

During this process, the fertilized ovum has been making its way toward the uterine cavity, and about seven days after fertilization, the blastocyst implants in the endometrium. Small projections on the trophoblast, called chorionic villi, burrow into the uterine wall so that the blastocyst becomes completely embedded, obtaining its nourishment by diffusion from the uterus. Once implantation has occurred, conception is complete, the normal menstrual cycle is suspended, and pregnancy is established. Occasionally, the fertilized ovum fails to reach the uterus and instead implants elsewhere in the reproductive tract. This is known as ectopic pregnancy and almost invariably requires surgery.

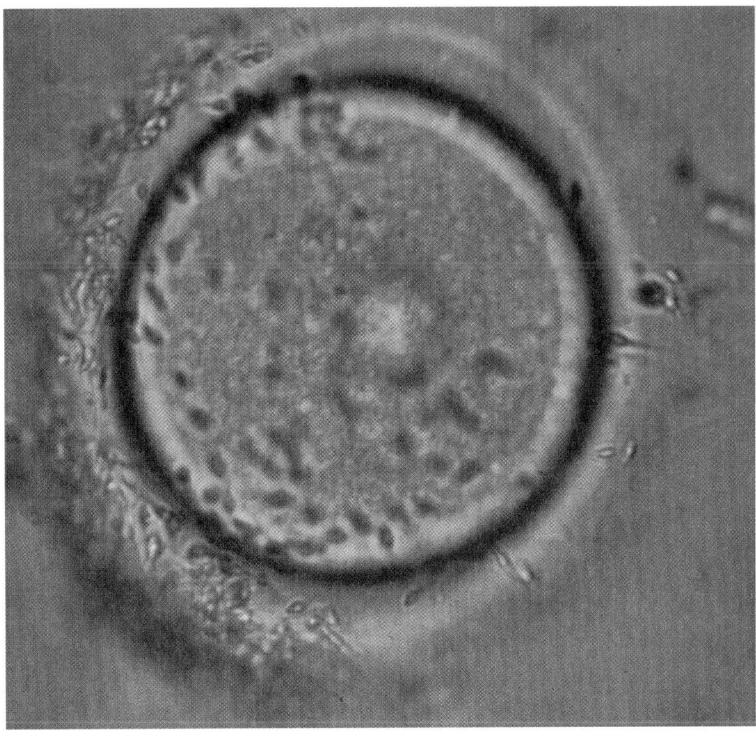

An ovum is a female reproductive, or germ, cell. This photograph shows its nucleus, approximately central, surrounded by cytoplasm, which in turn is surrounded by the zona pellucida, in which a number of sperm can be seen.

Boy or girl?

The sex of the new infant is determined at the very instant of fertilization and depends entirely on the pattern of sex chromosomes present in the nucleus of the sperm. The nucleus of every cell in the body, except the germ cells (sperm or ovum), contains a "blueprint" of information determining how that cell functions. Forty-four of these chromosomes are somatic—not concerned with reproduction—while two are sex chromosomes. These are of two types, X and Y; females have two X chromosomes (XX), and males have one X and one Y chromosome (XY). Germ cells, however, only contain 23 chromosomes, half the normal number. Each female ovum therefore contains 22 somatic chromosomes and one X chromosome; each male sperm contains 22 somatic chromosomes and either an X or a Y chromosome.

At fertilization, the fusion of the cells ensures that the newly fertilized ovum contains its full complement of chromosomes but its sex depends on the sperm. An ovum fertilized by an X-carrying sperm will develop into a female embryo; one fertilized by a Y-carrying sperm will develop into a male.

Infertility

Infertility—the inability to produce children—affects about one in ten couples. There are many causes. In about 40 per cent of cases, infertility is due to male sterility—low sperm count, abnormal sperm, or impotence. In women, the most common cause is blockage of the Fallopian tubes. Other causes are failure to ovulate and cervical disorders. In one case in ten, no cause will be found, but in other cases, medical investigation will reveal a cause that can be treated successfully.

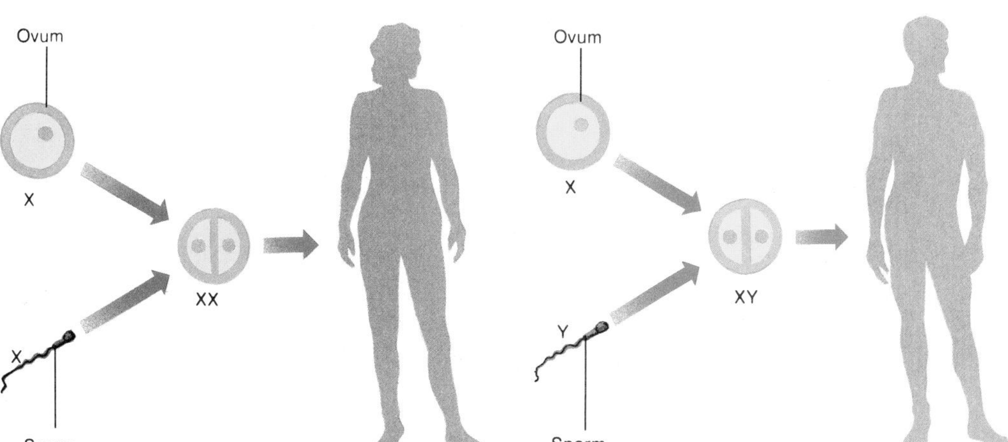

Sex chromosomes in the nuclei of body cells are of two types, called X and Y. All cells in a female have two X chromosomes; all in a male, one X and one Y. Germ cells have only one sex chromosome, however an ovum has an X, but a sperm can have either an X or a Y. When a sperm fertilizes an ovum, the resulting cells will therefore have either two X chromosomes and be female or one X and one Y and be male.

Pregnancy and childbirth

Pregnancy, or gestation, is the period during which one single cell develops into a fully formed human being within the mother's body. It begins at the moment of conception and normally continues for approximately 266 days, or nine calendar months, until the child is born.

Stages of development

The embryo starts life as a single fertilized egg no larger than a pinpoint. Contained within its nucleus, however, are the hereditary or genetic units that determine the infant's ultimate development. These are carried on twisted ribbonlike strands of DNA within the chromosomes, which provide the "instructions" for and control the manufacture of the proteins that will build up the new body.

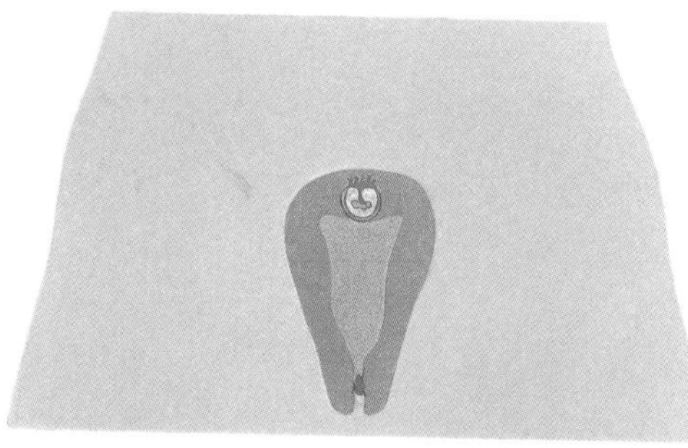

At 4 weeks, the embryo's spinal column, nerves, some blood vessels, and the heart have started to form. Length is about .25 inch (0.5 centimeter).

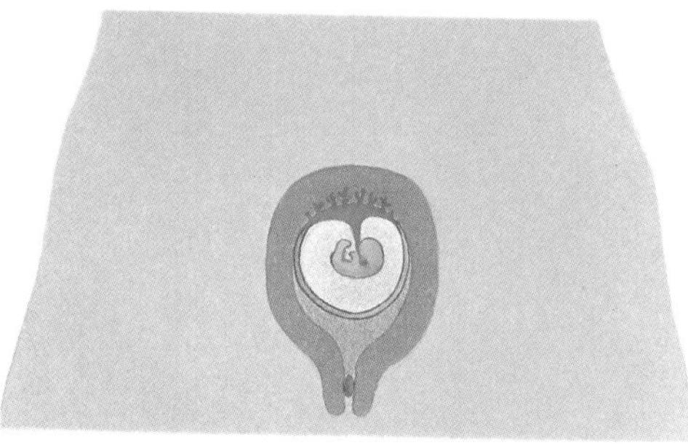

At 9 weeks, most basic development is complete. All major body systems have formed. Length is about 1.25 inches (4 centimeters).

At 14 weeks, facial features—eyes, nose, mouth, ears—are recognizable. Sex organs start to develop. Length is about 4.75 inches (12 centimeters).

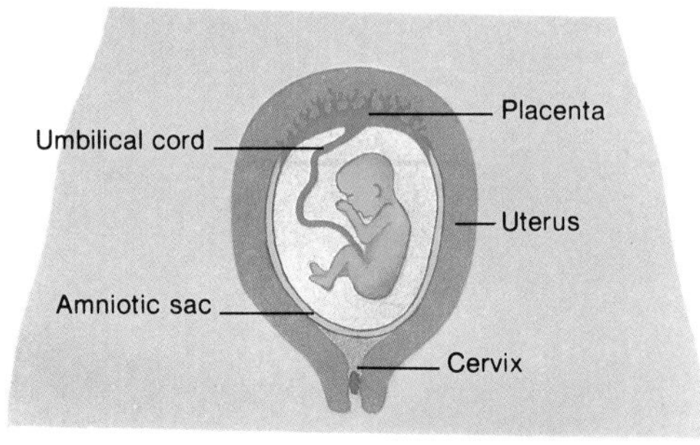

At 20 weeks, the baby has formed hair and nails. A fine fur—lanugo—covers the body. Length is about 8 inches (20 centimeters).

Development begins with cleavage, or cell division. The initial single cell undergoes repeated mitotic division to form firstly a solid, many-celled morula, and subsequently a hollow sphere, the blastocyst, which on about day seven implants in the endometrium. Clustered to one side of the blastocyst is a mass of cells—the embryo—which continue to divide but also undergo gastrulation. This is a complex process of rearrangement whereby cells migrate into layers and take up approximately definitive positions inside the embryo. The embryo invaginates, or pushes in on itself, so that it at first resembles a diminutive cuplike structure and subsequently an elongated pouch. By about the 12th day after conception, two distinct layers of precursor cells—an inner endoderm and outer ectoderm—have formed. And during the following week a third middle, or mesoderm layer, is produced between them.

As the cells migrate they also differentiate, changing structure and function to be transformed into the specialized cells, tissues, or organ types of the mature body. As individual cells differentiate, so too the entire mass begins to develop a rudimentary human shape.

All body systems and vital organs are formed within the first three months, though nearly all the body systems still have much developing to do. From the endoderm develops first a primitive gut, then the respiratory tubes, lungs, liver, and digestive organs; from the ectoderm develop the skin, sense organs, and nervous system; the mesoderm is the source of all the body's connective tissues, bone, cartilage, muscles, heart, blood vessels, and urogenital system.

Nourishment is obtained from the mother's body via a complex life-support system. First to develop is the amniotic sac, a fluid-filled bag of membranes in which the developing embryo is cushioned and protected at constant temperature. A cap-shaped pad of tissue—the placenta—forms at the point of implantation and to this the embryo is attached by the umbilical cord. Maternal and embryonic bloodstreams remain separate but nutrients and waste are exchanged from one to the other via the placenta.

By the end of the third month, although the fetus is only about 3.5 inches (9 centimeters) long, it is easily recognizable as human. Most of the major internal organs are fully formed, the circulatory system functions, and rudimentary genitals have appeared. From this point (or in some cases from as early as eight weeks), the embryo is called a fetus, which grows and matures during the remaining six months until birth.

The course of pregnancy

For most women the first sign of pregnancy is the absence of menstruation. Other early signs include feelings of nausea (morning sickness), increased urination, and some heaviness in the breasts. Pregnancy can, however, be confirmed by a urine test six weeks after the last period. This will detect chorionic gonadotropin, a hormone produced by the placenta.

Most symptoms of pregnancy are caused by changed hormonal levels in the body and, from the third month, by the increased pressure and size of the fetus. High levels of estrogen and progesterone are responsible for feelings of nausea and possibly for the emotional swings of the first months. After about six weeks, hormonal activity also prepares the breasts for nursing. Breasts may feel itchy or heavy as they begin to enlarge; veins become prominent and, from about the 12th week, a thin fluid—colostrum—is secreted. The areolae become mottled as pigmentation increases, and increased pigmentation may also appear on the face, lower abdomen, and genitals.

As the fetus increases in size, the abdomen swells and the mother's weight gradually increases—an average gain of 20 to 25 pounds (9 to 11 kilograms). Posture may alter to compensate, and many women experience backache and lethargy. Other uncomfortable side effects may include constipation, hemorrhoids, indigestion, and varicose veins.

The movements of the developing infant can usually be felt by about 20 weeks; by about the 32nd week, pressure may lessen as the baby engages, when the fetal head passes the pelvic inlet, having turned head down in the pelvis.

Ensuring health

Pregnancy is a natural condition, not an illness. Nevertheless, a good diet, exercise, regular prenatal care, and medical supervision are the best way to ensure a good pregnancy and healthy baby. A woman should visit her physician as early as possible for a thorough medical examination during which weight, blood pressure, blood group, and medical history can be checked. Thereafter, regular visits to a clinic or physician are essential to monitor progress. Prenatal medical care can help prevent or arrest complications, such as threatened miscarriage or toxemia—a serious condition in which there are any two of the following: excessively raised blood pressure; swelling of hands, face, and feet; and the appearance of protein in the urine.

A woman can do a great deal herself to ensure health. The baby obtains all its nourishment from the mother, so a balanced diet with adequate iron and calcium is essential. Smoking, excessive alcohol, and certain drugs cause damage and must be avoided. Drugs should only be taken under strict medical supervision.

Contact with infectious diseases, particularly rubella, during the first three months can also cause damage to the fetus. Some factors are uncontrollable, however, notably chromosomal abnormalities resulting in such genetic disorders as Down's syndrome. These may well cause early, spontaneous miscarriage but if not, some can be detected by amniocentesis—the testing of the amniotic fluid—at a relatively early stage (between the 12th and 16th weeks).

Birth

Birth, or parturition, marks the culmination of nine months of pregnancy. For the expectant mother it can be exciting and alarming, but

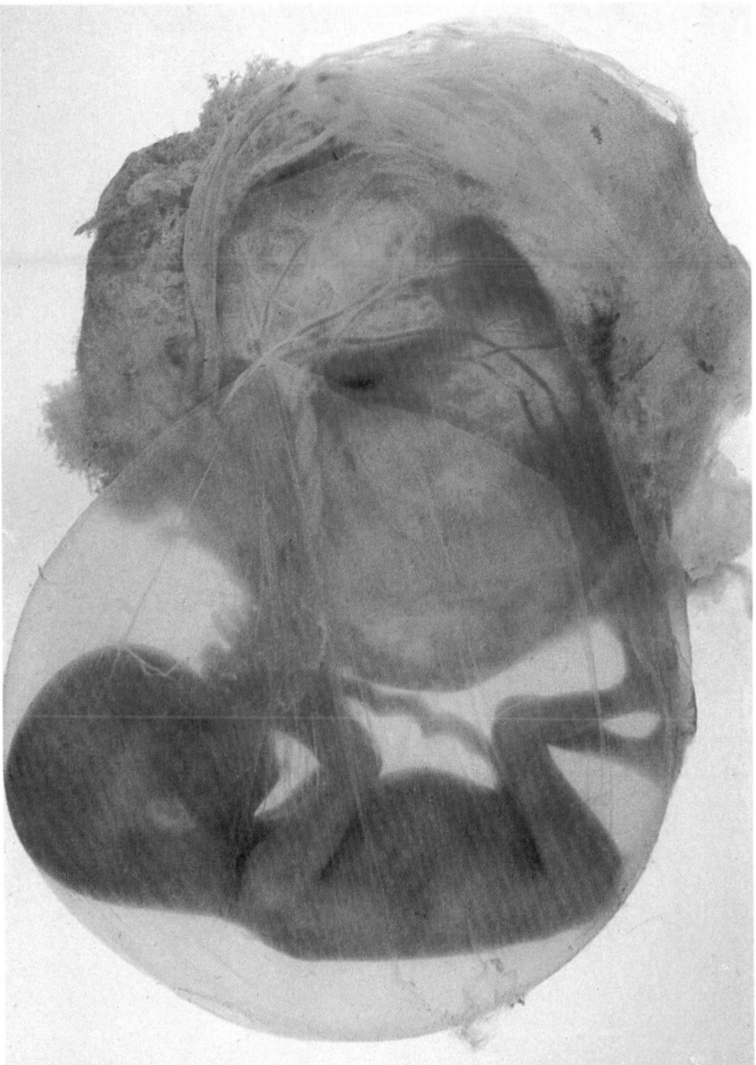

A fetus at 16 weeks is only about 6.25 inches (16 centimeters) long but already has recognizable features and shape. The fetus lies within the amniotic sac and is attached to the relatively large placenta by the umbilical cord.

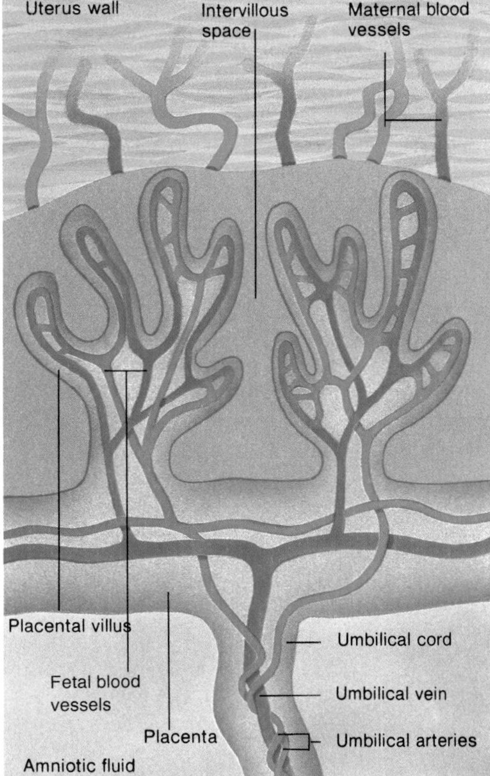

The placenta is the physical link between mother and child. Through it the maternal and fetal blood circulations provide a fetus with everything it needs to develop and grow. The transfer between maternal and fetal circulations occurs in the intervillous space, which is filled with maternal blood. Microscopic projections from the placenta, called villi, allow the fetal circulation to exchange dissolved oxygen and carbon dioxide as well as nutrients and wastes.

anxiety can be lessened by an understanding of the processes involved.

During the final weeks of pregnancy, the woman's body prepares itself for labor. The cervix softens and uterine contractions that have been occurring throughout pregnancy become more noticeable. Finally, the ligaments of the pelvis soften and become more flexible, the cervix begins to be "effaced" and the baby's head "engages" low in the pelvis.

Stages of labor

Labor is divided into three stages. First, the cervix dilates so that the baby can pass through; second, the baby is delivered; and third, the placenta and membranes are expelled. These stages are not clear-cut but tend to merge into each other. No one knows for sure what actually initiates labor, although it is thought that hormones produced by the mature fetus may stimulate the production of prostaglandins, which in turn act on the uterus. Various signs indicate that labor is imminent. Regular contractions occurring every 15 or 30 minutes are the most common sign; others include the expulsion of a mucous plug from the cervix—called the "show"—and a gush of fluid as the amniotic sac ruptures.

The first stage is characterized by increasingly intense muscular contractions as muscle fibers pull the lower uterus and cervix up and around the head of the fetus. This stretching and pulling in turn dilates the cervix to allow the baby to pass through. The process may take anything up to 20 hours; usually, however, it lasts about 8 to 14 hours for a woman having her first child, and about half this for subsequent children.

As dilation proceeds, contractions become more frequent and intense until toward the end of the first stage—the transition period—when they occur every two to three minutes, each contraction lasting about 60 seconds. This period is particularly painful and a woman may also experience nausea, backache, and leg cramps. Increasing too may be an uncontrollable desire to push or bear down as the pressure from the baby's head against the cervix intensifies.

Once the cervix is fully dilated, the second stage is entered and the powerful "bearing down" reflex is accentuated. From this point, the woman can participate actively, bearing down with each contraction to push the baby out of her body. In a normal delivery the baby is born head first. The head rotates beneath the pubic arch and, as it emerges, rotates back to its original position. Shoulders and trunk follow in the same way and the baby is born. The baby breathes in and makes a first cry. The umbilical cord is usually cut at this stage.

The third and final stage occurs within the next 15 minutes as the placenta and umbilical cord are expelled. This is a painless process that may be aided by light pulling on the cord. Once delivered, the placenta is checked to ensure that nothing has been left in the uterus that might cause hemorrhage. Subsequent contraction of the uterine wall usually stops further bleeding.

Relief of pain

Childbirth is painful and the damaging effects on both mother and child of a prolonged and distressing birth are now well known. Today the emphasis is on "natural" drug-free labor, and the woman who understands what is happening and who is adequately prepared with breathing and other exercises can frequently give birth unaided and with a minimum of pain and discomfort. It is also essential that a woman in labor is not left alone; the sympathetic presence of her partner or another relative is actively encouraged. Most women do, however, choose some form of pain relief. Among drugs available are: the epidural anesthetics, which are administered in the spine and block out all sensation in the lower part of the body; analgesics such as pethidine; and inhaled anesthetics. These drugs can affect the baby, however, and today they are used with considerable caution.

At 28 weeks, the baby is lively and is about to turn head downward in the uterus. A greasy material—vernix—covers the body.

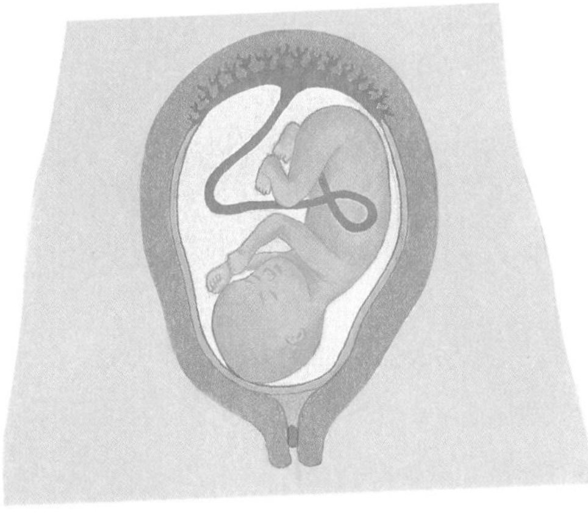

At 34 weeks, the baby has turned head down and can no longer move easily in the uterus. The uterus lies at about the maximum height in the abdomen.

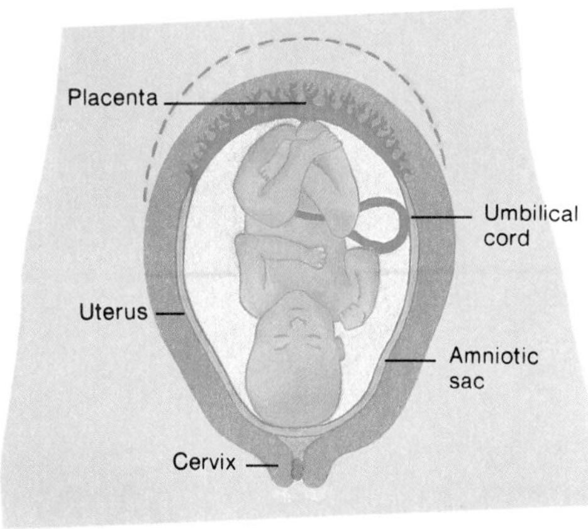

At 38 weeks, the baby is ready to be born. The uterus has "lightened," settling lower in the abdomen. The cervix of the uterus begins to be "effaced," and the baby's head "engages" in the pelvis.

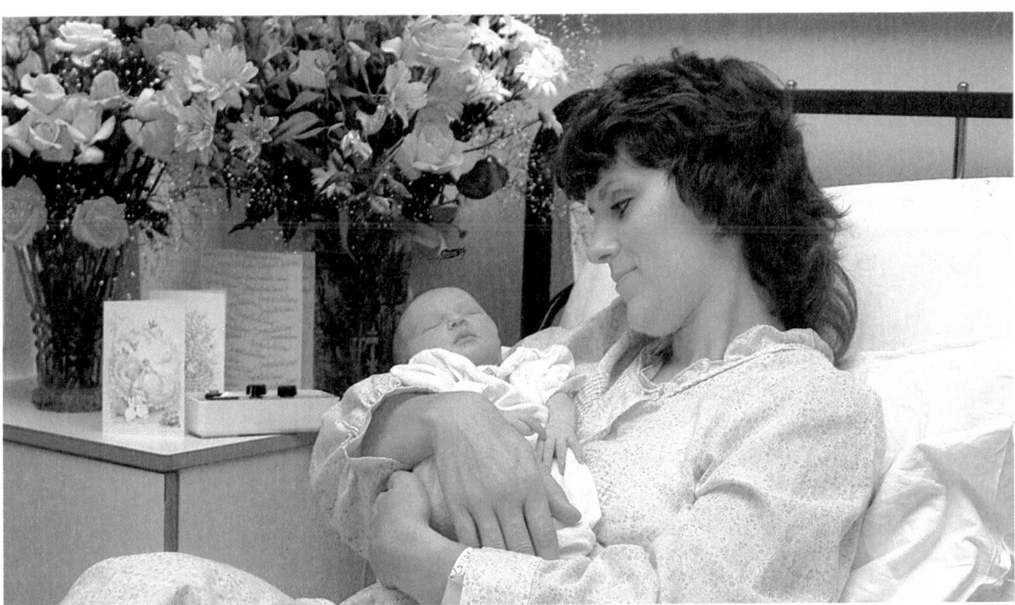

Birth is a profound experience for both mother and baby. Close physical contact between them immediately after birth may help to lessen the shock and strengthen the natural bond between mother and baby.

Problem births

Most births are perfectly normal but problems can and do occur. Breech presentation, where the baby is born feet or buttocks first, is one example. In this case, duration of labor is critical: too fast a labor may result in damage; too long a delivery may cause oxygen starvation. In a breech presentation, delivery is usually in three stages: breech and legs, shoulders, and then head, forceps (large surgical tongs) being used to ease the head out. Where a normal vaginal delivery is impossible, a baby may be delivered by Caesarean section. This involves making an incision in the mother's lower abdomen and delivering the baby through it.

Labor may sometimes be induced artificially—a controversial practice but one usually carried out where the health of mother or baby is at risk. Reasons for induction include preeclampsia, postmaturity of the fetus, Rh factor incompatibility, or diabetes. Induction may involve artificially rupturing the amniotic sac or the intravenous infusion of oxytocin to stimulate contractions. Finally, where there is a danger of the baby's head tearing the perineum, an incision in the vagina—an episiotomy—may be made.

After the birth

The body returns to normal remarkably quickly. Initially there is a steady loss of a bloody substance—lochia—from the vagina as the placental site and uterine lining break down. This should end after 10 days, and within six weeks uterus, cervix, and vagina should have returned to normal. Postnatal exercise helps to tone up stretched muscles. Breasts secrete colostrum for the first two or three days after birth, before the milk flow begins.

One common feature of the postbirth period is depression, which may be caused by hormonal imbalance or emotional and social factors. Whatever the cause, however, postnatal depression is distressing, and sympathetic treatment and support from family and friends are essential for a speedy recovery. It should not be confused with the much rarer postpartum depression, which is a far more severe form of mental disturbance.

Premature babies, born before the 36th week, and very small babies—for instance of less than 5.5 pounds (2.5 kilograms) in weight—may not be fully developed and may need to spend their first few days in an incubator. This controls the baby's environment, keeping it sterile and at a constant temperature and humidity. Premature babies usually grow fast and can soon catch up with those not born prematurely.

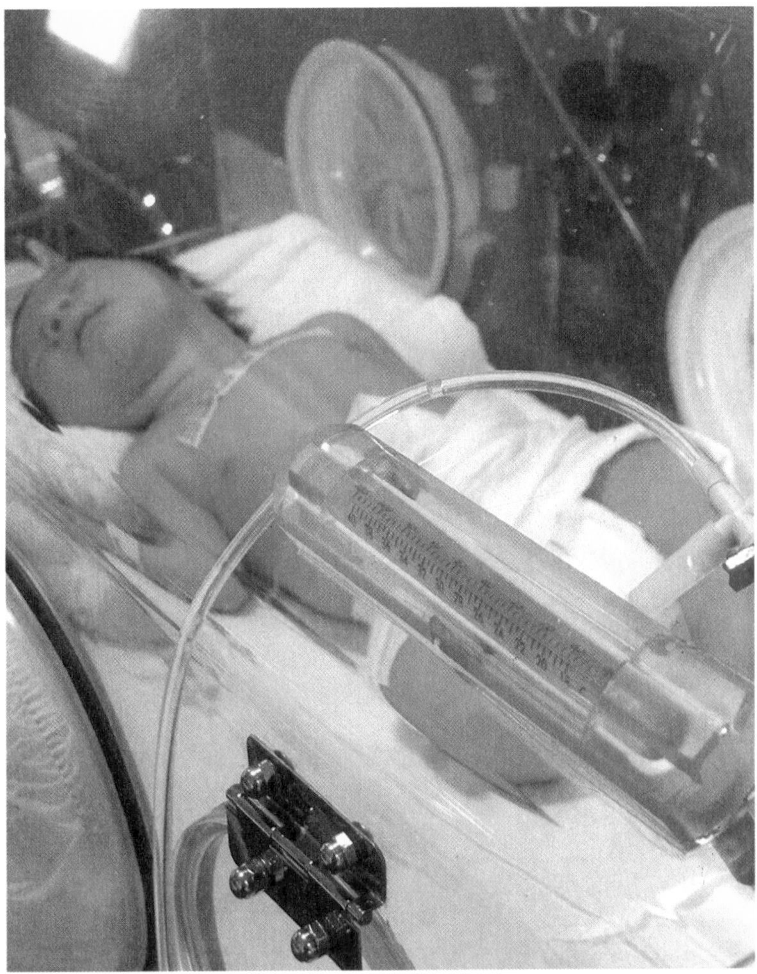

Human development

The development of an individual is a process of physical, intellectual, and emotional growth and change. Two main factors—heredity and environment—determine a child's development from birth onward.

Physical development

The most rapid period of physical growth occurs during the first two years. Intellectual development is equally rapid during this time. In the first 12 months, the average infant's weight triples and its body size increases by about half. As a general rule, by the age of two a baby's height is already about half what it will be as an adult. The brain also develops rapidly and brain growth is largely complete by the age of two years. Motor skills and learning abilities improve as nerve tracts acquire their outer coating of myelin and develop new pathways between cells. These two processes continue up to about the age of five. The cartilaginous elements of the fetal skeleton also gradually harden into bone. Between the ages of five and seven, the first permanent teeth appear, and the bones of trunk and limbs continue to lengthen. The growth rate becomes less perceptible after about the age of six but speeds up again just before puberty.

During adolescence a person develops from a child to an adult—a process that involves profound physical and emotional changes. Puberty—the onset of sexual maturation—occurs when, under the stimulation of the pituitary gland, the sex glands begin to release their hormones into the bloodstream. As a result, the reproductive organs mature and secondary sexual characteristics develop. Long bones undergo a burst of growth before attaining their final adult size. Muscles, brain, and central nervous system also complete their physical development at around this time, although some of the bones of the skull do not fuse permanently until the late thirties.

The early twenties mark the peak of physical development as muscles, heart, blood, and lungs all operate at maximum efficiency. Emphasis switches then from growth to maintenance and repair of the body. In the late twenties, however, the body begins its gradual physical decline. This process is hardly notice-

The elderly and the very young often have a special affinity. Both are at extremes of human development, need more than average care from others, and tend to be kept slightly apart from normal everyday adult life. For these reasons they are often left to look after each other. Commonly, both also have a special affinity with animals. In many rural communities the care of farm animals is the responsibility of the older and younger members of society.

able at first and—in active people—may not become apparent for many years. In most people, however, it becomes increasingly evident in their thirties and forties.

Exactly what causes aging is still uncertain, although genetic factors and wear and tear all play a part. The symptoms of old age are essentially an accumulation of defects: the nervous system, muscles, and skin deteriorate, major organs become less efficient, and disorders such as arteriosclerosis become more common.

Mental and social development

Mental and social development depend both on physical factors and on learning. According to the Swiss psychologist, Jean Piaget, intellectual development also moves through regular and recognizable stages. Until about the age of two, sensation and reflexes are closely linked. Gradually, the use of language develops and, as hand-eye and eye-ear coordination increase, mental processes develop from intuition based on incomplete perception to reasoned thought. By about the age of 12, a child has usually developed an adult ability to conceptualize and reason.

Less measurable, perhaps, is the process of social development, or socialization—the acquisition of a "social self" with values and beliefs that influence an individual's personal behavior and aspirations. This process begins in childhood, with the family being the chief socializing agent in most cultures. The family, and subsequently, school and peer groups, interpret the prevailing culture and present the child with a social pattern of desirable actions and probable results.

One of the most crucial aspects of the socializing process is "sex typing," by which a child adopts behavior patterns considered appropriate to his or her sex in a process of copying and encouragement reinforced by reward.

Heredity versus environment

One of the most controversial questions surrounding human development is the extent to which an individual is the product of his or her environment and upbringing on the one hand, or of genetic inheritance on the other. The question of "sex typing" can be seen as a specific example of this. The controversy affects such aspects of development as personality, aptitude, and intelligence particularly. Although various tests have been carried out, for example, on identical twins raised in the same or different environments, findings remain inconclusive. All that can be said with certainty is that heredity, culture, socialization, economic factors, and experience all play important roles in transforming the newborn infant into an adult individual.

Women, traditionally, have the chief responsibility for rearing children, either in the home or in play groups and nurseries, as illustrated here. With more women returning to full-time employment after having had babies, however, these traditional roles are changing. Some are even being taken over by men, for whom the role of "house-husband" is becoming increasingly common.

The change into manhood coincides with the peak of physical development and fitness, which many men maintain by taking part in sports and games.

The first 12 months

For a newborn baby, the outside world is a frightening but exciting place. The first year is a foundation year, during which a normal baby acquires basic skills that will be built upon through the rest of its life. For instance, in these months the baby's eyes, ears, and tongue develop abilities that will be necessary for learning to read and speak. The baby begins to learn how to control its muscles; it also experiences emotion, and begins to understand language. It grows its first teeth and learns to smile, laugh, and eat solid food.

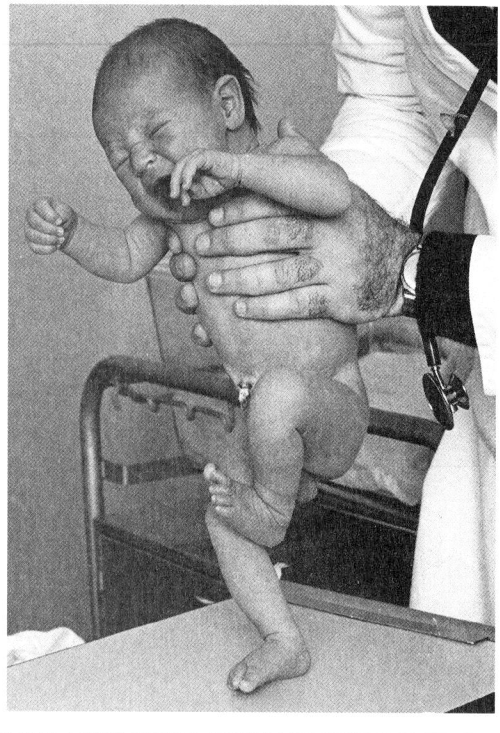

A newborn baby shows primitive reflexes in the first few weeks of life. An example is the step reflex: when one foot is placed on a horizontal surface the baby raises the other leg, as if in an attempt to walk.

A baby's curiosity increases rapidly after the first few weeks. Objects are observed dimly at about two weeks. Familiar shapes such as a parent's face may be recognized at about three or four weeks. The eyes begin to focus at about eight weeks, though rapidly moving objects cannot be followed with the eyes until a baby is about one year old.

Physical changes

An average newborn baby weighs 6-9 pounds (3-4 kilograms) and is approximately 20 inches (50 centimeters) long. By 12 months, it weighs roughly 19-26 pounds (9-12 kilograms) and has increased its height by approximately 28-33 inches (70-80 centimeters). A newborn baby's brain is around 25 per cent of its final adult brain weight, although the baby's body is only 5 per cent of its adult weight. During the first year, the brain grows very fast, allowing the baby to learn an enormous amount.

A newborn baby's skeleton is soft and incompletely formed, and its skull has gaps (fontanels) between the main bony plates. This softness and flexibility allows the baby to pass through the mother's birth canal without damage. The fontanels close during the first 18 months, and the bones harden as the child grows. In fact, the whole process of ossification, which changes soft cartilage into hard bone, begins before birth and continues until about age 20.

In the first 12 months, the skeleton strengthens until the legs are able to support the baby's weight. The first tooth usually appears about the sixth or seventh month, and the baby usually begins to take solid food, rather than just milk, at around two months.

Reflexes and senses

Newborn babies show a number of instinctive actions and responses known as reflexes. They include the rooting reflex, where the baby turns the head if the cheek is gently touched; the grasp reflex, in which the hands tightly clutch anything placed against the palm; and the step reflex, in which the baby steps when a foot is placed on a horizontal surface. These reflexes are later superseded by more complicated reactions, such as turning toward a familiar sound, and reaching out to grasp an object the baby can see. By 12 months, a baby has developed the full width of vision he or she will have as an adult, and can focus on small objects at a distance.

From the earliest months, babies gaze longer at patterned and colored shapes than at plain white or gray ones. A normal baby's hearing develops rapidly, and improved coordination helps it to turn toward sounds it has located. By eight weeks, a baby utters the first recognized phonemes—sounds that later join to form speech. By one year old, he or she has mastered some of the more difficult sounds, such as "b," "g," "p," and "t"; many babies say their first recognizable words just before the first birthday.

Physical abilities

A baby's motor (movement) development is very rapid; through the first 12 months, it develops from a helpless infant into a mobile, inquisitive individual. Noticeable muscle control begins at about three months, when the baby can hold up the head. As the limbs and muscles strengthen, coordination improves and, by about six months, a baby is able to roll over and sit up without support; by about nine months, he or she can reach a standing position; and by about 12 months, the baby walks when one hand is held. The baby learns first to clutch objects in a closed fist, then to grasp them with the thumb on one side and fingers on the other, and then to pick up fairly small objects with finger and thumb.

Personality and emotions

In the mother's womb, a baby is comfortable, warm, dark, and soothed by the mother's heartbeat, so for the first few weeks after birth, bright lights, loud noises, and sudden movements can be very distressing. Babies gain tremendous pleasure and security from warmth and physical closeness, and benefit from as much as they can get.

By about six weeks, the baby has learned to smile, and at four months he or she laughs and giggles. Through the first year the baby gradually comes to feel more complicated emotions such as jealousy, petulance and affection.

By its first birthday, a baby is able to respond to simple commands, such as "come here," and to understand the meaning of "yes" and "no"; babies love imitating adult behavior, and will "burble" contentedly, although incomprehensibly, while playing. In these vitally important, formative 12 months, the foundations are laid for all types of adult behavior, emotions, and skills.

Immunization

Babies receive some immunity from the mother before birth, and some from antibodies in breast milk. Nevertheless, they are vulnerable to infection and so are usually immunized against certain infectious diseases between the ages of 3 and 12 months, with a booster dose at about age 5. Inoculations against diphtheria, tetanus, and poliomyelitis are the most common. In Europe, vaccination against pertussis (whooping cough) is fairly common, but reactions causing brain damage have occurred in a tiny percentage of cases. Vaccination against measles and mumps is also available. Vaccination against tuberculosis is only given to babies who are at risk; otherwise, children are usually vaccinated at about age 10 to age 12.

Walking, with clumsy, staggering steps, starts at about ten months, but a child needs to hold something for balance at first. The first unaided steps usually occur at about age one, although even then a child may still move faster on hands and knees.

Teething is painful and babies do not suffer in silence. The upper and lower incisors appear first, at about six to twelve months, and it is these that are hurting the child in the photograph *(left).* Other childhood, or "milk," teeth emerge in the approximate sequence shown diagrammatically below.

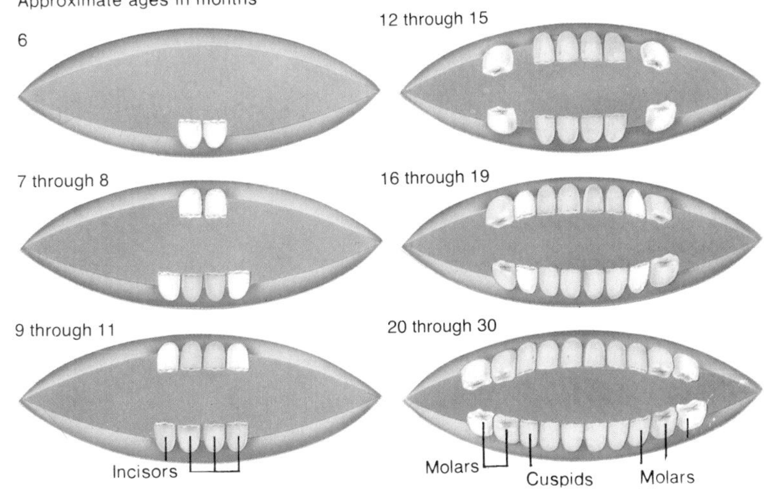

Fact entries

Freud, Sigmund (1856-1939), Austrian psychoanalyst, whose research into neuroses led him to postulate a theory of childhood sexuality, which in turn showed him the significance of sexuality in many aspects of human behavior.

Montessori, Maria (1870-1952), Italian child psychologist and educator, whose work with preschool and retarded children stressed the importance of a stimulating environment, in particular one full of things children can handle and touch, in the education of young children. The first woman ever to graduate in medicine at the University of Rome, she then lectured there, and was appointed government inspector of schools in 1922. She traveled the world supervising training courses.

Piaget, Jean (1896-1980), Swiss psychologist whose study of the thought processes of children and of the growth of their intelligence helped to establish child psychology as a science and also has had considerable influence on educators.

Spock, Dr. Benjamin (1903-), American pediatrician whose book on *Baby and Child Care* (1946) became a standard reference for many parents in the 1950's to 1970's. Although he retracted some of his teachings, his methods remain popular.

Age 1 through 5 years

A child never learns faster and grows more quickly than in its first 12 months, but the next four years are also times of astonishing development, particularly of the mind.

By the age of five, most children have grown to over 3 feet (1 meter) tall—more than half their adult height—but a five-year-old's brain is 90 per cent of final adult brain weight. At about 18 months, a normal child can walk reasonably well on its own; at two years, it can run steadily; and by five, it can jump, skip, and hop and walk along a bench without falling off.

Conceptual development

Conceptual development begins from the time that a child first begins to understand actions and spoken words. It continues throughout life, as there is a need to deal with all sorts of abstract ideas, from the simple to the complicated. Nutrition in infancy plays a very important part in this development, and inadequate feeding up to the age of 18 months may permanently impair a child's conceptual abilities.

At age two, children's abstract concepts are limited; they know their first name, and can point to common objects such as eyes, hair, or shoes. At this stage, a child cannot match pairs of three-dimensional shapes, but can use pencil and paper to copy simple lines.

By age three, a child knows its age in years, and is beginning to be able to match shapes by trial and error. The child can copy circles, name some colors, and count up to ten. There is also considerable understanding of the concept "where," "what," "who," and "whose."

At four, a child can speak well and can understand simple comparisons such as "bigger" and "colder," and constantly asks questions beginning "Why. . . ?", "When. . . ?" and "How. . . ?"

At age five, a normal child has a vocabulary of 1,500-2,000 words and can repeat its full name, age, birthday, and address. A child of this age can copy a square and eight or nine simple capital letters and, when matching three-dimensional shapes, has learned to compare objects by eye before moving them to their correct positions.

Achievements

Coordination improves rapidly through the first five years. At 18 months, a child can build a small tower of bricks and shows the first signs of being right- or left-handed. At two years, he or she can throw a ball and turn the pages of a book. At three years, a child can stand briefly on one leg and use a spoon and fork.

Preschool children paint using colors freely, but showing little control of line and form.

Two- and three-year-olds are often happiest playing alone and tend to be preoccupied with their own games even in the company of other children. Nevertheless, most welcome the security of an adult's presence nearby and will complain loudly if they feel neglected.

Health

Toilet training occurs between the ages of one and four, beginning (usually at 15-18 months) when the child is able to signal that a diaper is wet or soiled. Most children have stopped wetting the bed at night by age three, with maybe a few accidents up to the age of four.

Children aged one through two require approximately 1,200 calories per day; by age five, this need increases to around 1,600 calories. At age five, most children sleep for about ten hours a night. Nightmares, however, can send a child screaming to the parents for reassurance and the warmth and comfort of the parents' bed. A child may also need reassurance before bed, particularly about fears of the dark. By the age of six, most children have given up daytime naps.

As children become more active, so the risk of illness increases—in this age group, however, major infectious illness is less common than minor injuries from accidents. Exploration can also lead to serious accidents, particularly from poisoning, but also from burns or scalds. General health care includes sensible safety precautions, particularly in the home and garden; choice of clothing and footwear that inhibits neither movement nor growth; personal hygiene, including care of the teeth; nutritious diet; and a friendly acquaintance with both doctor and dentist to ensure that the natural anxieties about such encounters are minimized.

Emotions

Through these years, emotions can change drastically as children discover their individuality. The two- to three-year-old stage can be particularly trying for the parents, as a child tries rebellion, demands constant attention, shows jealousy and possessiveness, and throws temper tantrums. Not all children show all these characteristics and some show them more vigorously than others. Nevertheless, these problems are familiar enough to most parents, and few families avoid the experience completely.

Emotions generally fluctuate a bit less in a four-year-old, and at this age, children start to play and share happily with other children. By the age of five, a child can show considerable concern and responsibility in protecting the interests of younger children.

Emotional upsets through these years are common particularly when new babies are born in the family. These can trigger rebellion or nervous habits, and a child may develop irrational fears. If at this age the child must be separated from its parents—for instance, to enter the hospital—great reassurance can be needed to quell fears of permanent separation. Starting school may also be difficult, but is often more traumatic for the parents than the child! Generally, if parents have encouraged their child's independence and have tried to understand and relieve any fears, the child should be able to make the transition to the next stage of life easily.

Physical skills develop at different ages. The illustration shows certain "landmarks" in the development of an average child—but of course, individual children's development may vary considerably from these stages.

Playing with other children reveals a child's emotional development and usually begins during the fourth year. Playing together encourages imagination but also leads to quarreling—particularly if toys have to be shared or desires conflict in other ways, for instance, where two children both want to be the center of attention. At this age, children can be generous, even altruistic, to those they regard as friends, but they also can bully smaller or less confident playmates ruthlessly.

Age 5 through 10 years

Mental and physical development are extremely rapid between the ages of five and ten. The illustration identifies some representative stages. Children have almost unlimited energy and curiosity—often to their parents' exasperation, but to their pleasure and entertainment too, because the first clear indications of a child's individuality and character start to appear at this age.

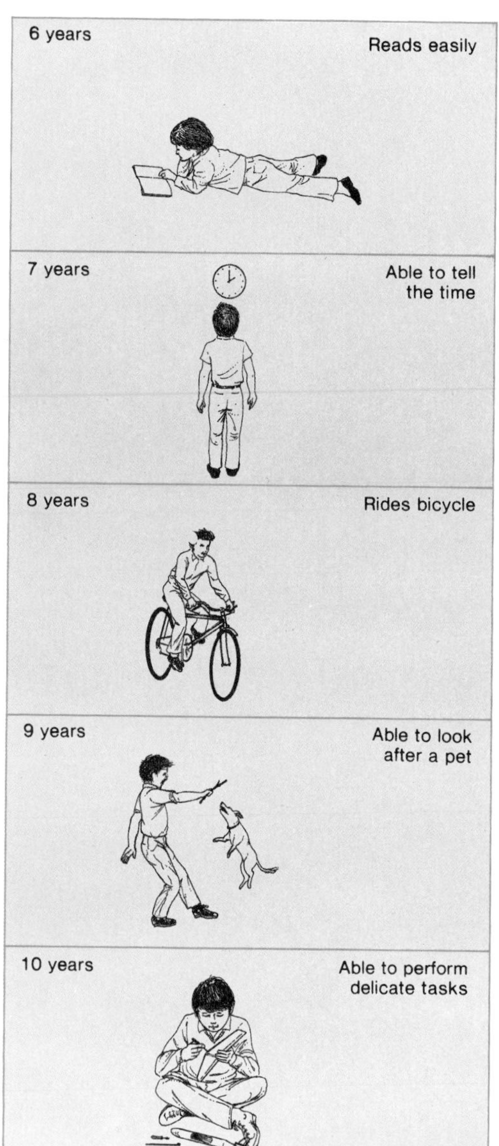

Abundant energy, channeled into physical activity, typifies children in the five- through ten-year-old age group. They develop their physical prowess and coordination through all kinds of play. This gives them ample opportunity to interact with other children—with friendship and with aggression—and helps them develop their individual and social characters.

The years from ages five through ten take a child from the first experience of formal education to the months preceding puberty. At five, a child is still very dependent, physically and emotionally, on the parents. By age ten, the child is much more an individual, exhibiting personal talents and tastes, and is independent in many everyday activities. The skills and coordination learned in early childhood are used at this age to develop new interests and hobbies, and carry the child further along the way to full independence.

Through these years, a child can learn to cook simple meals, be totally responsible for a pet, use books for self-directed studies, and carry out many other activities that serve as landmarks of independence.

Achievements

During the years five through seven, the normal child finally masters the more difficult sounds of speech and becomes confident about using them. The soft consonant sounds, such as "r," "th," and "ch," are the last to be learned—up to this age the child may still be confusing or mispronouncing them. By age six or so, the language center in the brain has developed an intricate network of interlocking nerve pathways, which through the rest of life allow the person to construct complex sentences in speech, thought, and writing.

Coordination continues to improve, helped by practice, and a child can learn to draw and to write neatly. By age six, simple words are usually written confidently; cursive writing is learned soon after. The child becomes increasingly adept at skills such as model building and sewing, which require very fine and well-controlled hand movements. By age ten, most children can draw objects realistically. Children at this age have a great deal of energy and often occupy themselves with activities such as bicycle riding, playing games with other children, exploring, and pursuing their favorite hobbies.

Conceptual development

At the age of five or six, a child's grasp of abstract ideas is based on simple comparisons such as "hotter," "younger," "more," and so on. From about age seven, the child slowly learns to make decisions and solve problems based on logic rather than intuition or guesswork. This skill improves rapidly through the next years—by the age of about 12 a child can reason, on a simple level, in the same way as an adult. From the age of eight, the child begins to use many adjectives as he or she learns more about the quality of objects and actions.

It is not until about the age of ten, however, that a child begins to have a thorough grasp of ideas involving time. Simple time descriptions such as "today," "tomorrow," "at four o'clock," or "on Saturday" are understood first, then more abstract concepts, such as "when you were a baby" and "next November," follow later.

Mental problem-solving also begins at about this age, and a child no longer needs to see every stage of a simple problem either physically or on paper to be able to work out the answer.

Health

As soon as they start school children are exposed to many common infections—from colds to measles, mumps, and chicken pox. Normally, they are very resilient and recover from these illnesses quickly if they contract them. Generally, however, vaccination against most of these disorders is carried out before the child starts school. This form of conferred immunity not only protects the children and their contacts at school, but also protects any parent who has not been immunized and who would suffer more seriously from the illness as an adult if the infection were contracted.

School is also the place where learning difficulties first become evident, though not always in obvious ways. An apparent reluctance to attend classes may mask dyslexia, for instance. Because everyone goes to school, and most enjoy (or at least accept) it, children who do not—for whatever reason—tend to hide their fears. These are likely to show nevertheless, but not directly. Abdominal pains, bed-wetting, fatigue, and even an obvious "unusual" change in behavior may all reflect a child's unhappy mind.

Children are notoriously picky about food, but it is essential that they have a balanced and nutritious diet, with adequate quantities of fresh fruit and vegetables, protein, bread, and milk. Up to the age of ten, boys and girls have similar calorie requirements: about 2,400 calories per day. After this age, boys and men need around 500 calories per day more than girls or women of the same age.

By nine, children of both sexes are about 4 feet 8 inches (120-140 centimeters) tall, although during adolescence, boys begin to grow faster than girls. During these years, the milk teeth are gradually lost and replaced.

Finding out about the world and practicing independence are among the dominant concerns of this age group, but this process can have its dangers, and supervision and adequate precautions are still needed. About half the deaths that occur between the ages of five and fifteen are caused by accidents.

Emotions

Young children react badly to anything that upsets them deeply. Such upsets are caused by many things, including parental discord, or losing physical or emotional security (for instance, by moving or starting a new school).

Children are also strongly influenced by their peers, and often goad one another into behavior that they know is generally unacceptable. Many children at this age go through phases in which they do precisely what they have been told they should not: lying, cheating, stealing, fighting, swearing, smoking, and going where they have been forbidden to go are all common. Views differ on the best parental reaction to such behavior on the assumption that it is a temporary aberration rather than a permanent character defect or psychological fault. Overall, however, it seems that a natural reaction (disapproval, annoyance, or anger) is most appropriate and can do little harm, so long as the child recognizes that this reaction is a direct response and does not imply any genuine or permanent rejection.

Team sports help children learn how to direct their energy and competitiveness toward common rather than individual ends.

Books stimulate the imagination and so appeal to many children in this age group, if they have not yet associated books with discipline and schooling.

Puberty and adolescence

Through puberty and adolescence, girls become women and boys become men. Puberty sees the start of the physical aspects of this transformation and occupies roughly the first half of the teenage years. Adolescence covers the second half of the teenage period up to the usually undefined point at which a person is seen to be "adult." It is a time of learning independence and emotional maturity and of coming to terms with adulthood.

It can be a difficult time for the teenager because of mood changes, the strength of sexual feelings, and the desire or even the need for ever-increasing independence.

Physical changes in girls

The physical changes of puberty usually occur in girls between the ages of 10 and 14, although there is considerable individual variation. Nutrition, heredity, body weight, and social factors all influence the age at which any particular girl begins puberty. The changes are started by hormones released from the pituitary gland at the base of the brain; these hormones cause the ovaries to mature and to release estrogen into the bloodstream. Estrogen causes the nipples to darken and the breasts to grow, slowly at first, as the milk ducts enlarge and increase in number. Pubic hair, followed by axillary (armpit) hair, begins to appear, then gradually grows coarser, darker, and more prolific.

About a year after these changes begin, the menstrual periods start, when the uterus sheds its lining each month. The menarche (first period) is usually preceded by a monthly clear discharge for one or two months. The first periods may be very light, not much more than a slight, bloodstained discharge, or may start immediately with a normal adult level of menstrual flow.

The estrogen causing the external changes of puberty also induces growth of the uterus, vagina, ovaries, and labia (the folds of skin around the entrance to the vagina), and changes the vaginal secretions from alkaline to acid. The pelvis grows wider to allow for childbearing, and other hormones (androgens) in the bloodstream cause a slight hair growth on the upper lip.

Ovulation (production of an egg for possible fertilization) usually starts a few months after the first menstrual period.

Adolescents are particularly adept at learning new skills and benefit enormously from careful teaching and encouragement—probably more than any other age group. Skills acquired at this age often serve as the basis for future employment, or at least serve as interesting hobbies in adult life.

Physical changes in boys

Changes in boys at puberty are also started by pituitary hormones, which cause the testes to grow and the scrotum to enlarge and become ridged and darker in color. Spermatozoa

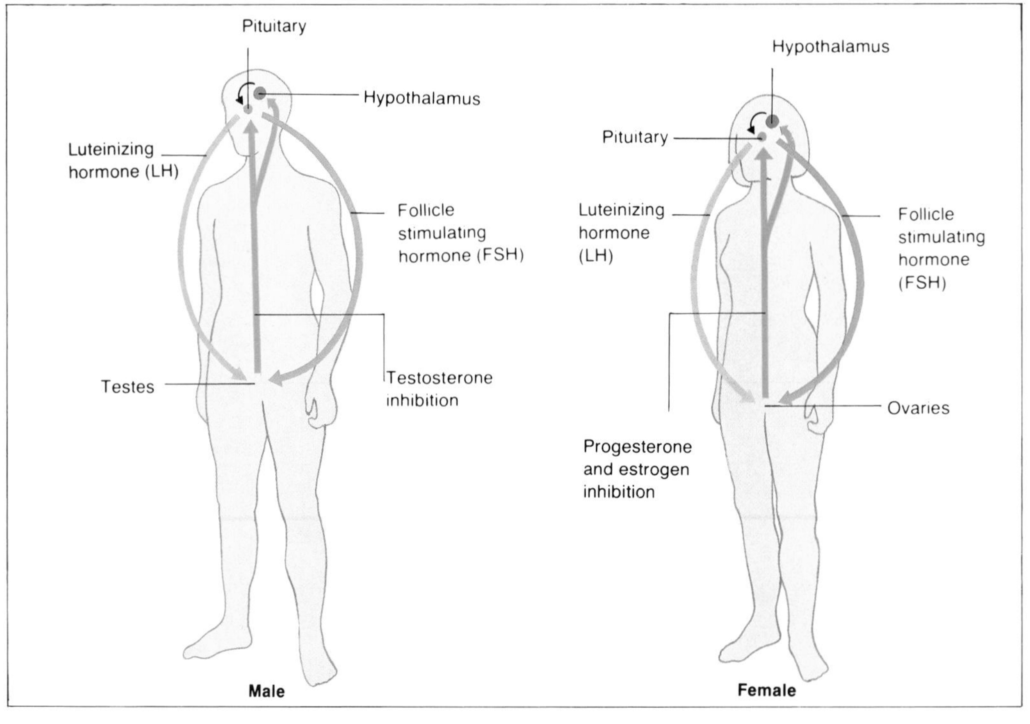

Physical development in boys and girls is controlled by hormones released from the anterior pituitary, which is stimulated by a releasing factor (black arrow) from the hypothalamus in the brain. In boys, pituitary hormones make the testes produce testosterone, which causes the body to develop such male characteristics as facial and body hair, male sexual organs, a deeper voice, and heavier musculature. In girls, pituitary hormones stimulate the production of progesterone and estrogen by the ovaries. Progesterone initiates the development of the breasts and affects the menstrual cycle; estrogen causes the body to develop female sexual characteristics. In both boys and girls, the levels of sex hormones in the blood are monitored by the hypothalamus: this feedback mechanism controls the hormone output of the pituitary.

begin to be formed, although many of these do not reach maturity in the early years. Testosterone released into the bloodstream causes a sudden increase in height and weight. The penis increases in size, and hair begins to appear in the armpits and in the pubic region. In early puberty, boys may also experience uncomfortable swelling in one or both breasts. This is caused by sensitivity to hormones in the blood, and soon disappears.

The hormones that bring about a boy's gradual physical and emotional development into a man have various direct and indirect effects on the body. The vocal cords enlarge as changes occur in the larynx, and the voice slowly deepens. The prostate gland starts to secrete substances that form part of the seminal fluid. Hair begins to grow in the pubic region and on the face. The muscles grow, the shoulders broaden, and the body thickens generally. Boys usually complete these physical changes by about age 18.

Changes in both sexes

At puberty, both boys and girls tend to accumulate extra fat. It disappears later in most boys, but girls tend to retain it around the hips, thighs, and breasts. Because of increased hormonal action, the sebaceous glands increase their activity, causing the skin to become oilier and coarser. Blood pressure and lung capacity increase, but average heart rate, respiration (breathing) rate, and body temperature all tend to fall as the child gets older. The muscles become stronger and, particularly in boys, more noticeable. Sexual urges grow stronger as hormonal action increases and the sex organs develop.

Hygiene

When axillary (armpit) and pubic hair starts to grow, perspiration also increases in those areas, and teenagers become conscious of the need to pay extra attention to personal hygiene. When their periods start, girls should be advised how sanitary napkins or tampons are used and how often they should be changed. The overactive sebaceous glands in the skin, which are frequently the cause of teenage skin problems (notably acne), can be controlled by careful washing and specially medicated soaps and creams.

Social transitions as well as physical ones occur at puberty and in adolescence. Often this transition takes a symbolic form, even if the symbol is no more obvious than wearing "adult" clothes or makeup. Sometimes, however, the symbolism is formalized, as in the Jewish ceremony of *bar mitzvah*, shown here, which symbolizes a child's acceptance into the adult community.

Social and psychological development

The psychological changes involved in puberty and adolescence are immense, as teenagers face adulthood, gain independence, and

Many adolescents enjoy group activities, particularly if they help channel exuberance and energy into physical activity. Intensely loyal to their team, these cheerleaders are trying to arouse enthusiasm within the crowd before the ball game.

Sports and outdoor activities are almost as important as study and social life to many teenagers. Those activities with marked social aspects—like surfing, for instance—understandably have the greatest appeal. Such activities also provide an opportunity to show great personal skill, which is important for the social competitiveness of teenagers.

come to terms with their maturing bodies and sexual feelings. Teenagers need great understanding from their parents, teachers, and other concerned adults during puberty but providing this can be difficult, because teenagers can be very unlovable when they are confused by mental, physical, and emotional changes beyond their control.

Most teenagers at around the age of 15 or 16 become involved in heterosexual relationships. These may be very casual, as emotional attachments move easily among several different boyfriends or girlfriends, or they may be far more profound. Romantic love is a common feature of the teenage years, and many relationships formed at this time are taken very seriously.

Mood changes

Adolescence can be a worrying time because hormonal activity often induces sudden and inexplicable mood changes, which may surprise the teenager as much as the family. The teenager does not really know whether he or she is a child or an adult. An adolescent is expected to obey parental and school discipline, and yet is also expected to be self-motivated about work, looking after money and other responsibilities. Most teenagers also worry that they are developing too fast or too slowly, or that they are not changing in the same way as everyone else. Any negative feelings about puberty that have been acquired in childhood come to the forefront during the teenage years.

Adolescent girls may suffer additional problems due to menstruation, specifically premenstrual tension and menstrual cramps. Premenstrual tension is a mixture of physical and psychological symptoms that may include fluid retention, temporary weight gain, skin disturbances, headaches, depression, fits of temper, breast tenderness, and a feeling of heaviness and lethargy. The syndrome occurs for several days before, and during the first few days of, each period, and can be aggravated by stress. Menstrual cramps also may begin in adolescence and may be severe enough to cause temporary absence from school. These problems can upset a girl's life considerably and cause substantial distress.

Sexuality

Sexual feelings emerge slowly during puberty and become a dominating influence during adolescence. Curiosity about sexual matters and the physical characteristics of the opposite sex is intense for most adolescents. This curiosity may take the form of questions to parents or teachers, but is also pursued by reading as much as possible relating to sexuality and by sharing information with other children of the same age group. Sexuality has a social as well as a physical aspect, and many young teenagers feel happier meeting the opposite sex in groups, or at least with another couple, before they are confident enough to go out with their date alone.

Social and psychological problems

For most people the changes of adolescence are at worst merely temporary troubles. For some, however, they can cause serious problems. Compulsive eating, leading to excessive weight gain, or self-starvation, called anorexia nervosa, may occur. Periodic depression—as an aspect of mood changes—is common, but can become acute and, in extreme cases, result in attempted or actual suicide.

Social problems tend to be associated with an adolescent's desires for sexual discovery, novelty, excitement, independence, and rebellion. They are most likely to occur when circumstances or an individual's reaction to them get out of control. The main areas of teenage social problems in Westernized societies are concerned with sex (in particular with sexual diseases or unwanted pregnancies), drug abuse, and crime.

An awareness of the causes of sexual problems and the willingness of parents to advise helpfully about their avoidance or, if necessary, their treatment, is the easiest solution to the first of these problem areas. Professional advice and treatment centers such as Family Planning or contraception clinics, pregnancy advisory centers, and clinics for the diagnosis and treatment of sexually transmitted (venereal) diseases are alternatives or adjuncts to parental guidance.

Criminal activities, such as drug abuse or petty theft, are often tempting to teenagers because of the excitement of risk and the gesture of rebellion they embody. But minor "risk-taking" leads all too easily—usually through association with friends who take similar or greater risks—to deeper involvement. The penalties are also serious because they don't stop when the "debt to society," whether a fine or a prison sentence, has been paid. A criminal conviction can, and usually does, literally change a person's life.

Such difficulties affect only a minority of teenagers, however, and most families cope with the emotional upsets of adolescence with a minimum of antagonism. Even where conflict occurs it tends to pass quickly because it is

Study is a dominant feature of the teenage years for most adolescents. As they grow older, emphasis shifts gradually from organized classes to more independent study. Examinations usually mark the various stages of formal education.

Discos appeal to all ages, but perhaps to adolescents most of all, because they provide a context in which young people can meet others away from the critical eyes of their elders. Loud, emotive music and the excitement of dancing also helps some adolescents to overcome shyness.

more likely to be an expression of reaction to change—by either parents or children—than a reflection of deeper hostility.

Conflict

As they begin to develop into adults and seek their own standards, teenagers naturally tend to become resentful of rules and restrictions imposed by others. School and family discipline is irksome, and rebellion against authority is a common reaction. Parental values are superseded by influences from school, the media and, in particular, the opinions of friends. Many adolescents become strongly concerned about moral questions, especially those relating to social issues such as justice, politics, religion, war, and class. As a result, they frequently come into conflict with their families, especially over specific principles or details of ideology.

Most adolescents live at home during this transitional period, while they are finishing their schooling or while training for a job. Meanwhile, they become old enough to drink, smoke, vote, drive, and marry, and crave emotional and financial independence. This wrestling with two different roles—as an independent individual on the one hand and as part of a family on the other—has a maturing effect that probably does as much as anything else to equip the adolescent for adulthood.

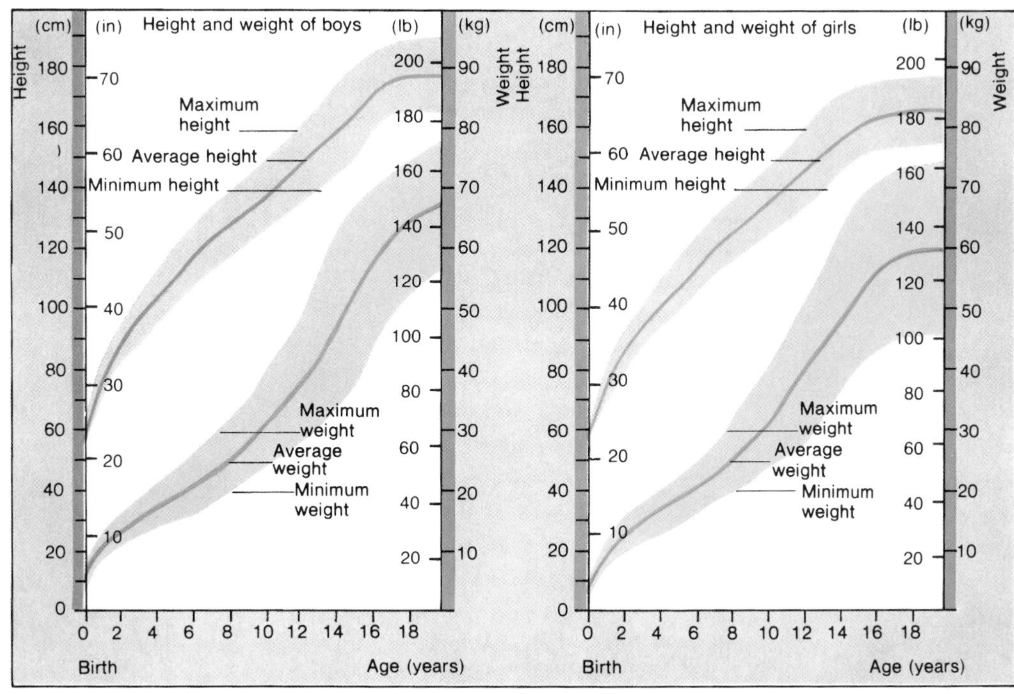

The growth of boys and girls follows similar but not identical patterns from birth to the late teens, when height and weight stabilize. The graphs show the increase in height and weight for each sex. The average height and weight of each sex (the dark mid-lines of each graph) remain almost identical until the mid- to late-teens, when young men continue to grow after young women stop. Differences occur chiefly in rates of growth—with girls growing faster in the early teens—and in variations between maximum and minimum heights and weights, with girls showing a greater variation in weight.

Adulthood

Adulthood begins when the genetic program of growth is complete—that is, when the body has grown to its full height and has also undergone the sexual changes that make adolescents physically mature. This stage is generally reached between the ages of 16 and 20. It occurs slightly earlier for females than males, who may still be growing in their early twenties. Today, a person legally becomes an adult at age 18 in most states of the U.S., in most Canadian provinces, and in most European countries.

Emotional maturity is not yet complete at the onset of adulthood, however, and is consolidated during the twenties. There is still great potential for learning and for improving society-related skills, such as independence, business acumen, and responsibility.

In all societies, there is social pressure to conform, and most people bow to this pressure on reaching adulthood. Another dominating factor in Westernized societies is the work ethic, and nowhere are the two more obviously combined than in a crowd of similarly dressed commuters on their way to work.

Physical concerns

The peak of physical health, for both males and females, occurs in the last few years of the teens and in the early twenties. Furthermore, opportunities for maintaining fitness are readily available at school and college and in leisure hours. Work responsibilities grow, people marry and have children, opportunities for physical exercise become fewer, and many people even in their mid-twenties take no physical exercise at all.

Few people cut down on their food consumption in adulthood—instead, it often increases as family life is established. At the same time, actual physical requirements decrease steadily, and as a result, many people eat far more than they need. This can rapidly cause overweight, which in turn contributes to numerous disorders, such as high blood pressure, heart disease, diabetes, and varicose veins. Smoking and drinking may also increase, contributing to unfitness and ill health. Regular exercise is therefore important, not only to maintain fitness and health, but also as a form of relaxation from stress. The need for a balanced and moderate diet is also essential.

Motivation

During early adulthood, personal motivation tends to be at its strongest. A young adult may be keen to establish a successful social role and career, to build up satisfactory emotional relationships, to earn money for necessities

The nuclear family, consisting of mother, father, and children, is the basic social unit in adulthood in most societies. Social scientists also recognize the concept of the extended family, which may include grandparents, and brothers or sisters of the adults (and their children, if any).

and luxuries, and to explore new ideas—in short, to define and fulfill ambitions, and to face the challenges that the adult world offers. So, providing the opportunities are available, many young adults tend to be ambitious, enthusiastic, zealous, and dedicated, whether in choosing a marriage partner, rearing children, or pursuing a career.

This motivation is likely to persist until at least the age of 35-40, but thereafter, there is a tendency for it to diminish. Although a few people find their 40s to be some of the most productive and energetic years of all, a typical 40-year-old has established a satisfactory way of life, which may include a home, a family, and a career, through a high level of output in the previous years. From this age onward, energy is more likely to be directed into consolidating these established positions, rather than breaking new ground. Consequently, if something goes wrong—perhaps resulting in divorce, illness, bereavement, or unemployment—people in mid-adulthood find it much harder than do young adults to start afresh.

Emotions

Emotional maturity lags behind physical maturity because it involves some social skills and experience that can be gained only in the adult world. A mature adult has to learn to handle emotional responses, and how and when to show feelings or conceal them. Some emotional responses are expressed principally in social reactions, which come into play, for example, when standing up for one's rights at work or coping with shyness in oneself or in others. Other aspects of emotional maturity are learned in interpersonal relationships, especially between marriage partners. The individual has to learn to deal with anger, fatigue, pleasure, frustration, professional or sexual jealousy, physical attraction, and many other emotions. Sexual maturity is reached physically in adolescence, but emotionally takes somewhat longer to develop as lasting sexual relationships are initiated and established.

Stress

Stress is a normal physiological condition that, to a certain degree, is both healthy and necessary for people to function at their best. Too much stress without relaxation, however, tenses the body chemically and physically, and, over a period of time, can cause significant harm.

Stress occurs particularly in people who work long or irregular hours and in those who are experiencing emotional difficulties. It can also be caused by poor working conditions, poor housing, poverty, and lack of satisfaction and can be aggravated by major incidents that are not unpleasant in themselves, such as moving home, getting married, or having a baby.

This condition contributes to many disorders, psychological problems, and emotional and sexual difficulties. A successful and relatively stress-free adulthood can often be achieved by balancing work, emotional life, relaxation, exercise, sleep, sexual activity, and leisure pursuits.

Sports keep people fit, and physical fitness helps minimize the effects of stress. Some sports, such as tennis, have a strong social aspect, too. If this generates too much social competitiveness, however, it can actually increase stress and counteract any benefits the physical activity itself may bring.

Stress, an important aspect of life in industrialized nations, has a number of different effects on the body. In themselves, these effects are harmless, and in certain circumstances are necessary and can even be beneficial. The illustration below shows the normal bodily reactions to stress and indicates the parts of the body that stress affects.

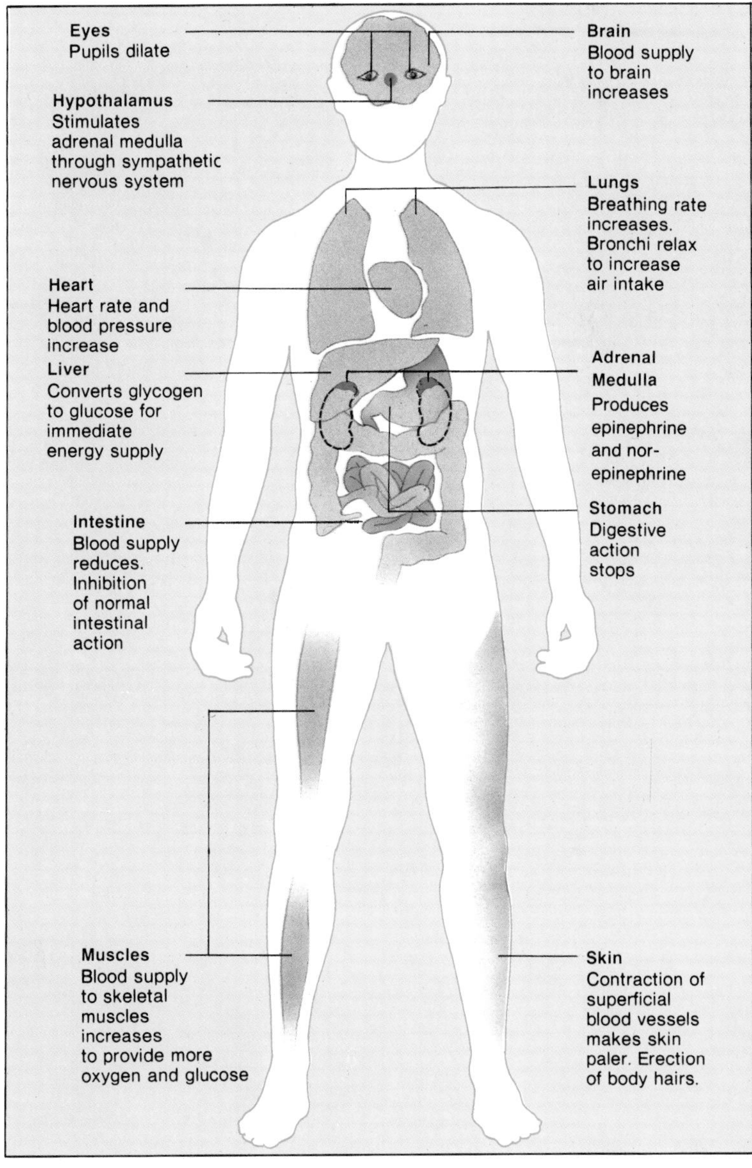

A healthy outdoor life can improve longevity, although it may also accelerate the visible effects of age. The wind and sun, in particular, age the skin, as the wrinkled face of this Portuguese fisherman shows.

Aging

The average life span of people in the Western world today is approximately 70 years—a little less for men, a little more for women. It has increased enormously since the middle of the last century, when the average life expectancy at birth for either sex was only about 40 years. During this century, better medical care and improved working and living conditions have also helped to prolong life significantly.

The human body begins to deteriorate in the 20's and 30's, and as age advances, all of the body's systems become less efficient. One of the major concerns of middle and old age, therefore, is the need to come to terms with the physical, psychological, and social changes this deterioration involves.

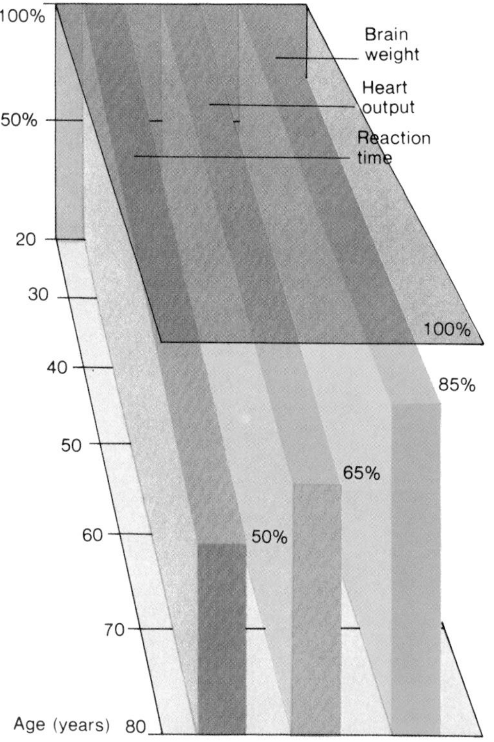

Aging is accompanied by the gradual physical deterioration of the body. The diagram shows three factors—brain weight, heart output, and reaction time—that deteriorate steadily from age 20. By age 80, these have deteriorated to 85, 65, and 50 per cent, respectively, of what they were 60 years before.

Coming to terms with old age is usually made easier by the fact that the mind normally deteriorates less rapidly than the rest of the body. A person who is mentally alert can often find great pleasure in a life that allows time for peace and reflection, particularly if these are balanced by stimulating interests and adequate physical activity.

External changes

Many physical changes are immediately obvious. White hairs appear as hair follicles lose their sources of pigmentation. Wrinkles increase as the skin loses its elasticity. Middle age is often associated with an increase in weight, followed by a significant decrease as old age advances. Muscle tissue is often replaced by fat, particularly around the trunk, while the arms and legs generally become thinner. Older people tend to lose height because of the compression of the vertebrae in the spine that results from the gradual loss of calcium from bone (osteoporosis)—which affects post-menopausal women particularly—and because of the tendency to stoop as muscle tone is lost.

Internal changes

Changes associated with aging also take place within the body's systems. Many internal organs, such as the kidneys, spleen, pancreas, lungs, and liver, become smaller in normal elderly people and less efficient at performing their tasks. The circulation of the blood is also affected by aging. The heart's pumping action is less efficient, and its response to exercise or stress, by increasing the heart rate, is more extreme. The blood vessels (veins, arteries, and capillaries) throughout the body lose some elasticity and tend to become convoluted. The bones become more brittle—also a result of osteoporosis—which makes older people more liable to fractures from falls or other accidents. The body becomes more sensitive to extremes of temperature and may take longer to recover from illness. Susceptibility to infection is increased, and the risk of cancer and some other disorders is greater.

Loneliness afflicts the elderly more than anyone. It is one of the main social problems of aging, and particularly affects those whose family does not live nearby, whose husband or wife has died, or who have outlived their friends. The problem is especially acute in towns and cities where people tend to be unconcerned with the welfare of others, but it also occurs wherever family and community ties have broken down.

The nervous system

Other changes associated with aging affect the nerves and their related functions. Nerve cells degenerate in old age and are not replaced, and the blood supply to the brain and other parts of the nervous system is affected by any general deterioration—for instance, caused by arteriosclerosis—that involves the circulation. This tends to reduce the brain's efficiency, and a decline in intellectual performance may follow the brain's gradual physical decline. Aspects of intelligence most likely to be affected by aging include logic, understanding three-dimensional images, problems involving numbers, and the ability to grasp new ideas. Other functions related to the brain also lose their efficiency: reflexes and physical movements become slower, and the memory—especially for recent events—may deteriorate. In severe cases, this can lead to senile dementia, which is characterized by loss of memory, unreasonable or childlike behavior, disconnected or incoherent speech, and a lack of awareness. The senses, too, are affected. Smell, taste, sight, touch, and hearing all deteriorate, causing increasing isolation of elderly people as everyday tasks and conversations become more difficult.

Menopause

Menopause literally means "stopping menstruation," although much more is involved than simply the end of the monthly periods. The menopause usually begins any time between the ages of 45 and 50, and has various physical and psychological effects. The cause of this "change of life" is an alteration in the usual monthly female hormone cycle, particularly affecting the production of progesterone, estrogen, and FSH (follicle-stimulating hormone). The woman stops ovulating and menstruating, although this rarely happens suddenly. She may also experience insomnia, headaches, severe mood swings, "hot flashes," and emotional disturbances, all related to hormonal changes. After the menopause, women become more susceptible to heart disease and bone deterioration.

Prospects for the elderly

Although aging does undoubtedly bring problems, in most cases these are no more than limitations; only rarely are they incapacitating. Furthermore, these limitations tend to be reduced by improvements in communal and personal health care—important aspects of which are health screening, improved diet, and an appreciation of the benefit of exercise to both body and mind—and also by medical advances, particularly in combating killers such as cancer and heart disease. Consequently, it is also likely that with life expectancy increasing, people are seeking to ensure that the quality of their lives improves too. To this end, some elderly people engage in social and political activities to improve their circumstances, while others tend to concentrate on developing satisfying leisure pursuits or even starting new careers.

Persons over the age of 60, most of whom have retired, form a substantial segment of the voting population. Pensioners demonstrating in England show the political significance of this group, which will grow larger as health care improves and life expectancy is extended. As a group, it is likely to be more eager than most to see results quickly. It is also likely to be more skeptical than most of promises that can be deferred.

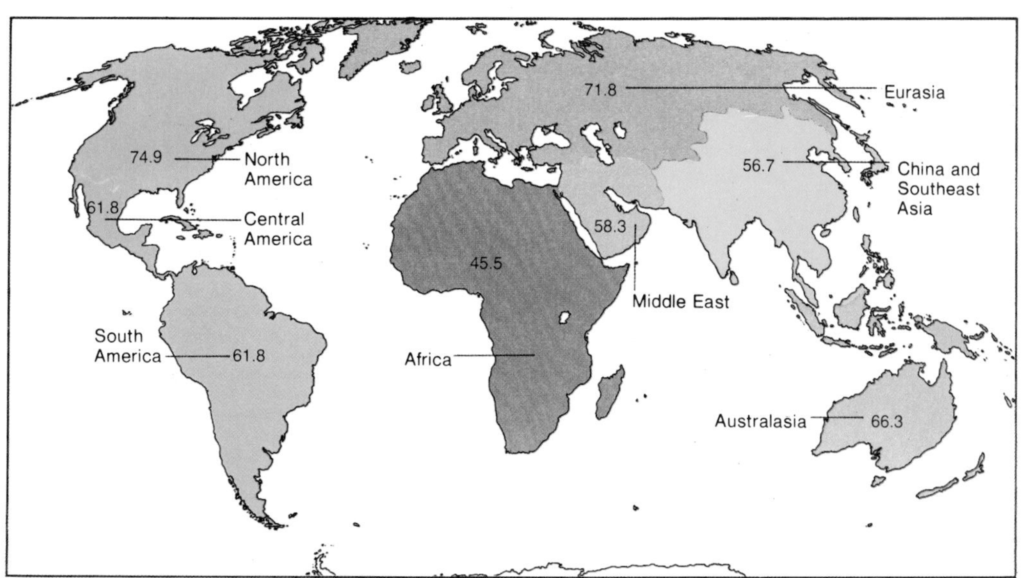

Life expectancy, calculated as the average age to which people live, varies from country to country and continent to continent. The map shows the average life expectancies of populations in eight broad geographical areas.

Illness and health

All of the body's organs and systems have specific functions to perform; illness basically results from the failure of any of them to function normally. Illnesses may be acute, producing severe short-lived symptoms, as in influenza; chronic, with symptoms that are prolonged, as in arthritis; or recurrent, as in malaria or various allergies. Good health is ensured not only by avoiding disease, but also by preventing illness through general health care, hygiene, or such specific methods as vaccination, and by strengthening the body's natural defenses through diet, exercise, and avoidance of stress.

Viruses are tiny, simple organisms that live off cells, which they attack for their nutritional and reproductive needs. This electron micrograph shows rows of viruses—called bacteriophages—attacking a bacterium. When viruses attack body cells they cause disease.

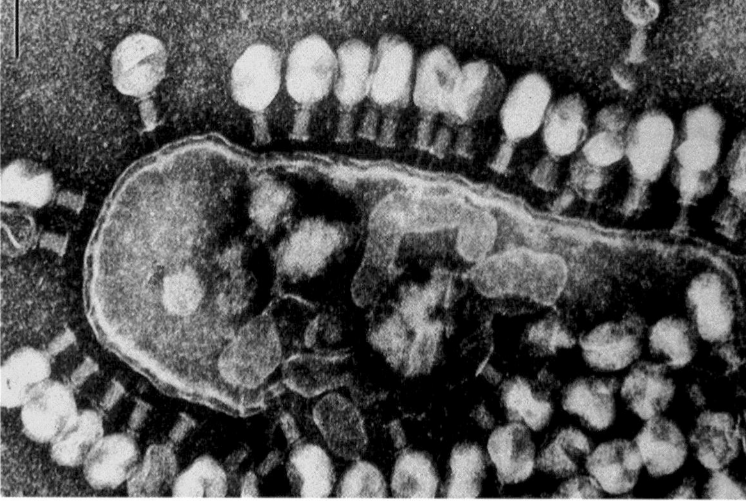

Garbage causes disease if it is allowed to collect in public places. It concentrates decay and provides a breeding place for bacteria and vermin, such as rats, which can spread infection. The removal of refuse is an important aspect of community health—particularly in an urban environment.

Causes of illness

Illness usually results from a combination of factors, such as the coincidence of an infection and low natural resistance. This is not always the case, however—for example, hereditary and congenital disorders originate before birth.

Congenital disorders affect the developing embryo and may be caused by chromosomal abnormalities or cellular damage. The best known examples include cleft palate and Down's syndrome (commonly called mongolism). Embryonic development may be seriously affected by diseases such as rubella. If contracted by the mother in the early stages of pregnancy, rubella can cause abnormalities in the child's heart, eyes, and ears. Certain drugs taken by the mother during pregnancy may also result in congenital disorders, and a pregnant woman should take no drugs without medical supervision.

After birth, a person's health is at the mercy of various external factors. Good health depends, to a great extent, on adequate nutrition and maintenance. Vitamins and minerals are essential for the proper working of the body and their lack may give rise to various deficiency disorders. For example, insufficient iron, needed to make hemoglobin, may result in anemia. And lack of vitamin D is the cause of rickets, an uncommon disorder in developed nations but only too common in the Third World.

The best-known causes of illness are living organisms, which range from microscopic viruses and bacteria to larger parasites such as tapeworms; they affect the body in many different ways. Viruses attack the cell structure of the body. The poliomyelitis virus, for instance, causes paralysis by growing in and destroying certain types of nerve cells in the spinal cord. Other viral diseases include influenza, mumps, smallpox, rabies, and herpes. Bacteria cause disease by producing poisons (toxins), or enzymes, which harm living cells. Bacterial infections include pneumonia, tetanus, and pertussis (whooping cough). Other pathogenic organisms that affect the body include various protozoa, such as amebas, which cause a form of dysentery, and fungi, which cause disorders such as athlete's foot.

Normal body tissue has the ability to repair itself, but with aging, this mechanism becomes less efficient and may gradually give way to degenerative disorders. Arteriosclerosis, or hardening of the arteries, is one of the most significant of these. Causing reduced blood flow, it can lead to vascular thrombosis (clot in a blood vessel) and coronary heart disease.

Tumors and cancers stand in their own category and are the result of abnormal cellular growth. Many tumors are benign—they develop slowly and do not spread—but, if sited in delicate areas, such as the brain or spinal column, may cause damage by pressing against sensitive tissues. Cancers, in contrast, are malignant tumors caused by cell mutation. They can spread rapidly and cause death by destroying healthy tissue.

Changing patterns

As little as 100 years ago, four out of ten babies failed to reach adulthood. Today, life expectancy in the Western world is approximately 70 years for a man and a little more for a woman. There are many reasons for this dramatic improvement, among them rising living standards in housing, nutrition, working environment, and sanitation, which have removed many of the conditions in which disease once thrived. Medical advances also have played a large part. Some of the most significant contributions to present-day health include a greater understanding of the causes of illness, the use of preventive measures such as vaccination programs, major advances in surgery, and the development of antibiotics and other drugs. As a result of these advances, infectious diseases, such as smallpox and poliomyelitis, have been eradicated in many parts of the world, and a person's chance of a long and healthy life is better than ever before.

Health and society

Illness may not just be a question of the failure of one of the body systems. Often it is also closely tied to climatic, social, and environmental factors. Although many infectious diseases have been eradicated in the Western world, most are still common in the Third World, that is, in developing countries, where malnutrition and poverty combine to perpetuate high levels of infant mortality and low life expectancy.

Ironically, the material benefits of improved social living in the Western world have themselves created new health problems. As traditional killers have disappeared, new ones have taken their place. Heart disease and cancers, once little known, are now common and account for a large proportion of all deaths.

Today it is known that such diseases of affluence are directly related to diet, sedentary occupations, smoking, and the stresses of twentieth-century living. Medical cures for these illnesses remain elusive, but some of them can be prevented, and current medical views emphasize the importance of healthy diet and regular exercise, and the dangers of stress, smoking, and alcohol. Good health may, ultimately, depend as much on changes in the way we live as on current or future developments in medical science.

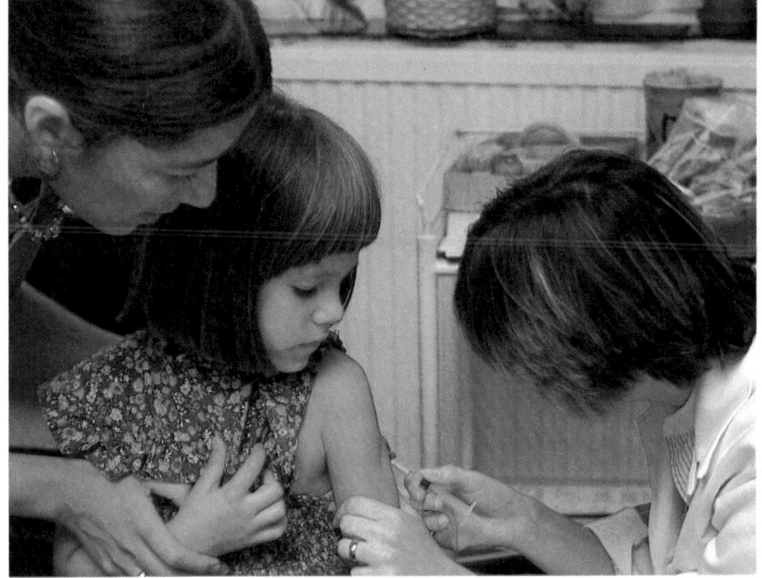

Vaccination gives immunity to specific diseases. Children are usually vaccinated against diphtheria, tetanus, pertussis (whooping cough), and poliomyelitis.

The main causes of death reflect factors such as climate, diet, and standards of medical care. In the U.S., for instance, diet and life style can be linked with the high proportion of deaths from cardiovascular disorders.

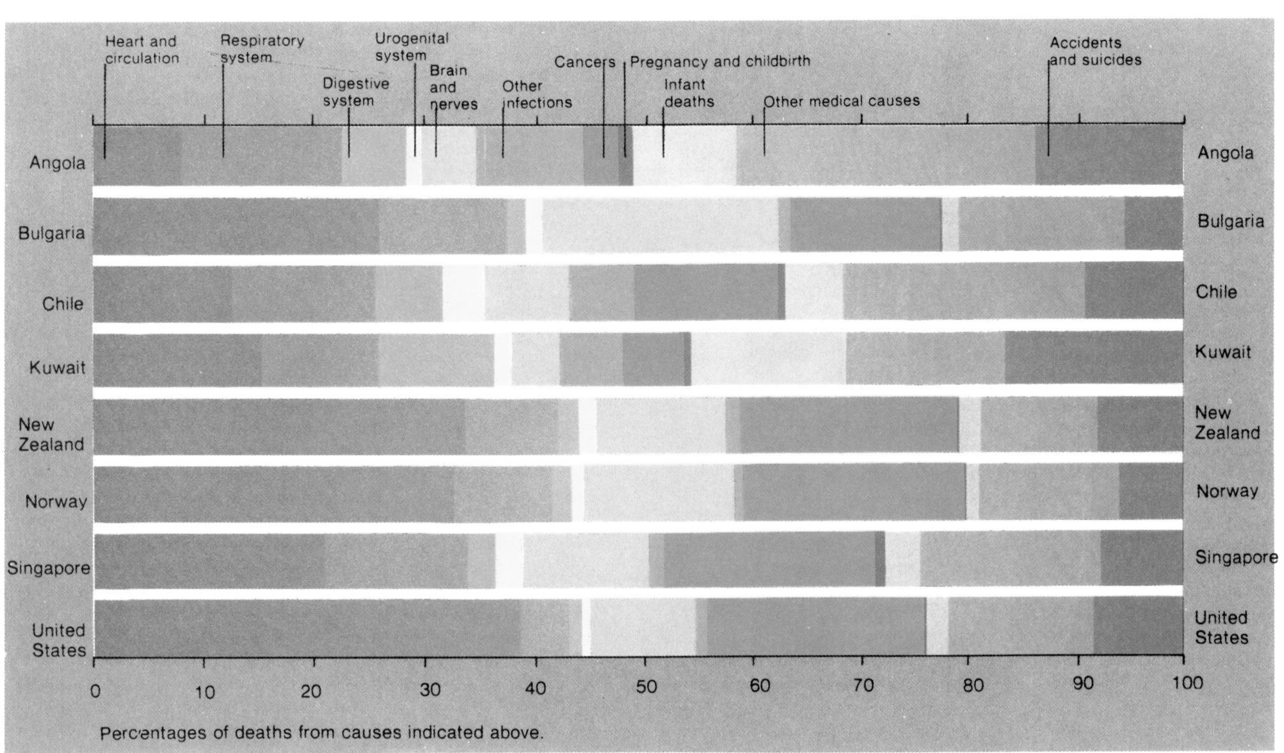

Disorders and deficiencies

Most people go through life in general good health, suffering occasionally from temporary disorders, which are more inconvenient than threatening. The common cold is a typical example of an infectious illness that is a great nuisance, but not permanently debilitating.

The human body is, however, susceptible to a wide variety of more serious disorders and diseases, which include hereditary conditions; defects present at birth; disorders caused by dietary defects or deficiencies; disorders that affect one or other of the body systems; neoplasms, whether benign tumors or malignant cancers; conditions that affect the brain or nervous system (or both); psychosomatic disorders—mental disturbances that produce the physical symptoms of illness; and many complaints associated with occupation, environment, and the body's natural degeneration.

Hereditary disorders

Some disorders may be inherited from one or both parents and may affect a child directly. In other cases, an inherited disorder may not be apparent for one or more generations. Severe hereditary disorders include hemophilia (in which a person's blood fails to clot, resulting in excessive bleeding from even minor injuries), some types of dwarfism, sickle-cell anemia (in which a person is anemic because of abnormally-shaped red blood cells), and the rare Friedrich's ataxia (which causes problems with muscular coordination). Color blindness is an example of a less serious inherited disorder. Certain hereditary disorders such as hemophilia, like some birth defects (for example, the condition known as Down's syndrome), can be detected during pregnancy by the technique of amniocentesis.

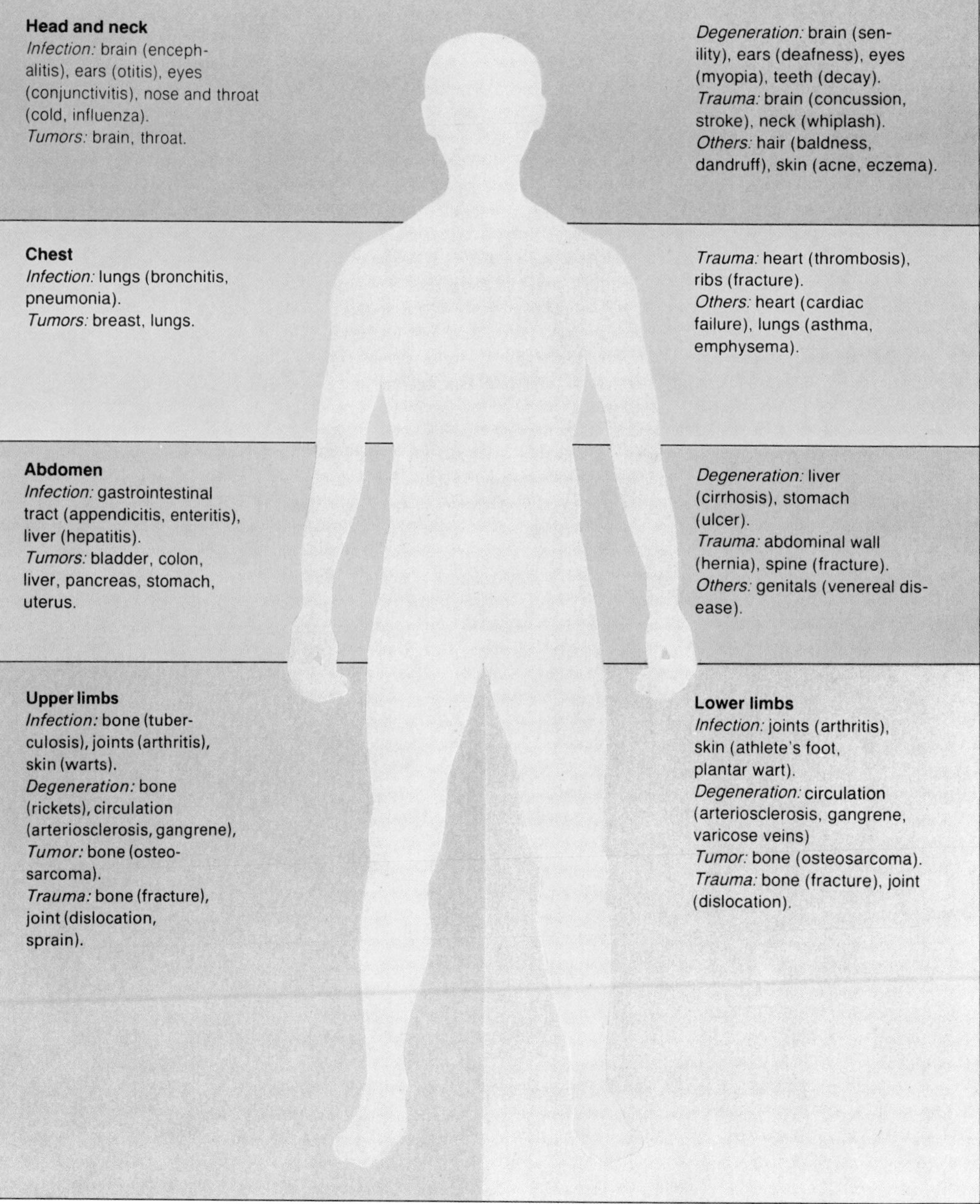

Each part of the body is susceptible to its own set of characteristic disorders, and there are other conditions that affect the body as a whole. The chief categories are infections (which often cause inflammation of a tissue or organ); traumas, which usually result from injury; tumors and other abnormal growths; deficiency diseases; and degenerative disorders, generally resulting from the process of aging. Disorders that affect the whole body include, as well as generalized infections, those involving the skin, the skeleton, the circulation, the lymphatic system, and the peripheral nervous system. Certain glandular disorders, particularly those involving hormones, may also have a profound effect on the whole of the body. The illustration indicates some of the disorders that can affect the various parts of the body.

Other birth defects

Some defects are not inherited but acquired while the fetus is in the uterus. Faults in normal physical development may cause such disorders as cleft palate, harelip, spina bifida, hydrocephalus (water on the brain), and congenital heart abnormalities. Faults in the chromosome distribution can lead to Down's syndrome, in which the child has an abnormal number of chromosomes.

Other disorders appear as a result of abnormal circumstances during pregnancy. For instance, a baby may be born deaf, or with cataracts in the eyes, or even with heart disease, if its mother contracted rubella (German measles) during the first three months of pregnancy. And certain drugs taken by a pregnant woman may cause abnormalities in her child. Damage to the baby may also be caused during complicated births. For example, if the fetus does not receive sufficient oxygen during the birthing process, brain damage (cerebral palsy) or even death might result.

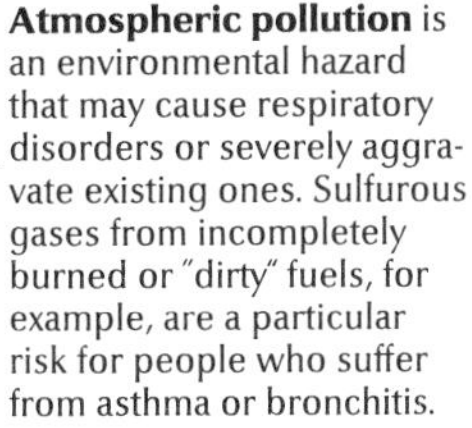

Atmospheric pollution is an environmental hazard that may cause respiratory disorders or severely aggravate existing ones. Sulfurous gases from incompletely burned or "dirty" fuels, for example, are a particular risk for people who suffer from asthma or bronchitis.

Dietary defects and deficiencies

The necessity for a normal, well-balanced diet is well known, and generally the body compensates for variations, losses, and temporary excesses in diet. At its simplest, this is illustrated by the body's desire for liquids (thirst) after an insufficient intake of fluids or after eating salty food. But certain disorders are actually aggravated by a normal diet. Celiac disease makes the intestines react to the protein called gluten (an ingredient of wheat flour) in such a way that normal absorption of other nutrients is prevented. A gluten-free diet is usually prescribed in order to relieve the symptoms and prevent further deficiency disorders from developing. Phenylketonuria (PKU) is a hereditary deficiency disorder in which enzymes that normally break down the amino acid phenylalanine are absent, so that this substance (which occurs in many foods) accumulates in the blood and damages the brain, causing symptoms that range from irritability to convulsions. In most countries, babies are tested at birth for this deficiency, which can be corrected by adjusting the baby's diet.

Malnutrition, resulting from a diet that lacks essential vitamins, is responsible for diseases such as rickets, scurvy, and beriberi. Severe malnutrition in children up to the age of eighteen months causes an irreversible reduction in intellectual ability. Overindulgence can also lead to problems. For instance, a diet rich in sugar may lead to obesity and aggravate diabetes, and diets rich in animal fats contribute to heart disease and disorders of the circulatory system.

Some foods that have no ill effect on most people cause abnormal, allergic reactions in others. The reaction can vary from a temporary rash or digestive disturbance to water-filled blisters over most of the body.

System failure

Occasionally, one of the body's systems fails completely. Disease or damage to the kidneys may lead to kidney failure, which can be fatal if both kidneys are affected and the condition is untreated. Cardiac failure may cause the heart to stop pumping blood around the body, and unless the heart is restarted quickly this will result in death. The term cardiac failure also describes partial failure of the heart, which results in an accumulation of blood in various organs because circulation is impaired. Liver and lungs may be damaged by disease or toxic substances, and this damage may also be fatal.

The body's systems are finely balanced, and although some effect usually occurs if a system is only partly faulty, nevertheless the body has a remarkable capacity to cope with—and

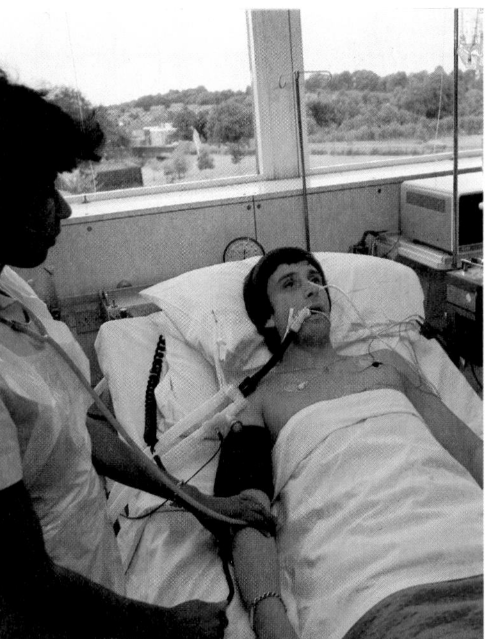

A chronically ill person usually needs a prolonged course of treatment, sometimes involving a long stay in a hospital. The aim is to support the patient so that he or she can live at home and lead as normal a life as possible.

Rickets is a deficiency disease caused by a lack or insufficiency of vitamin D. The vitamin is supplied in sufficient quantities in a balanced diet containing such foods as eggs and fish; it is also formed in the skin on exposure to sunlight. Its deficiency affects calcium metabolism and results in deformed bones in children. In adults, vitamin D deficiency causes osteomalacia, which is also characterized by a softening of the bones.

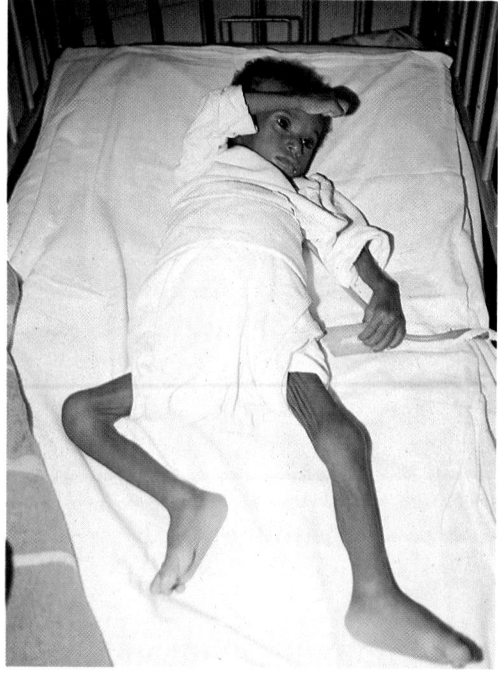

even compensate for—partial failure of its systems.

Old age is associated with general slow degeneration and gradually decreasing efficiency of all the body's systems. The lungs, heart, liver, kidneys, and brain all work less well, and the senses tend to deteriorate. Sight and hearing in particular are liable to suffer quite rapid decline in older people; this probably contributes more than anything else to the problems of aging.

Hemophilia is a comparatively rare but serious inherited disorder. People with the condition lack an essential clotting factor in their blood, and, as a result, bleed excessively from even a minor cut or bruise. Most hemophiliacs are males; they inherit the disorder from their mothers, who are carriers but do not themselves suffer from the disease. However, as the diagram shows, it is possible for a girl to be a hemophiliac if her father has the disease and her mother is a carrier.

Causes of disease

Some diseases and disorders seem to occur without obvious cause, as with some cancers and other growths and with many of the disorders that affect the nervous system. Many conditions, however, are brought about by specific identifiable circumstances.

Certain lifestyles give rise to particular hazards, and some occupations are associated with specific diseases. For example, cardiovascular disorders are particularly prevalent in sedentary workers who are also subject to stress; and respiratory diseases such as asbestosis, bagassosis, or silicosis, are likely to affect the lungs of those who work in conditions in which large quantities of certain types of dust are inhaled.

There are some disorders that may occur at particular stages of life; for instance, one type of leukemia is more common in children and young adults than in older people, and gallstones are particularly likely to affect middle-aged people. Other conditions, such as allergies and chilblains, can occur at any age.

External factors

Excessive use of alcohol or tobacco, abuse of drugs, stress, obesity, and poor diet can all cause or aggravate certain disorders. For instance, smoking is associated with bronchitis and with several other conditions, best known of which is lung cancer. Women who smoke or drink during pregnancy also risk causing significant harm to the child in their womb. Stress is a significant cause of ulcers of the duodenum, and is strongly associated with cardiovascular disease. Lack of exercise, especially in combination with a sedentary occupation, has been associated with obesity and circulatory disorders, and especially with cardiovascular disease.

Neoplasms

New growths of normal or abnormal body tissue are known medically as neoplasms. They can take many forms—some are harmless; some cause discomfort, irritation, or pain; and some are potentially fatal. Examples of harmless (benign) growths are common warts, moles, and fatty growths known as lipomas. Growths capable of causing pain or difficulty include fibroids (fibrous lumps in the uterus), and polyps in the nose, rectum, or vagina.

Malignant growths of excess tissue are called cancers. Such growths can be found in almost any part of the body, including the brain, lungs, breasts, uterus, bones, kidneys,

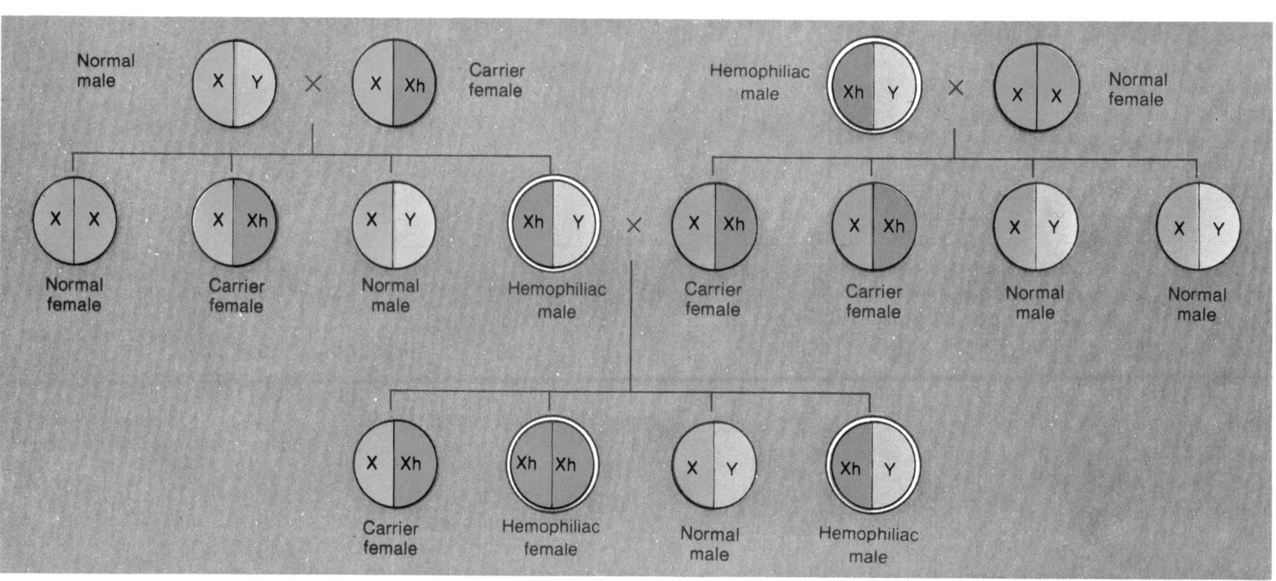

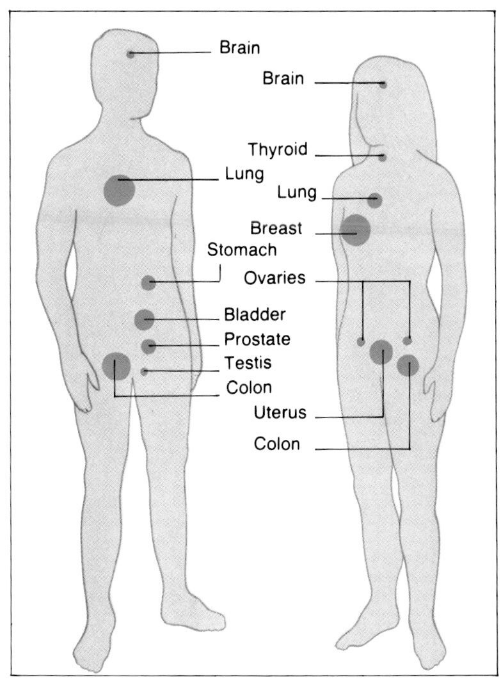

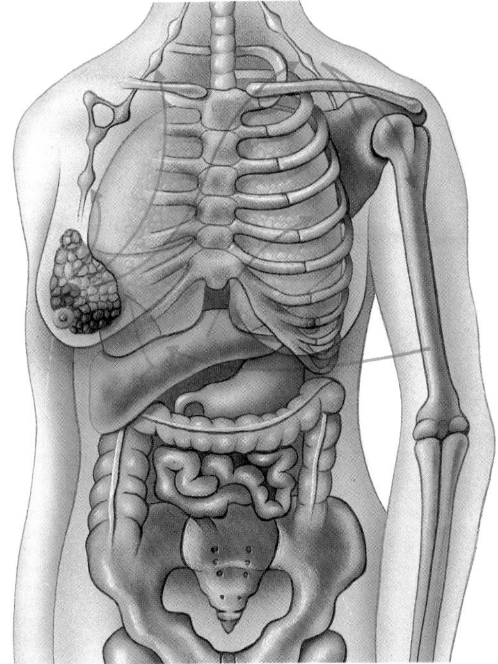

Cancer takes various forms and can affect almost any body tissue or organ. The diagram *(far left)* shows the most common sites in men and women, with the size of the colored spot indicating the relative incidence. Untreated cancer can spread from the primary site by the process of metastasis. The diagram *(left)* indicates how breast cancer can progress first to the lymph nodes and then to the bones, from which it moves to the liver and finally the lungs.

mouth, stomach, liver, and colon. Cancerous cells multiply abnormally fast and so starve surrounding tissue of nutrients. If the malignant growth is confined to only one accessible area, it can often be removed by surgery or destroyed by radiation or chemotherapy. Once cancerous cells have entered the bloodstream or lymphatic system, however, they may spread to almost any part of the body. If this happens, it is very difficult to halt the disease. Some cancers are caused by known cancer-producing agents (carcinogens) such as tobacco smoke, ultraviolet rays, and X rays.

Neurological conditions

The brain and nervous system are also subject to various disorders. The brain is the most complex organ of the body and is—directly or indirectly—involved in all bodily functions. If something goes wrong with the brain's functioning, for example as a result of epilepsy, injury to its tissues, a brain tumor, a stroke, or encephalitis (inflammation of the brain), the results can be far-reaching and sometimes unpredictable.

Diseases can also attack the nerve pathways. One of the best known, and most serious, examples is multiple sclerosis. In this disorder, the cause of which is unknown, the protective cells around the nerves of the brain and spinal cord are damaged, causing a variety of symptoms that may become progressively more severe and can eventually lead to invalidism. Infections of specific parts of the nervous system, such as poliomyelitis (an infection of the spinal cord), can also result in paralysis.

Psychological and similar disorders

The mind can affect the body, and many physical disorders are thought to be caused or aggravated by emotional disturbances. Stress is perhaps the most common of such causes, and can be a significant factor in disorders such as indigestion, stomach ulcers, headaches, palpitations, high blood pressure, heart disease, and diabetes. It may aggravate disorders like asthma, eczema, psoriasis, excessive sweating, and migraine. Combined with emotional difficulties, stress can lead to such severe conditions as alcoholism, drug dependence, and anorexia nervosa.

Sexual difficulties may result from emotional problems, perhaps related to irrational guilt or fear or to feelings of inadequacy, or they may be a result of stress. The most common physical symptoms associated with sexual difficulties of this sort are inability to achieve an erection or experience orgasm.

Sympathetic advice and possibly psychotherapy may be needed to resolve psychologically based physical problems—the physical symptoms are unlikely to disappear unless the underlying emotional problem is dealt with.

Curvature of the spine in the elderly may result from osteoporosis, a degenerative disorder in which a gradual loss of calcium causes porosity of the bones. The vertebrae, in particular, may become deformed and compressed, leading to a stiff neck and a characteristic stoop, which in turn affects the way the person walks.

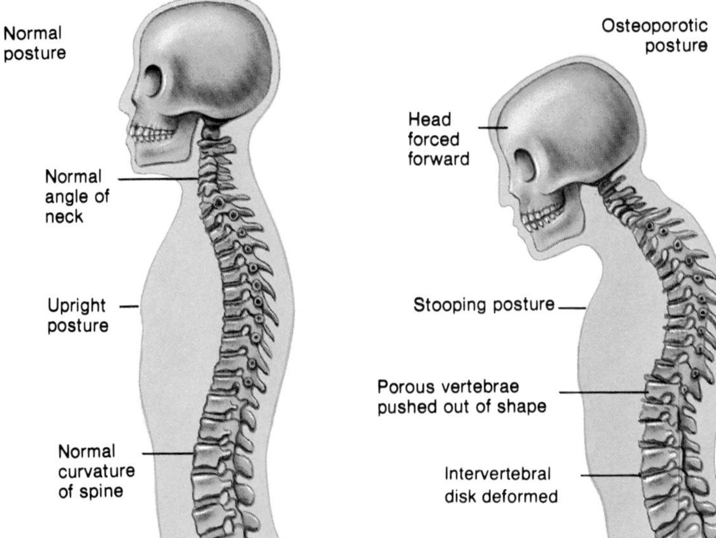

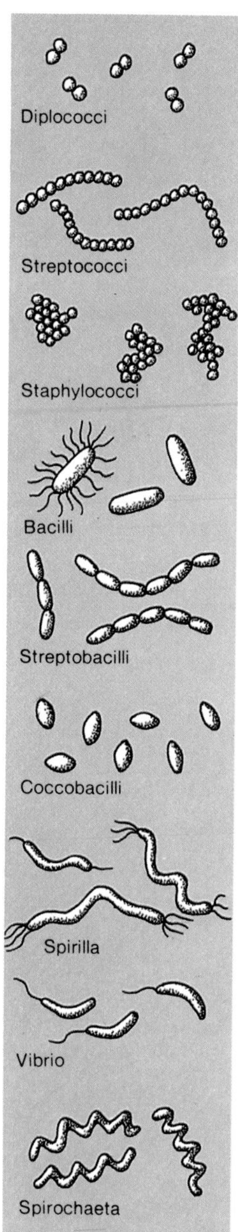

Bacteria have a variety of forms, several of which are shown above. Among these there are three main types—cocci, which are roughly spherical or oval; bacilli, which are elongated, or rod-shaped; and spirilli, which have a spiral shape. Size varies considerably, but most bacteria are between 0.2×10^{-3} and 2.0×10^{-3} millimeters in length. The photo-micrograph is of a *Salmonella* bacterium, the type that causes various infections of the gastrointestinal tract, including typhoid.

Infection

Everyone—including healthy people—carries some microorganisms on the skin or in the body, but normally the body's natural defenses prevent these from causing harm.

Infections occur when the body is invaded by disease-causing organisms—bacteria, viruses, fungi, protozoa, or larger metazoa, such as tapeworms. They may enter the body by various means: through the nose or mouth; through a break in the skin; or through physical contact with an infected person or thing, as in sexual or skin infections.

Some infections, such as a common cold, are minor and short-lived; others, such as athlete's foot, are more persistent, but are still not life-threatening. Certain infections, however, for example those that cause meningitis, poliomyelitis, typhus, and rabies, are extremely dangerous. Infections by protozoa or larger organisms are more properly called infestations, and are caused by organisms that live on humans as parasites.

Agents of infection

The most common infective agents (pathogens) are bacteria. Many forms live harmlessly in the human body, particularly in the lower digestive tract, but others cause minor or severe infections such as boils, tonsillitis, and pneumonia.

Viruses are smaller than bacteria, and can be seen only with the aid of an electron microscope. Viral infections include the common cold, chickenpox (varicella), poliomyelitis, and herpes.

Rickettsias are unusual agents of infection found on fleas and lice; they have characteristics in common with both bacteria and viruses, and can transmit diseases such as typhus to humans.

Fungi are plantlike organisms that can cause various diseases, including ringworm and thrush—the common name for moniliasis or candidiasis.

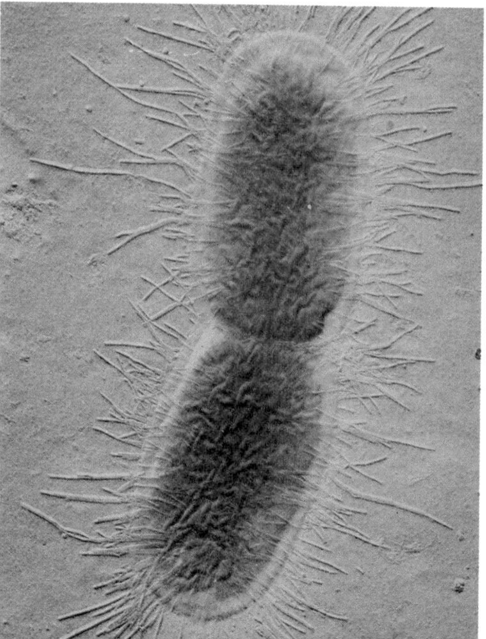

Protozoa are single-celled parasites that cause diseases such as malaria, amebic dysentery, and toxoplasmosis. Metazoa are many-celled parasites, such as tapeworms and lice.

The spread of disease

Diseases spread in various ways. Poliomyelitis and cholera are transmitted by contaminated water. Many viruses, such as those causing chickenpox, are spread by airborne droplets that are sneezed, coughed, or breathed out by someone with the disease. Diseases such as gonorrhea, syphilis, and AIDS (Acquired Immune Deficiency Syndrome), which are transmitted by sexual contact, are known as venereal diseases.

Infectious organisms can be contained in the saliva, sputum, vomit, blood, pus, or excreta (waste products) of an infected person. Food may be a carrier of disease, particularly if it is neither fresh nor freshly cooked, or if it is contaminated with animal- or insect-borne diseases such as tapeworm or salmonella.

Some diseases are caught directly from animals. For example, psittacosis can be caught from certain birds, and rabies is transmitted through the saliva of infected mammals.

Open wounds can become infected by any bacteria that come into contact with them. Most serious of such infections is tetanus, caused when tetanus bacilli—which are commonly found in soil—enter the body through a dirty wound. Tetanus can be prevented by vaccination. If the disease develops, however, it can be fatal.

Prevention of disease

Hygiene is the key to preventing the spread of many diseases. Important principles of hygiene include: washing the hands after going to the toilet and before handling food; covering any wounds before handling food; keeping a sickroom clean, and disinfecting or destroying any soiled handkerchiefs or dressings; and washing a sick person's dishes, eating utensils, and clothes separately from those of the rest of the family.

It is also important to take extra care of hygiene when traveling abroad because of the presence of infective agents to which the body is unaccustomed, and to have any recommended inoculations before starting a trip. Keeping pets and farm animals as clean as possible, and washing the hands after handling them—particularly before touching food or anything that might come into contact with it—is another good principle. In any case, it is sensible for each member of a household to have his or her own facecloth, toothbrush, and hairbrush.

The body has various systems for preventing and fighting infections. The skin prevents many organisms from entering the body, and blood clots and tissue repairs soon seal any minor wounds in the skin. The tonsils, adenoids, and mucous membranes of the nose and throat help to trap any inhaled germs. The lymph nodes together with the spleen manufacture antibodies against infections that penetrate the outer defenses, and the liver can destroy various disease-produced toxins. White blood cells attack invading germs, and blood also contains antibodies, produced by white cells in response to infection, which provide protection (immunity) against further attacks by the same infecting agents.

Immunity is mostly developed by the body's natural immune system, but some immunity can be conferred. Newborn babies inherit antibodies from their mothers and acquire others from mother's milk. Others again are developed in response to specific infections. Immunity can also be induced artificially by vaccination, which involves introducing dead or weakened disease agents into the body to stimulate the formation of antibodies.

Curing infections

Antibiotics are the most successful agents that mankind has created to combat infectious diseases. Most work only against bacterial infections, however, such as tonsillitis and pneumonia. Sulfonamides and other drugs can also be effective against bacteria.

Viruses are far more resistant to known drugs. The symptoms of viral diseases can be treated—for instance, decongestants relieve the symptoms of colds—but generally viral infections must be left to take their natural course.

Fungicidal drugs can ease such conditions as athlete's foot, and ultraviolet radiation from sunlight or from a sunlamp helps to kill the germs that are present in acne. Certain drugs are effective in eliminating parasites, such as threadworms and tapeworms. Drugs known as antitoxins counteract the effects of toxins produced in the body by infecting organisms. When drugs fail or are inappropriate, however, surgery is also a possible treatment—for instance, to remove an infected appendix.

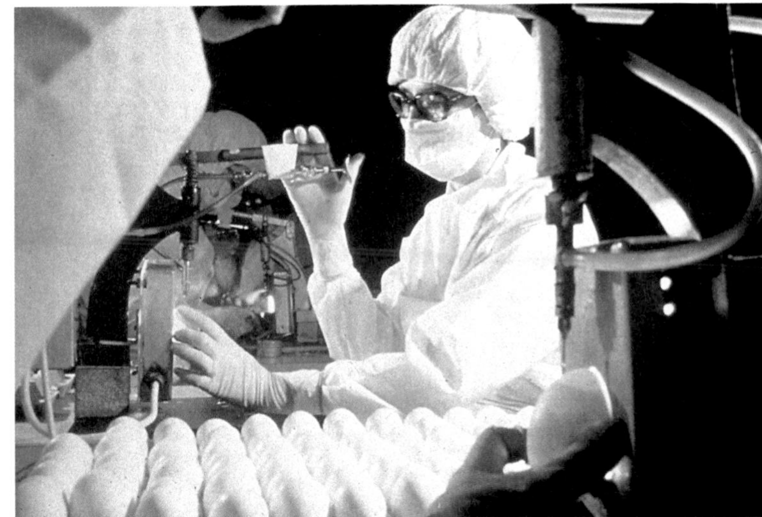

Fertilized hen's eggs are used as a living culture medium in which to grow viruses for making vaccines. Here eggs are being injected with a strain of influenza virus.

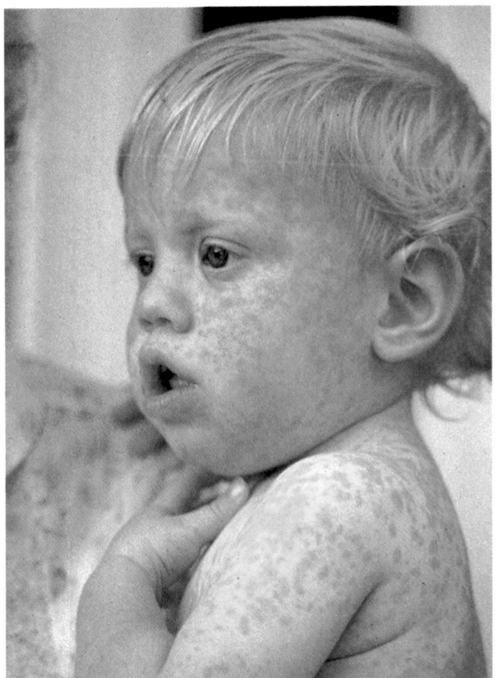

Measles, an infectious disease caused by a virus, causes a rash on the face and body. Contracting the disease usually confers immunity for life, but there is a vaccine available for immunizing babies.

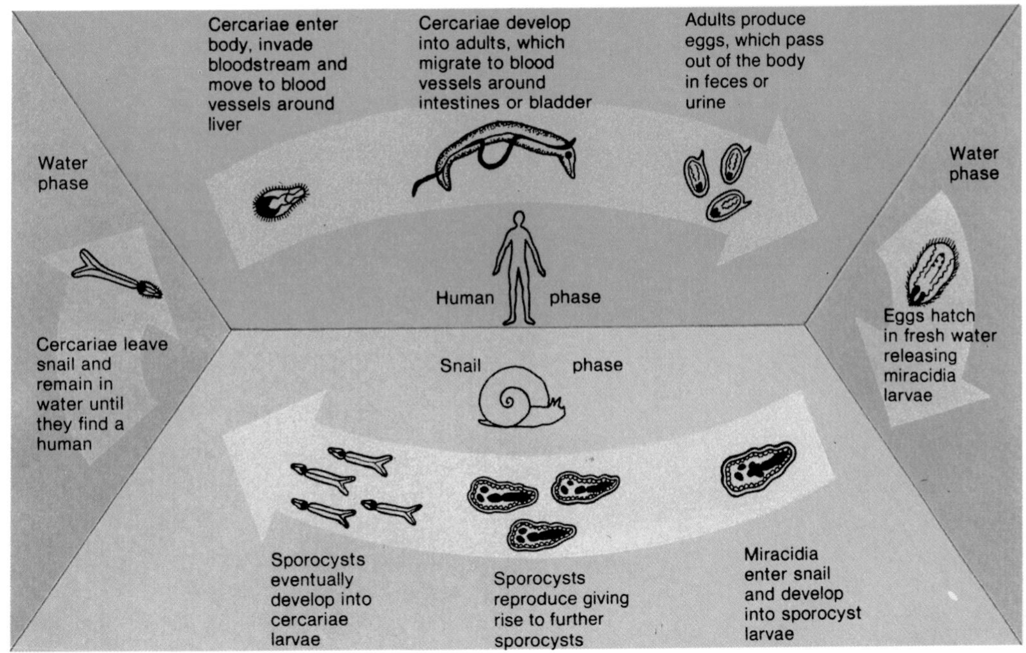

Schistosomiasis, formerly known as bilharziasis, is a disease caused by *Schistosoma* parasites, which are common in tropical America, Asia, and Africa. The parasite also depends on some types of water snail, and people become infected from water in which these snails live. The parasite's life cycle has four phases: one in snails, one in humans, and two intermediate stages in water, from which both hosts acquire the infestation.

Allergies

Although medical controversy focuses on the causes and mechanisms of allergy—even on the definition of the term—to the lay person the chief mystery is, how can a person suddenly become allergic to things that hitherto have caused no harm? And why do certain things affect one person strongly and others not at all?

Much remains to be learned. But from the beginning, the word "allergy" has been used to describe a type of adverse reaction by the body's immune system to a foreign substance. Normally, the immune system develops antibodies only as a response to the presence of a potentially harmful substance (such as a virus). The antibodies produced are then specific to that substance, and will be produced again immediately if that substance is encountered later. In an allergy, this mechanism is brought into operation by a harmless substance (like pollen or some foodstuffs). Re-exposure to this substance—known as an allergen—results in the production of antibodies, and a subsequent allergic reaction.

Food allergies in babies may be one cause of hyperactivity, in which the baby cries and moves incessantly. Among the chief culprits are food colorants added to some foods (such as orange juice), although even the staple food—milk—causes an allergic reaction in some babies.

Pollen grains, shown here greatly magnified, are the allergens that cause allergic seasonal rhinitis, better known as hay fever. Its symptoms may be relieved by antihistamine drugs, but the cause needs desensitization treatment.

Allergic reactions

Many allergic reactions involve a common mechanism—the over-production by the body of a type of antibody known as IgE. This antibody binds to the surface of a special cell called a mast cell. When the IgE antibody combines with the allergen, the mast cell releases its contents, called H-substances. These include histamine, prostaglandins, and leukotrienes, which are the most important mediators of allergic reactions. These mediators cause tissue swelling, because they increase local blood flow and also cause small blood vessels to leak fluid into the surrounding body tissues. Several common symptoms of allergy result, for example, in swollen, red, itching lumps in the skin (urticaria or hives), a stuffed-up, runny nose (rhinitis), or red, itching eyes (conjunctivitis).

Some allergic reactions are relatively minor, but mast cell allergic mediators also cause more severe reactions, such as anaphylaxis or asthmatic attacks. Anaphylaxis occurs when histamine is released into the bloodstream in large quantities. This produces a sudden fall in blood pressure, which causes physiological shock. There also may be intense swelling of tissues in the throat, which can cause asphyxiation. Anaphylaxis is rare, but can occur if a susceptible person is injected with a drug, such as penicillin, to which he or she is allergic, or suffers an allergic reaction to insect stings. In an asthmatic attack, the release of histamine and leukotrienes in the walls of bronchi in the respiratory tract causes the smooth muscle to contract, thus narrowing the bronchi and causing partial respiratory obstruction. The characteristic asthmatic wheezing and difficulty in exhaling results. Another common cause of allergic reaction is certain food, and recent studies suggest that migraine headaches may be associated with food allergies in some way.

Certain allergies, especially hay fever, asthma, and eczema, often run in families. This pattern is known as atopy, and those who are affected are described as atopic. Individual members of a family may be afflicted with one or all types of reaction, due to excess IgE production. The exact reason for this is not known, but it is probably due to a minor abnormality in the complex control systems that regulate immune responses to foreign substances. Because the immunoregulatory network changes during an individual's lifetime, new allergies may appear and old ones disappear in a totally unpredictable manner.

Allergy and the twentieth century

Current thinking suggests that the changes in diet, in the environment, and in the stresses of everyday life characteristic of modern times actually encourage the development of allergies, both by increasing the number of powerful potential allergens and by increasing the overall susceptibility of people.

Chemical fertilization, allowing the land to be overexploited, reduces the amount of trace substances in the harvested products. Refining common ingredients such as flour and sugar also reduces the level of trace elements that once probably afforded some protection against the development of various sensitivities. In addition, the use of chemical additives, especially colorants, in food has greatly increased.

A further dietary factor seems to be the contemporary fashion for early bottle-feeding and weaning of infants. A baby's own immune system is not fully developed until about nine months of age, and allergies—from which maternal antibodies in milk may afford some protection—can develop easily before this time.

Our natural environment is now heavily polluted. Many of the pollutants either bring on allergic states or are themselves potential allergens. They include many chemicals, such as gasoline, cosmetics, and cleaning products.

Another possible reason for the increasing incidence of allergies is that, with growing public awareness, it is becoming fashionable to diagnose them as a cause of illness.

Allergy diagnosis

If inhalation, contact, or ingestion of a substance results in an allergic reaction with obvious symptoms, diagnosis of allergy is easy. An example is a rash that develops after eating strawberries. But allergic symptoms may also derive from a cause that is less easily distinguished. The oldest method of tracking down the source of such "hidden" allergies is the exclusion (or elimination) diet, in which a simple, basic diet that produces no reaction is gradually enlarged over several weeks by adding suspect foods one after another until the reaction occurs. A recent study involving children with severe migraine has shown that marked improvements can be achieved by excluding certain dietary elements.

More modern means of diagnosis are skin tests and blood tests. Skin tests are of two types. Prick or scratch tests are suitable for some types of allergy; patch tests are better for other sorts of allergies. Blood tests are more accurate; the most common are the radio-allergosorbent test (RAST) and the cytotoxic tests.

Allergy treatment

Therapies range from the orthodox to the unusual. Some relieve the symptoms rather than actually treating the underlying allergy. This is particularly true of the suppressive drugs commonly prescribed, such as sodium chromoglycate, antihistamines, and steroid preparations.

The method known as desensitization attempts to reduce the allergic response gradually. This treatment starts with the administration of a very dilute form of the allergen, then slowly increases the amount of allergen that can be tolerated without producing symptoms.

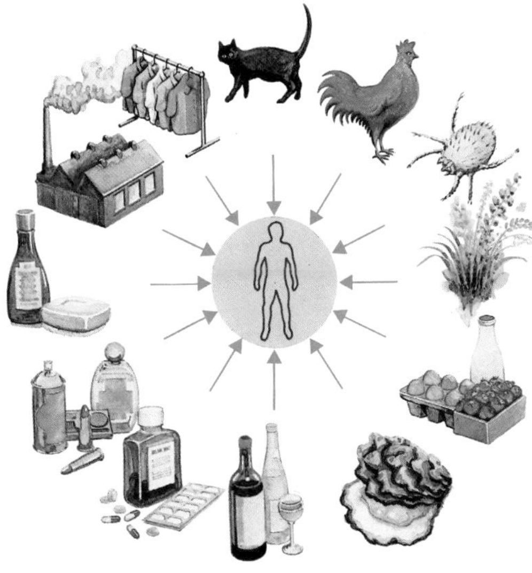

There are thousands of potential allergens, and the chief types are shown in the diagram: animal fur and dander, feathers, mites in house dust, pollen, foods such as milk, eggs, strawberries, and shellfish, alcoholic drinks, drugs, cosmetics, soaps and shampoos, atmospheric pollutants, and man-made fibers.

Another treatment is to avoid the allergen. Appropriate food can be excluded, or ionizers can be used to precipitate pollens out of the air, for example. And, given time, many allergies or sensitivities disappear of their own accord.

Finally, some people are apparently allergic to everything in their environment—a condition sometimes described as "total allergy syndrome." It is possible that they have a breakdown in their immune system that causes the easy development and endless accumulation of allergies. It is more probable, however, that their condition has been falsely blamed on allergies and is, in fact, something else that has yet to be properly understood.

Once an allergic reaction begins, the results can be rapid and dramatic—particularly on the skin. The woman in this photograph is allergic to adhesive tape, and contact with only a small area caused an eruption of lesions over nearly all her body.

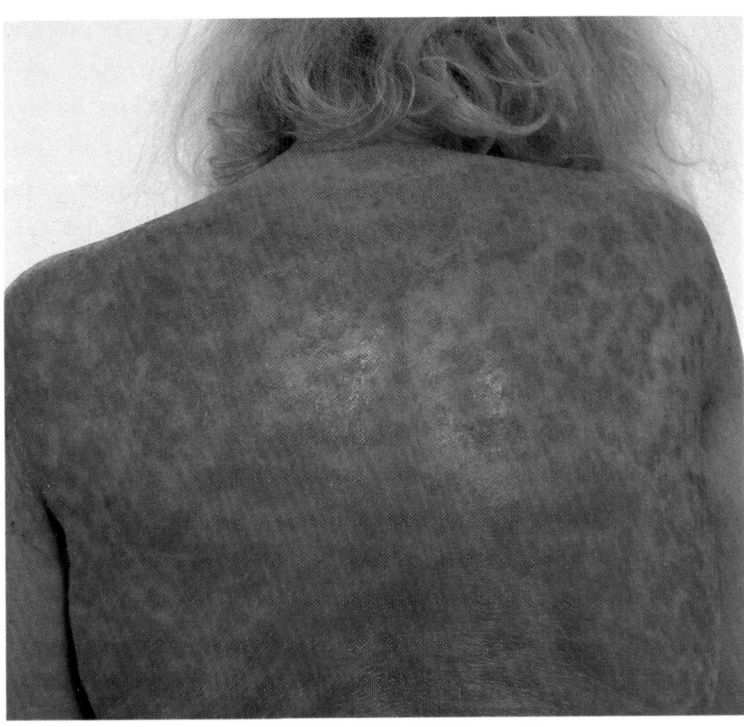

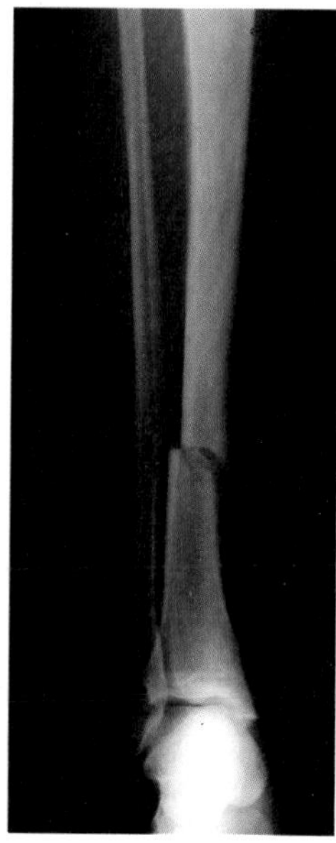

Broken bones are among the most common injuries that result from accidents. The limb bones—for example the tibia of the leg, shown in this X ray—are the most vulnerable, and need prompt specialized treatment if they are to heal properly.

Accidents

About one-third of all accidental injuries occur in the home, the majority of them to the very young or the elderly. Accidents affecting adults tend to be on the roads or at work, though older children and young adults are most likely to be injured while playing some sport. Among the otherwise healthy 10-30 age group, they are one of the most common causes of death. To a far greater extent than most people believe, however, accidents can be avoided by taking simple safety precautions in the home, at work, and on the roads, by an awareness of the dangers, and by using common sense.

Cuts, abrasions, bites, and bruises

These injuries are often superficial, and if so, can be treated at home or in the nearest convenient place, where the damaged area can be cleaned thoroughly and the flow of blood can be brought under control. A deep or extensive cut that persists in bleeding may require stitches (sutures), in which case it is treated by a qualified physician. Stitches are usually inserted under a local anesthetic, and removed about seven days later.

More serious cuts, abrasions, and some bites involve a greater possibility of infection and need more comprehensive treatment. An antitetanus injection is often administered, especially if the victim has not had an immunization course during the previous three years. In the case of an animal bite, extra precautions are normally taken, and these may include a series of antirabies inoculations. Snakebites are treated with a serum injected into the bloodstream.

Bruising (contusion) is usually a superficial injury that occurs when a blow or fall ruptures the tiny capillaries in the skin. Blood seeps out of the capillaries into the surrounding tissues and is slowly fragmented and absorbed. The red hemoglobin in the lost blood turns purple as its oxygen is dissipated and later turns brown and yellow as it is broken down into bile pigments.

Bruising rarely requires treatment, although a large collection of blood (hematoma) may have to be reduced by being drawn off with a syringe and needle. Contamination must be avoided scrupulously, and antiseptics and sterile dressings are used because stagnant blood is an ideal growing medium for harmful bacteria.

Burns

Burns are caused by a wide variety of accidents that need not involve a naked flame—merely heat. The damage common to all types of burns is the alteration (denaturation) of tissue protein at the affected site, which is followed by tissue death. Apart from fire, this damage can be caused by boiling liquids (when it is called a scald), hot gases (which are particularly dangerous to the respiratory system), an electric current, corrosive chemicals, friction, radiation from the ultraviolet rays in sunlight or from radioactive materials, and even by contact with extremely cold surfaces, particularly if these are metal.

Most accidents happen in the home, particularly the kitchen. Danger points include articles on a high shelf, an unlocked drugs cupboard, an overloaded electric circuit, a free-standing heater, poisonous household chemicals, broken glass and toys on the floor, burning-hot fat, and projecting saucepan handles.

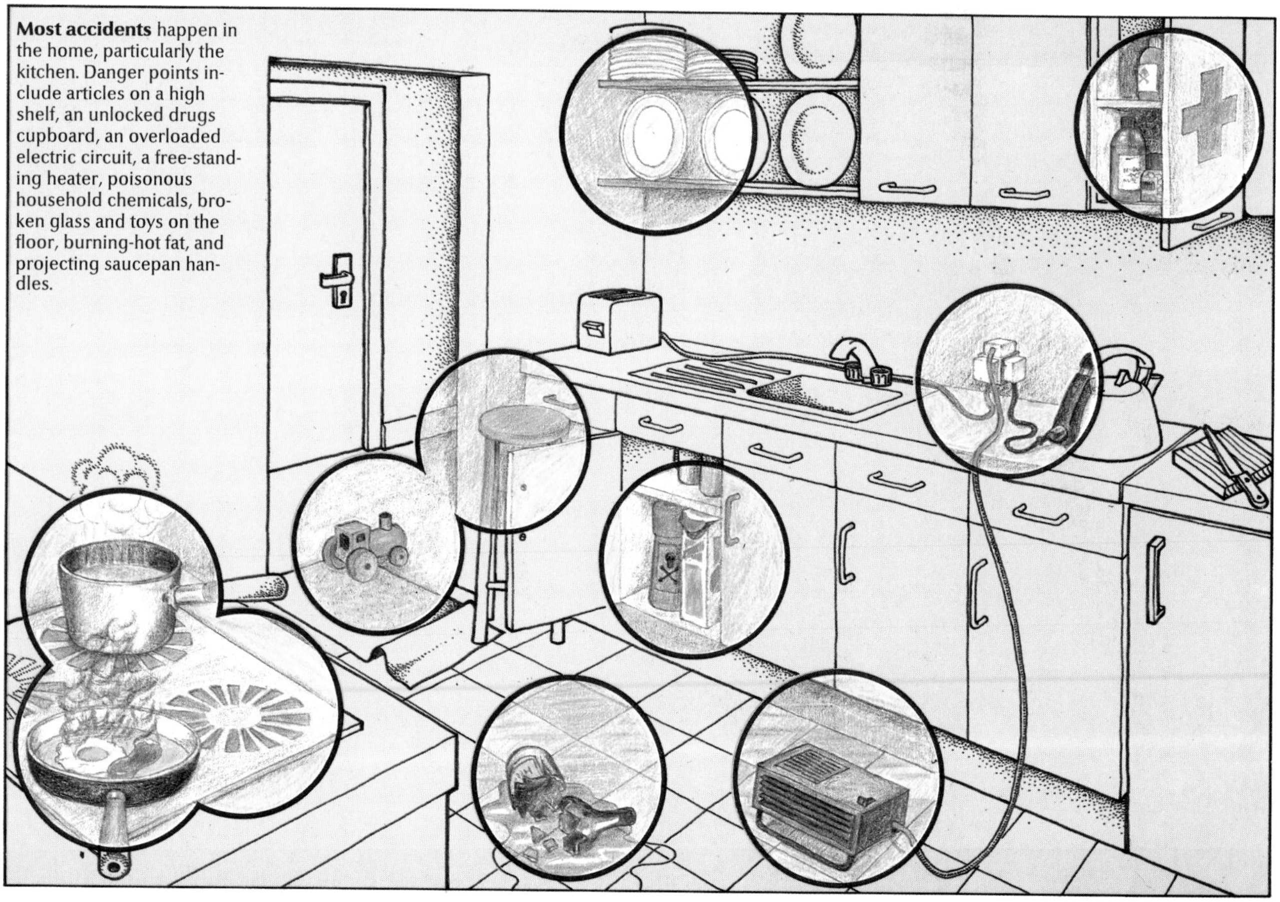

First-degree burns affect only the outer, inert skin layer. Second-degree burns destroy living tissue but leave sufficient growing layer for the surface to be restored. Third-degree burns involve the entire thickness of the skin and generally require skin to be replaced by grafting.

When tissue is burnt, plasma leaks out of the blood vessels and may form blisters under the skin. When the burning is extensive, the circulation may be adversely affected. This, and the severe pain, can lead to clinical shock.

Poisons

Poisoning can have the same effect on the circulation as shock, for instance, by interfering with the nervous system. A number of chemicals and vegetable poisons, such as strychnine and some of the fungal (mushroom and toadstool) poisons, affect the nervous and circulatory system in this way. Other poisons include corrosive substances, which affect the internal or external body surfaces, and metabolic poisons. The latter cause death by impairing cell function—cyanide, for instance, blocks oxygen transportation and causes chemical suffocation.

Fractures

Broken or cracked bones (fractures) are the commonest result of accidents. Shock may complicate fractures, especially when a large bone such as the femur is involved, because heavy bleeding may occur around the break. Pain and distress also contribute to the shock reaction.

Fractures are usually treated easily by orthopedic specialists, and heal more quickly in younger than older people. But a badly shattered bone may remain brittle for a long time and be in constant danger of breaking again.

Shock

This refers to a serious internal physical condition in which the blood pressure falls well below normal—in severe shock, the blood pressure can fall as low as 60/20 mm of mercury (the normal level is about 120/80 mm). In such circumstances, the blood circulation fails to maintain an adequate flow through the tissues and back to the heart. The brain cannot function because of lack of oxygen, and for this reason, shock is a common cause of death following a serious accident or acute illness.

Circumstances in which shock occurs include hemorrhage, which reduces the blood pressure directly by lowering the blood volume; reduced efficiency of the heart, for instance, after a heart attack (coronary thrombosis), when its pumping action is impaired; and the abnormal dilatation of certain blood vessels, which causes the pressure in the circulatory system to drop. To some extent, every accident—even a relatively minor physical injury—causes shock. Shock may also result from the body's reaction to surgical treatment, some drugs, emotional stress, and severe allergic reactions.

Sports and hobbies can also involve accidents. The protective clothing worn by this young skateboarder is about to be put to a severe test.

Highway traffic accidents are all too common. Relatively few are fatal, although almost all result in injury and considerable physiological and psychological shock.

Natural defenses

The human body is constantly bombarded by an incalculable number of microorganisms, of which bacteria and viruses are the most common. Most of them are harmless, but some are agents of infection (pathogens). The latter invade the body in various ways—through injuries, from infected people or animals, from contaminated food or drink, or in the air we breathe.

Pathogens have four main routes into the body: through the respiratory tract and the lungs; through breaks in the skin; through the digestive tract into the stomach and bowels; and through the reproductive and urinary tract. Once inside the body, infection may remain in the area where it arrived, or it may travel through the blood or lymphatic systems to other parts of the body.

In the face of such constant attack, the human body has a formidable array of natural defenses. It fights infections in two main ways: by preventing the entry of harmful microorganisms into the body; and by destroying or neutralizing those that do enter.

Barrier defenses

Skin provides the main physical barrier to infection. It has a slightly acid surface that is too cold and hostile for most germs and is further protected by bactericidal chemicals in sweat.

The natural openings into the body are protected too. The sensitive mucous membranes that line the body's orifices and internal passages are sticky so they can trap harmful invaders; they also contain bactericidal substances. The nose, for instance, filters air entering the respiratory tract. Mucus and hairs in the nostrils trap some unwanted particles; others are trapped farther along and removed by cilia of the trachea and bronchi, so that they can be expelled from the body by coughing or sneezing. Specialized dust cells in the lungs produce macrophages that engulf minute particles that pass the other defensive barriers. The acidic conditions of the stomach kill most invasive agents that are swallowed. The secretions of certain glands also serve as barriers: tears, nasal and vaginal secretions, saliva, and the digestive juices all contain antibacterial enzymes or other chemicals.

Internal defense systems

Where pathogenic organisms do manage to gain access to the body's tissues, complex internal defenses take over, responding directly to the physical presence of invading organisms and to the toxins produced by them.

Phagocytes are specialized cells that engulf and digest harmful bacteria. Some of these are highly mobile, such as the white blood cells called polymorphonuclear leukocytes or the single-nuclear monocytes that circulate in the

Respiratory System
Respiratory Defenses
Nose
Throat
Trachea
Bronchi
Lungs
Nasal cilia and mucus
Nasal hairs
Adenoids
Tonsils
Cough reflex
Tracheal cilia and mucus
Bronchial cilia and mucus
Macrophages in dust cells of lungs
Natural defenses in blood supply to lungs

The respiratory system *(above)*—from the nose through to the lungs—is continually exposed to harmful agents, but has a formidable array of defenses to combat them. Hair and mucus in the nasal passages filter out dust and dirt; lymphatic tissue of the tonsils and adenoids kill bacteria and viruses; hairlike cilia *(right)* sweep mucus up the bronchi and trachea to the throat; and cells called macrophages *(far right)* engulf dust particles in the lungs.

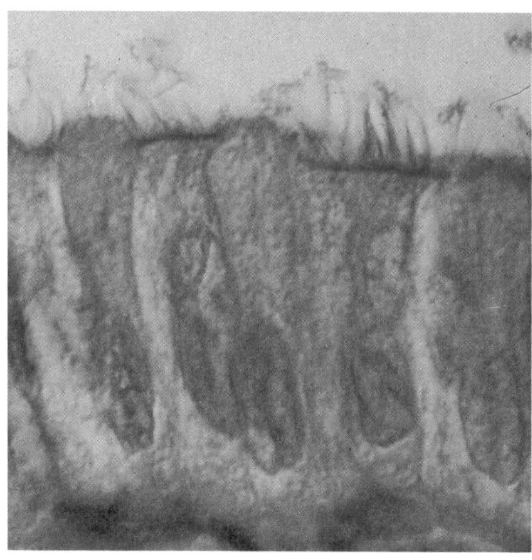

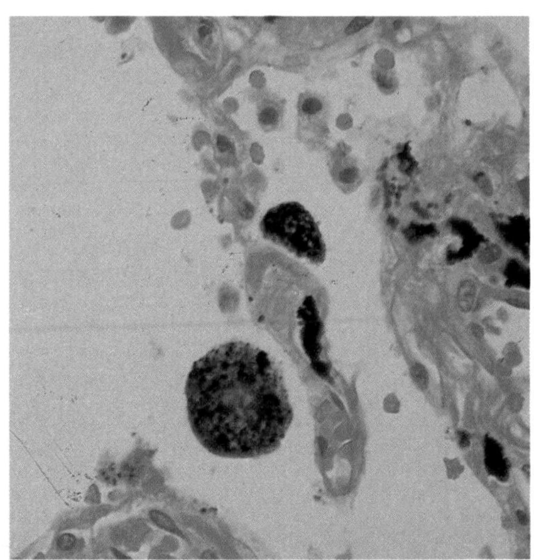

blood. When a cut or abrasion results in local bacterial invasion, increased numbers of phagocytes migrate to the invaded area, where they surround and ingest the bacteria to prevent them from spreading.

Other phagocytes, called macrophages, are more permanently located in specific parts of the body—particularly the lungs, spleen, liver, and lymph nodes—where they filter infective agents out of the blood and lymph circulation.

The lymphatic system plays a crucial role in the body's "immune response," the highly complex defense mechanism by which antibodies are formed in direct response to the presence of antigens—foreign substances, usually proteins, produced by invading organisms. Special white blood cells called lymphocytes, which are formed in the lymphoid tissue of the bone marrow, thymus, lymph nodes, spleen, tonsils, and adenoids, detect any alien protein that enters the bloodstream. Lymphocytes and plasma cells then produce a protein called an antibody. Released into the bloodstream, the antibodies attack the antigens. Some cause bacteria to clump together, and so prevent their spread; others affect the surface of bacteria and make them vulnerable to phagocytes; still others (antitoxins) neutralize poisonous toxins produced by antigens.

Antibodies are not general in their action. Those produced in response to the antigens of diphtheria bacteria are not able to react with those of tuberculosis bacteria, for instance. Nor does the body produce large numbers of antibodies on immediate exposure to an antigen. Large-scale production of antibodies occurs only a few days after exposure; it recurs much more rapidly during subsequent exposure. Once antibodies have been formed in response to a particular bacterium or virus, however, they never completely disappear from the bloodstream and so form the basis of lifelong immunity against that particular illness. The best-known example is the immunity acquired to childhood diseases such as measles. Following the same principle, vaccines—containing dead or weakened pathogens—confer artificial immunity by stimulating antibody production.

Pathogenic microorganisms are not the only foreign proteins that bring about antibody production. The body's tendency to reject skin grafts or transplanted organs is also due to its built-in ability to recognize foreign tissue.

Self-repair

Infection usually results in cellular damage. Where this occurs, special mobile cells called fibroblasts lay down strands of fiber to form a scaffolding onto which new cells can grow from healthy, neighboring tissue. In open wounds, the ability of blood to clot is important in preventing excessive loss of blood. The process consists of a complex series of chemical reactions but culminates in the conversion of a fluid substance, fibrinogen, into a mass of thin protein threads (fibrin), which forms the core of the clot.

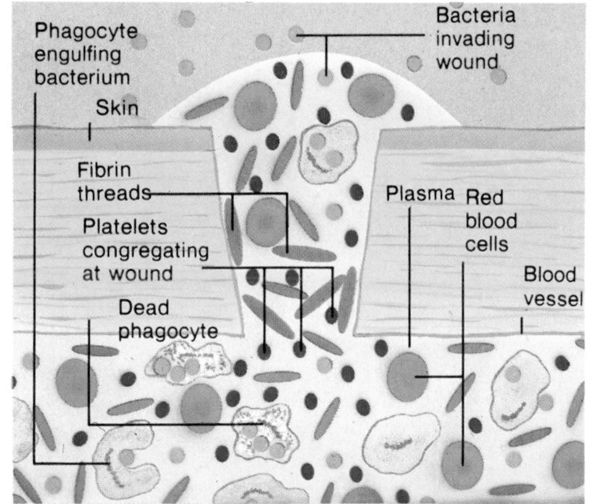

An injury to the skin results in invasion by bacteria, which are met by the body's second line of natural defenses, the blood. Phagocytes migrate to the injured area and engulf invading bacteria. Blood platelets, which have an important role in blood clotting, also concentrate at the site of bleeding.

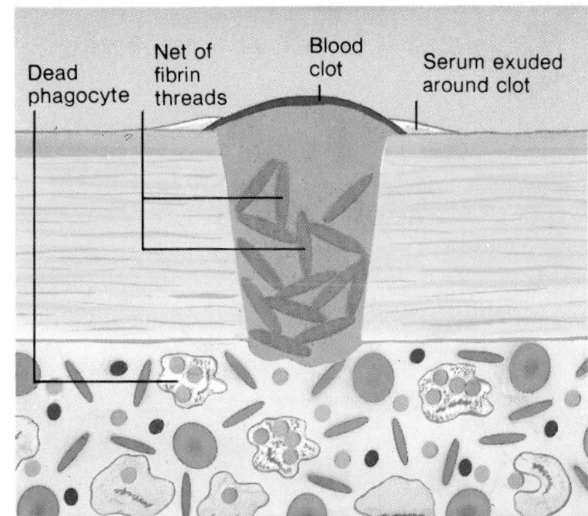

Blood clotting helps to seal the wound so that tissue repair can proceed. Phagocytes continue to destroy bacteria, while spent phagocytes and dead bacteria accumulate as pus.

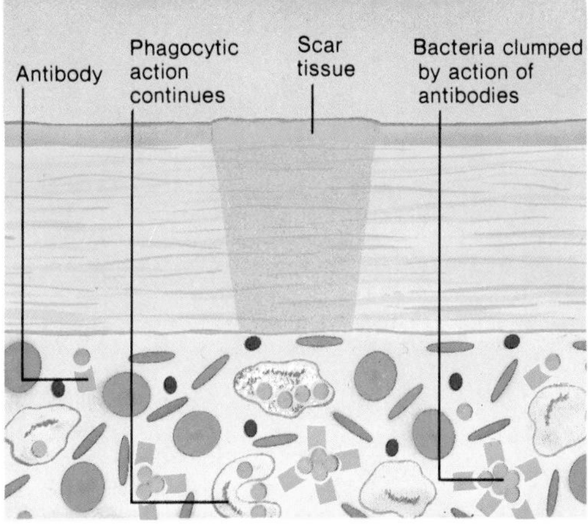

New tissue repairs the damage at the site of the wound. Antibodies formed in response to the invading antigens help to eliminate any remaining bacteria and confer a degree of lasting immunity.

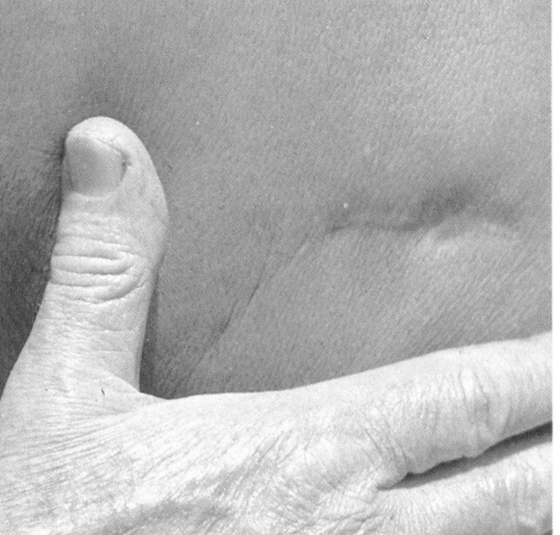

Scarring can be extensive at the site of a large and ragged wound. This photograph shows a spear wound that was stitched to close it and minimize scarring, but nevertheless the skin has been distorted by inelastic scar tissue.

Community health

Community medicine's prime concern is to prevent disease. Communal health responsibilities include: controlling housing standards and population density; the disposal of domestic and industrial waste; the maintainance of public hygiene; health screening; the elimination of sources of disease and infection, for instance, by vermin control or by neutralization (or drainage) of malarial swamps; and defining acceptable standards of burial. They can also extend to the provision of training and research facilities; the establishment and staffing of hospitals and clinics; the provision of medical emergency services; and the arrangement of financial support for sick people.

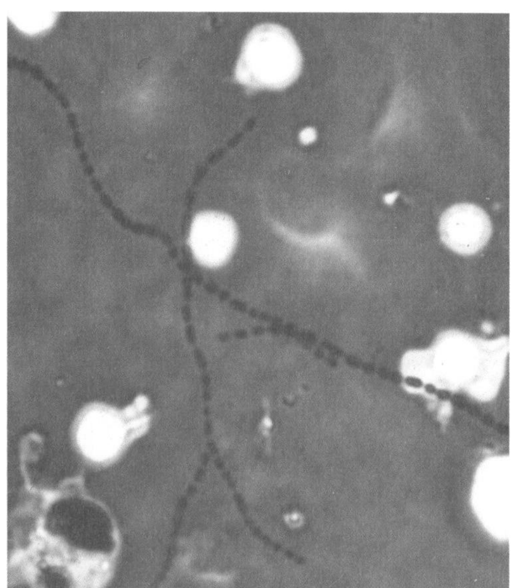

Milk is sterilized or pasteurized to kill bacteria such as these streptococci, which were photographed in a stained sample of untreated milk.

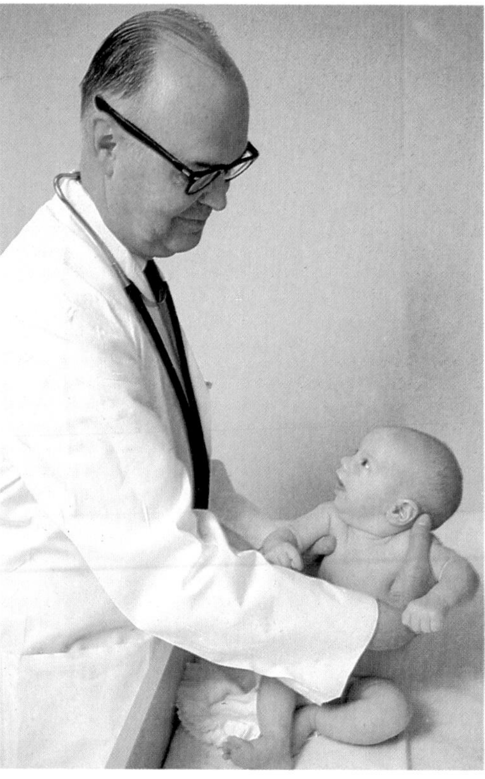

Baby clinics are a valuable aspect of community health because they allow pediatricians to regularly monitor the progress of growing infants. Any disorders are diagnosed and treated promptly. Parents are also given advice about vaccinations.

Water supply and sanitation

People everywhere need a constant supply of clean water for drinking, cooking, and washing, and also facilities for the removal of sewage waste. The latter must never contaminate the former, otherwise epidemics such as dysentery, typhoid, and cholera can result.

Water is collected from natural sources and stored in reservoirs. It is then purified and distributed for public usage. In some countries, one or two parts of fluoride per million are added to water, to help prevent tooth decay. Constant checks are carried out at all stages to see that no contamination occurs.

An adequate public and domestic water supply enables the sewage system to use waste water to transport the sewage from its source (washrooms) to sewage treatment works. This ensures that the transport is relatively swift and enables the system to be enclosed, which greatly reduces the spread of diseases, especially those such as food poisoning and dysentery, which are transmitted from feces to food by flies.

Vaccination programs

Children, adults, and animals are vaccinated against disease according to the principle established by a British doctor, Edward Jenner, in 1796. He discovered that people who had been given cowpox were protected against smallpox; this is because the cowpox virus, which causes a mild disease, stimulates production of antibodies that are effective against the smallpox virus. Babies are vaccinated against poliomyelitis, tetanus, and diphtheria and may also be vaccinated against measles and mumps. Susceptible children are vaccinated against tuberculosis. Girls who have not contracted rubella (German measles) naturally by about the age of 13 can be vaccinated against the disease at this age. Vaccination against typhoid, cholera, and yellow fever is also required for people of all ages who are traveling in areas where they may contract these diseases. Smallpox vaccination has effectively eradicated the disease.

Hygienic food processing

Hygienic controls are introduced at all stages of food production, from breeding and growing, to slaughtering and harvesting, to preparation and packing, to transporting and storing, and to selling, cooking, and serving. Such controls are obligatory in many countries, particularly where the food is being produced for storage and wholesale national or international marketing.

To prevent the spread of tuberculosis and brucellosis through dairy products, milk is pasteurized by being heated to 161° F. (72° C). This process kills most bacteria in the milk and improves its storage qualities without affecting its taste.

Cattle are vaccinated against brucellosis and tuberculosis, and meat is inspected for infections such as tapeworm after animals have

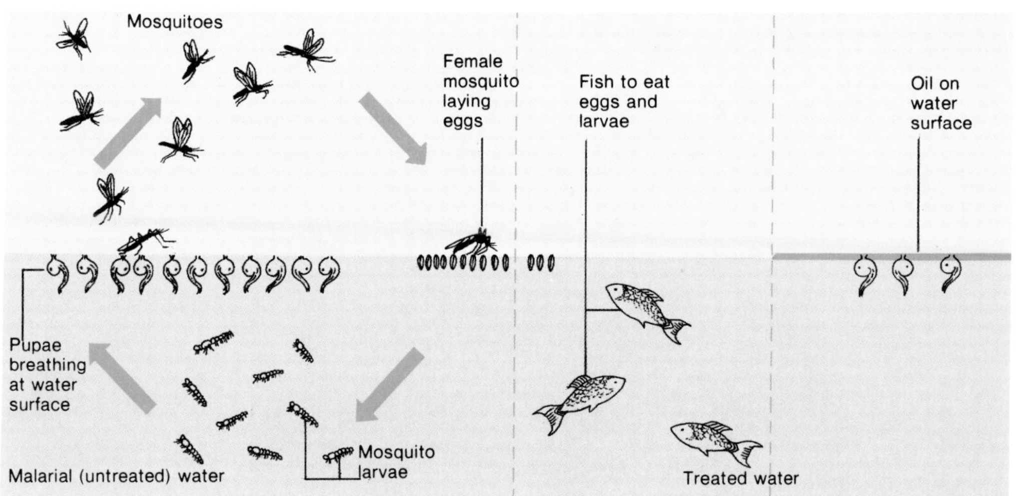

Malaria is spread by mosquitoes, so the disease can be prevented by destroying these carriers. The life cycle of a mosquito has three aquatic stages. Fish introduced to the breeding grounds reduce the population of mosquito eggs, larvae, and pupae. Alternatively, pupae can be killed by a thin layer of oil on the water surface, which prevents them from breathing.

been slaughtered in accredited slaughterhouses. Tuberculosis of the bone and brain tissue of cattle, which was common 50 years ago, is now rarely encountered in developed countries, as a result of scrupulous agricultural controls. Similar controls are applied to all other animals used as sources of food.

Food-processing factories, hotels, and restaurants are regularly inspected for the presence of vermin such as rats, mice, and cockroaches, and for evidence that adequate standards of hygiene are maintained in all parts of the operation where food might be contaminated. Stringent controls are also imposed to ensure that imported foods are fit for human consumption.

Food additives

During manufacture, processed foods may be enriched with substances that benefit health, particularly vitamins and minerals, which are sometimes destroyed in the commercial preparation of such foods. Iron and other minerals are added to bread and cereal foods, and glucose is sometimes added to drinks and candies. Some foods contain extra bran to provide roughage, which helps prevent bowel disease.

Health screening

In many countries, schoolchildren are tested for tuberculosis susceptibility. Chest radiography—which may be provided by companies, schools, or local health authorities—is available if necessary to check for disorders such as tuberculosis, lung cancer, chronic chest infection, and other conditions. Regular health checks and education programs are also instituted wherever possible, often under the direction of international bodies such as the World Health Organization.

Women, particularly in developed countries, are advised to have regular cervical smear tests and to examine their breasts for lumps. Both these examinations increase the chances for cancer being detected at the earliest opportunity, when it can be treated without much difficulty.

Mothers are encouraged to take their babies and children to clinics at special centers or at their doctor's office, where their development, weight, and rate of growth are noted against a chart of normal development, in order to identify abnormally slow or fast developers. Their feeding programs are discussed and dietary advice is given where necessary. Nursing mothers are advised to continue breastfeeding as long as possible. In some countries, however, the need to return to work and the availability of artificial milks has encouraged many mothers to stop breastfeeding too soon. Consequently, their babies fail to acquire natural immunity to certain diseases and also suffer from illness caused by contamination of the artificial food. An important aspect of health education is the identification and correction of such harmful trends.

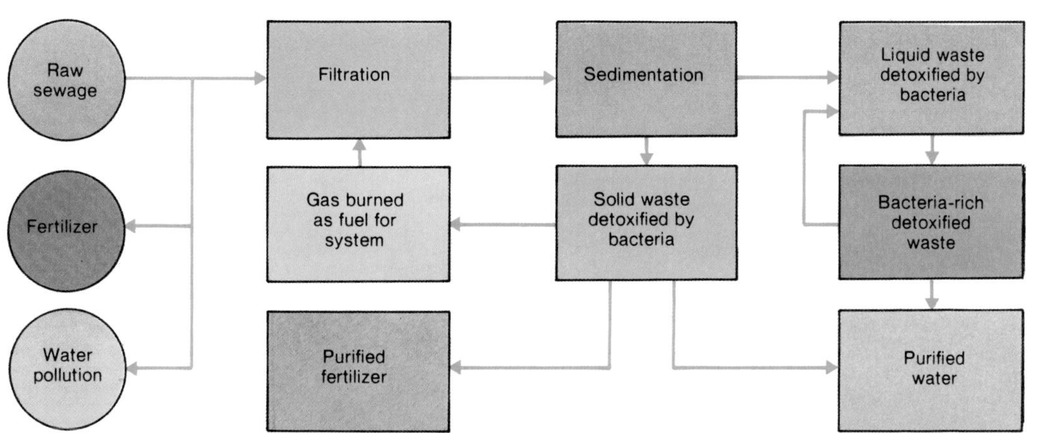

Safe sewage disposal is fundamental to community health. In primitive communities, sewage may be disposed of by using it as a fertilizer or by throwing it into a river. In an urban community, however, sewage can also be a serious source of disease if it is not properly treated.

Personal health

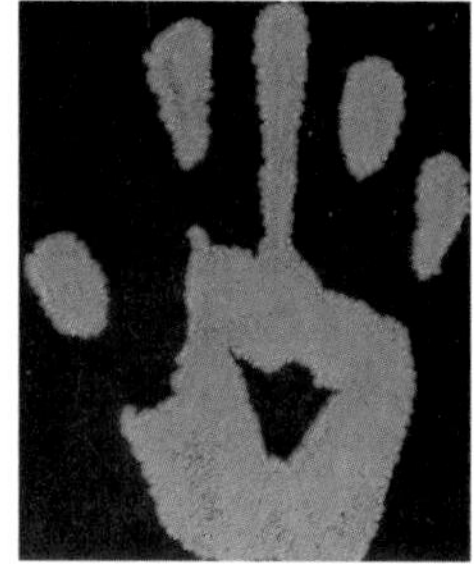

The hands are a source of infection, even after washing. This photograph shows the growth of bacteria after a "clean" hand was pressed palm-down on a culture plate.

In the second half of the twentieth century, good health is accepted as normal by most people who live in developed countries. This has resulted partly from improved standards of prenatal and child care, hygiene, nutrition, and preventive medicine; partly from better educational methods and communication; and partly from the astonishing advances that have been made in all areas of medical science. Unfortunately, many people take good health for granted and fail to treat their bodies with sufficient care and consideration.

Diet

A balanced diet containing the basic food types—proteins, fats, carbohydrates, vitamins, minerals, and fluids—is essential for satisfactory growth, development, and health. Babies require these in an easily digestible form, and breast milk is the best possible nutrition for an infant.

In Western countries, a large percentage of the daily protein requirement is supplied by meat. This is a good source of essential amino acids (protein building blocks), but red meat from farm stock also contains substantial quantities of saturated fat, which contributes to the development of heart disease. Research shows that communities with a diet containing a large proportion of fish, for example the Japanese, suffer less from heart disease, high blood pressure, and strokes. In contrast, a diet lacking even eggs or dairy proteins—for example, the diets based on rice, millet, or root vegetables that are common in poor nations—is likely to lead to some degree of protein deficiency.

In the West, it is possible to eat a perfectly balanced diet, but most people forego this opportunity. They tend to eat too much fat meat, sugar, and starch, and, as a result, suffer ill health from digestive problems, cardiovascular disorders, and obesity. An example of a balanced diet is one consisting of a small amount of meat; fish, eggs, and dairy products; raw or lightly-cooked fruit and vegetables; whole grain flour products; whole grains, nuts, and seeds.

Constituent of tobacco smoke	Acts against	Likely result
Nicotine	Natural defenses	Respiratory illness
	Heart	Heart disease
	Circulation	Circulatory disease
	Digestion	Stomach ulcer
Irritants	Respiratory tract	Chronic bronchitis
Carbon monoxide	Blood oxygen (reduced)	Damage to fetus
Carcinogens	Mouth, throat and lungs	Cancer of these and other parts of the body

Tobacco smoke is a major cause of illness and disease. Four main constituents—nicotine, irritants, carbon monoxide, and cancer-producing agents (carcinogens)—affect the respiratory tract (mouth, throat, and lungs) directly, and the circulatory system, stomach, and, in pregnant women, the fetus indirectly.

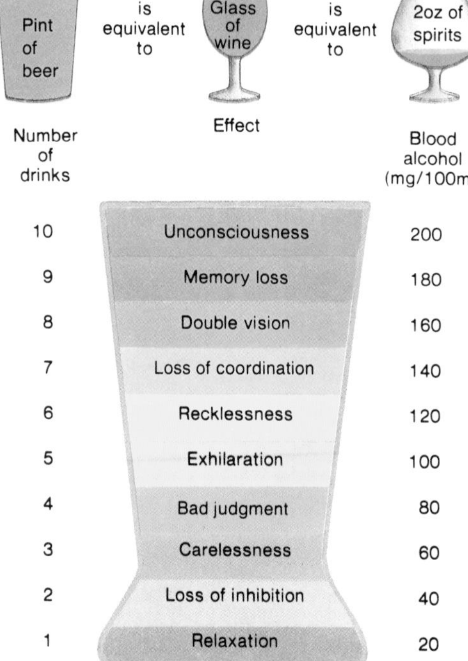

Alcohol produces a sense of euphoria and a loss of mental and physical control. The chart shows the approximate effects of an increasing number of drinks and the corresponding level of alcohol in the blood (expressed as milligrams of alcohol per 100 milliliters of blood).

Exercise

People living in agricultural societies are often much healthier than those in technologically developed ones. Outdoor activity keeps people strong and supple, whereas a more sedentary life style is more likely to produce joint degeneration and muscular weakness at a relatively early age.

Hard manual labor and physical exercise are not necessarily the same thing, however, as can be deduced from the poor physiques of some manual laborers. To be lastingly beneficial, exercise should rhythmically contract and relax the various muscle groups and should exercise the heart and lungs moderately. The best forms of exercise to avoid excess weight and keep the heart and blood vessels healthy are swimming, skiing, racket games, dancing, cycling, vigorous walking, and jogging.

Relaxation

People in developing countries are often undernourished and overworked, but in many respects they are better at relaxing than people in developed countries. Many practice meditation, and take part in sports, dancing, singing, and games, all of which are more beneficial than the passive entertainment of television that occupies so much of the leisure time of their counterparts in developed nations.

Exercise is an excellent way of combating the ill effects of stress. The "fight or flight" mechanism, which is the physiological basis of stress, is given an outlet through physical activity and so is prevented from harming the person, physically or mentally. Meditation is also a good way of calming the mind and inducing a sense of mental and emotional well-being. Laughter, too, is an excellent antidote to stress, and recreational pleasure is as important to health as is physical exercise.

Hygiene

Before the discovery of bacteria and viruses, and the identification of their role in causing disease, cleanliness was considered a luxury. Now, however, the importance of personal hygiene is accepted in nearly all countries of the world.

Personal hygiene includes washing the hands after visiting the washroom, as well as maintaining the washroom itself and the washing areas in a hygienic state. This involves regularly rinsing the sink and toilet with disinfectant and providing soap and either clean towels or hot-air hand driers. The hands should always be washed before preparing or eating food.

Preventive measures

There are certain preventive measures that most people can take against disease—and some which depend upon their availability. Principal aids to personal health are eating a balanced diet; taking regular exercise; learning to relax; and keeping oneself, family, and home as clean as possible. Others are to avoid smoking, drugs (except when medically essential) and excessive quantities of alcohol. Most peoples' environment is determined largely by their means of livelihood, but where an option exists, it makes sense to choose to live a life in which pollution and stress are minimal.

As additional aids to ensuring personal health, the following can also be beneficial: inoculation against infectious diseases, particularly for babies and young children; regular routine tests, such as breast examination and cervical smears; and regular tests of blood pressure and heart rate.

Regular exercise can help to maintain good health, and running—alone or in company—is popular because it allows people to keep fit relatively easily. Running in the countryside adds to the enjoyment and avoids damage to bones and joints that can be caused by running on roads.

Drinking and smoking are harmful but are great social pleasures nevertheless; many people tolerate or ignore the dangers for the sake of relaxation and conviviality.

Treatment of illness

The treatment of illness begins with the investigation of a patient's symptoms and the diagnosis of their cause. Treatment then aims to eradicate the cause, by means of drug treatment, surgery, modifications to lifestyle or, increasingly, where conventional methods seem inappropriate, by recourse to those alternative therapies that have been approved by scientists.

In all medicine, however, investigation and diagnosis must be the starting point. Laboratory tests, X-ray and exploratory techniques are now aided by computers, which speed up the rate at which diagnoses can be made and treatment started. Ten years ago, the fastest autoanalyzer could investigate the blood chemistry of several patients simultaneously and produce hundreds of results within an hour. Nowadays, medically computed analyzers are many times faster.

Antibiotic spots

Bacteria

Culture plate

Antibiotic drugs are tested on a culture plate containing a jellylike medium *(right)* with a colony of bacteria. Different drugs or different concentrations of drugs inhibit bacterial growth to varying extents, leaving a clear area in the culture. Similar techniques *(below)* are used in pathology laboratories to analyze samples as part of medical investigation and diagnosis.

Physical examination

No machine, however advanced, is ever likely to replace the physical examination of the patient by the physician. An easy physician-patient relationship has an important effect on the patient's mental state, which in turn may influence the healing process. At a more complex level, the physician may be able to make judgments more subtle than any machine can. Ideally, physician and machine complement each other in diagnosis.

Complete physical examinations are usually carried out in a clinic or a physician's office. The patient's case history generally indicates which body system requires initial exploration.

When the heart and major blood vessels are examined, the pulse is felt, the heart is listened to with a stethoscope (auscultation), and the blood pressure is measured. Air entry into both lungs is checked, and the chest tapped (percussed) to define air-containing areas. The abdomen is felt (palpated) with the flat of the hand to test for swelling, tenderness, or other abnormality. Internal examination, rectal (per rectum or PR) or vaginal (per vaginum or PV), explores the contours of the rectum and vagina, respectively.

Eyes are examined with a small flashlight for pupil size and reaction; each retina is studied with an ophthalmoscope that focuses on the light-sensitive membranes at the back of the eye. The eardrum is examined with the otoscope, and the mouth and throat with a flashlight and tongue depressor.

Cranial and spinal nerves are tested by the muscular power and surface sensation of the parts they supply. Spinal reflexes are gauged with the patellar hammer, used to elicit a series of reflexes, best-known of which is the knee jerk.

Laboratory analysis

Requests by a doctor for "culture and sensitivity" tests to be made on a particular specimen usually refer to urine samples. A drop is studied microscopically, by the laboratory analyst or pathologist, then "plated out" onto the surface of a culture medium (jelly) in special disposable plates, before being incubated for 24 hours.

Growths (cultures) of bacteria appear as small white or colored "colonies." Their sensitivity to antibiotics is tested by their reactions to paper spots in the jelly, each spot being impregnated with a different antibiotic. Those to which the bacteria are sensitive inhibit the growth of the bacteria colonies in their vicinity.

Sputum (phlegm) is treated similarly, and for whooping cough special "cough plates" are

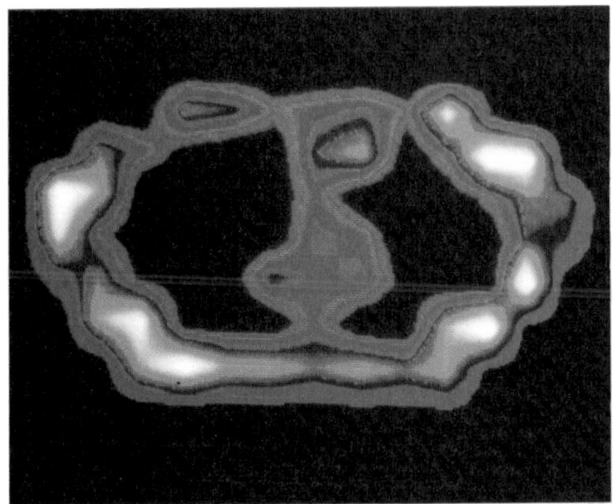

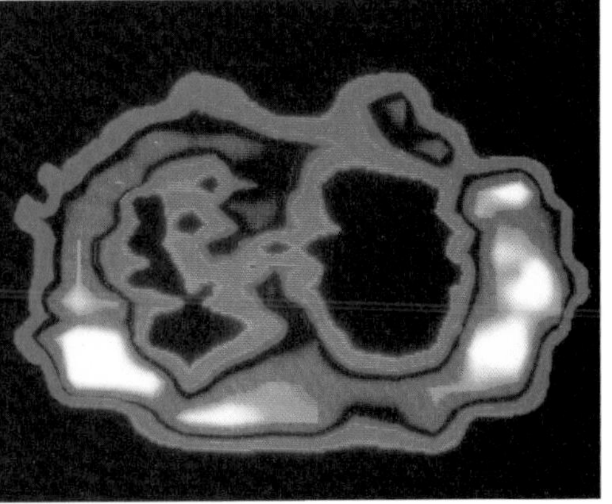

Nuclear magnetic resonance (NMR) techniques can be used instead of X rays to examine the interior of the body. NMR can reveal more detail than X rays and has no known side effects. One NMR image *(far left)* shows a cross section of a normal chest. The other *(left)* indicates the presence of a tumor in the patient's lung.

available to catch the droplets of infected sputum from suspected patients.

Urine and blood are also tested chemically for abnormal constituents, or abnormally high or low levels of substances that are usually present in known proportions. A raised level of urea in urine, for instance, suggests kidney disease, while a low level of thyroid hormone in the blood characterizes malfunction of the thyroid gland.

Blood samples are tested for clotting ability (erythrocyte sedimentation rate, or ESR). They may also be given a "blood count," in which the red cells per cubic millimeter are counted and examined for shape, size, and hemoglobin content. White cells are also counted and the various types identified.

Feces are examined for blood, which indicates bleeding in the gastrointestinal tract, and for evidence of infection or parasitic infestation.

Other techniques

The interior of the body can be examined visually by endoscopy, using a flexible fiberoptic tube that can be introduced either through natural openings or a small surgical incision.

Endoscopes are usually named for the part of the body they examine. A bronchoscope allows the physician to examine the windpipe (trachea) and the bronchi of both lungs. Cancerous growths can be detected in this way. A gastroscope shows the lining of the esophagus and the stomach. Similarly, a colonoscope, sigmoidoscope, and cystoscope view the interiors of the descending colon, sigmoid colon, and bladder, respectively.

Patients are given either a sedative or a general anesthetic before endoscopic procedures. During the examination, the physician can remove a tiny piece of tissue for a biopsy. Then the pathologist examines it for the presence of abnormal cells that might indicate an infection, cancer, or changes due to a disorder, such as ulcerative colitis (which affects the lower gastrointestinal tract).

As well as being used to diagnose skeletal problems, X rays can be used to investigate abnormalities of the soft tissues and internal organs. Tomography produces X rays of structures in a selected plane of the body, by computer-aided interpretation of a sequence of X-ray scans.

A physician, whether in a well-equipped office or, as here, without sophisticated technical aids in the open air of the bush, often remains the first (and most important) contact with the patient, making the first diagnosis and prescribing the preliminary treatment.

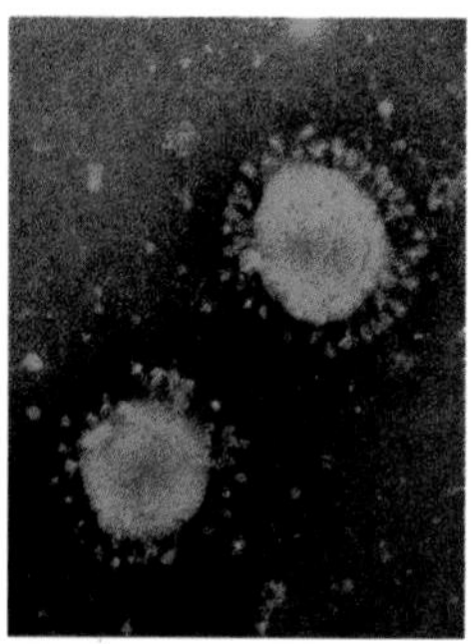

The common cold is the most common respiratory disorder in nontropical countries. Because it is caused by viruses (one type of which is shown above, much enlarged), it is difficult to treat, and most palliatives at best only relieve symptoms such as headache and sore throat.

Ear, nose, throat, and respiratory disorders

The respiratory system represents a compromise. On one hand, it must provide a large and effective area for exchanging oxygen with the environment; on the other, it must prevent harmful environmental agents from reaching deep into the body. Disorders of the system are generally characterized by ineffective gas exchange or failure of defenses. The whole system from the nose to the bronchioles (with an extension to the middle ear) is lined by specialized mucosa, and these structures are therefore considered together.

Ear disorders

Infections that spread from the nose or pharynx usually affect the middle ear. The Eustachian tube can be blocked by inflammation of nasal tissues, and this can cause acute ear infection (otitis media), or serous otitis, caused by accumulation of fluid in the ear (glue ear). The latter is usually treated with antihistamines, to reduce the inflammation and allow the fluid to drain, though surgery may be required to equalize pressure in the ear by inserting a small tube (grommet) in the eardrum. In some cases, the adenoids (lymphatic tissue at the back of the nose) need to be removed to cure persistent inflammation and blockage.

Untreated middle ear infections can spread to the mastoid bone behind the ear. The honeycomb structure of this bone allows infection to develop to such an extent that antibiotics may be ineffective, and if so, only surgery can eradicate the disease. Untreated mastoiditis can spread farther to destroy the inner ear, or to cause meningitis or an abscess in the brain.

Deafness can result from a scarred or ruptured eardrum—whether from infection or from an accident—but is more commonly caused by degeneration (ostosclerosis) of the small bones of the middle ear, which transmit sound. Persistent exposure to loud noise can also damage the ear and cause progressive hearing loss. Formerly untreatable, such damage can now be repaired by microsurgical techniques: a new eardrum can be fashioned from the lining of the ear canal and damaged bones can be removed or replaced by plastic components. Deafness can also be caused by obstructions of the ear canal (external auditory meatus), with wax, inflammatory tissue, or fibrosis after infection, or even a foreign body.

Sounds similar to those of bells, rushing water, rustling leaves, or even aircraft taking off, may all be generated within the ear, and afflict those who suffer from tinnitus. These symptoms may be due to aging or degeneration of the cochlea, but this is not known for certain. Until recently there was no treatment, but now many patients benefit from "masking therapy" which, paradoxically, produces actual noise in a device worn like a hearing aid.

Nose disorders

Most disorders affecting the nose are caused by pathogens—primarily viruses—or allergens, such as dust mites or pollen grains.

The common cold is caused by viruses. Treatment concentrates on relieving the symptoms; there is still no specific cure. A new drug, interferon, may help to prevent colds, but it is still undergoing clinical trials.

Many of the disorders that affect the ears, nose, and throat result from infections, often producing symptoms of soreness and inflammation. The major sites for such infections are the sinuses; nasal passages and adenoids; throat and tonsils; larynx and trachea (windpipe); and the ears themselves. The ear canal may become blocked with wax, causing temporary deafness; inflammation of the middle ear results in earache; and disorders of the inner ear may cause dizziness or loss of hearing.

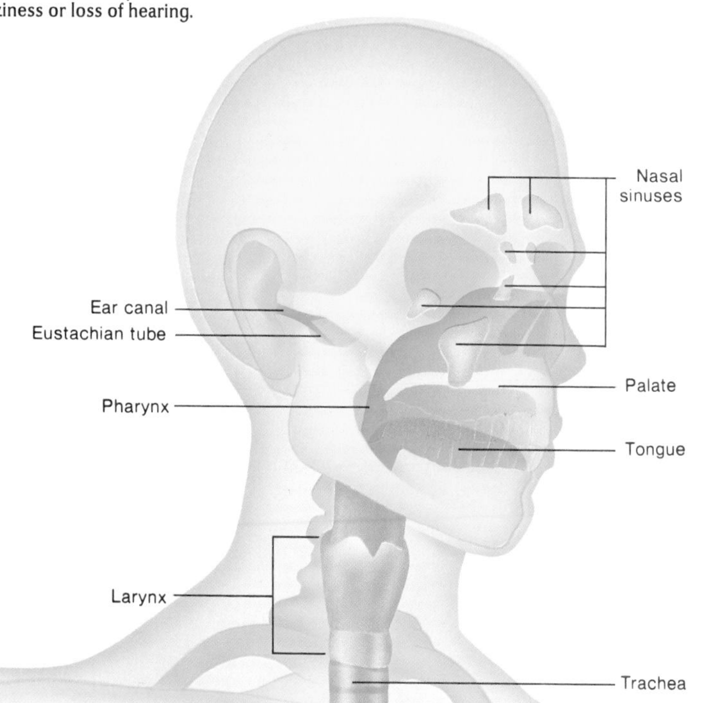

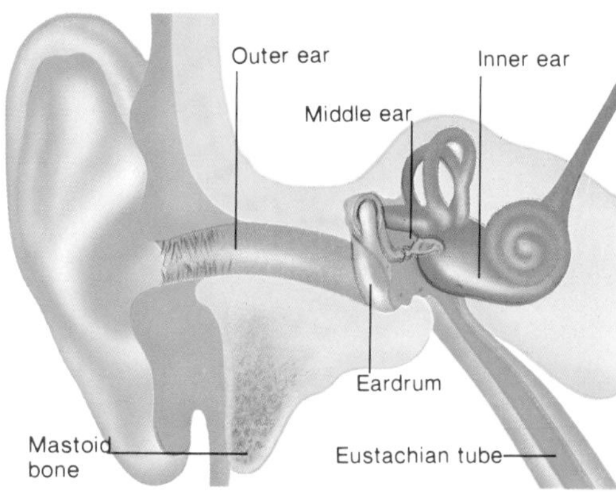

Throat disorders

Numerous bacterial or viral infections affect the throat. Medical names identify the main sites of infections—pharyngitis (pharynx), laryngitis (larynx), and tonsillitis (tonsils) are examples. Streptococcal throat infections are particularly dangerous because of the risk of complications such as rheumatic fever or glomerulonephritis. Throat swabs are taken to identify the infecting organism, which is then

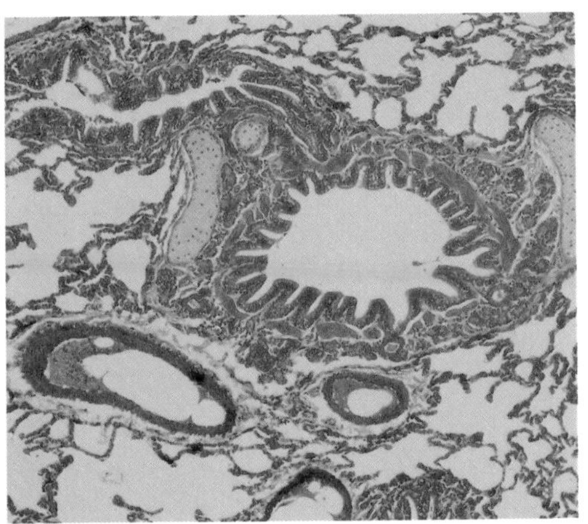

The lungs are susceptible to various infections that may cause inflammation that results in pneumonia or pleurisy. They are also vulnerable to the effects of inhaled chemicals and dust particles, whether from the atmosphere, working environment, or tobacco smoke. These photographs contrast tissue from a healthy lung *(left)* and from the lung of a smoker *(right)*.

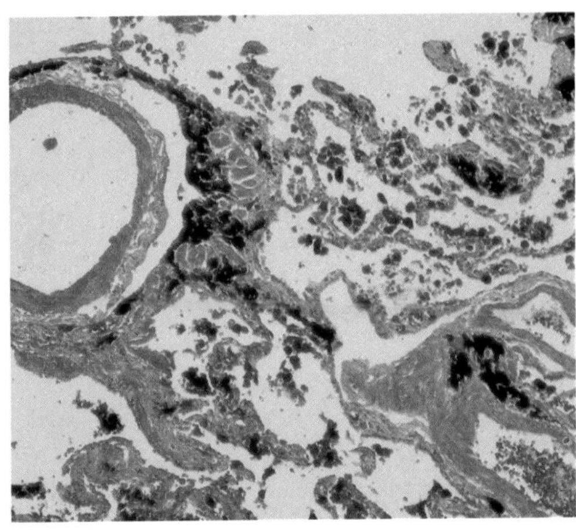

treated with antibiotics such as penicillin. Apart from infection, irritants such as cigarette smoke or alcohol, or even overuse—for instance, shouting—can cause laryngitis. Cigarette smoke and alcohol also encourage the development of cancer in the throat.

Lung disorders

Cigarette smoke and atmospheric pollution are among the commonest—and are certainly the most preventable—causes of lung disease. Disorders due to smoking range from minor ones, such as laryngitis, to serious, usually fatal, conditions, such as chronic bronchitis and lung cancer.

Chronic bronchitis—a persistent cough producing sputum—increases susceptibility to other chest infections. It may also lead to emphysema, in which lung tissue loses its normal elasticity and oxygen-uptake is reduced, causing breathlessness. Complications of chronic bronchitis can lead easily to respiratory failure. Treatment is with antibiotics and possibly oxygen therapy until the infection is controlled.

The most common infections of the lungs are lobar pneumonia, usually caused by pneumococci, and bronchial pneumonia. If an infection reaches the lining of the lung (pleura), pleurisy can result. The chief symptom is painful breathing, which is also a symptom of viral pneumonia. The bacteria causing a similar infection, Legionnaire's disease, has been identified recently as *Legionella pneumophila.*

The occurrence of lung cancer is almost entirely a result of smoking and is closely linked to total numbers of cigarettes smoked and their tar content. Although this is the commonest type of cancer in Western countries, the incidence has begun to approach a leveling-off as the public becomes more conscious of the dangers of smoking. Lower tar content and filtered cigarettes may also be beneficial. There are three main methods of treatment—surgery, radiation therapy, and cytotoxic chemotherapy, used alone or in combination. Surgery is most useful if the disease has not spread outside the lung, and may be curative. Radiation therapy is valuable in controlling more advanced disease, especially secondary deposits in the bones or brain, but it rarely provides a cure. Chemotherapy shows great promise, especially when combined with radiation therapy, in controlling and possibly even curing one particular kind of lung cancer, called oat-cell carcinoma.

Asthma

The symptoms of asthma are a combination of wheezing and a sensation of shortness of breath, caused by constrictions of the bronchial tubes and thickening of their walls by fluid. It is a common disease, affecting approximately 3.8 per cent of the total population and is thought to be an allergic reaction to inhaled dust particles.

In most cases, the allergen is unknown and treatment is directed toward relieving the airway constriction. Depending on the severity and frequency of the attacks, this may mean taking bronchodilators by an inhaler or may require powerful steroids and, occasionally, hospitalization. Recently developed drugs that patients inhale show great promise in preventing asthmatic attacks, especially in children. Treatment by desensitization injections and by special exercise programs have not been shown to alter the frequency or severity of attacks.

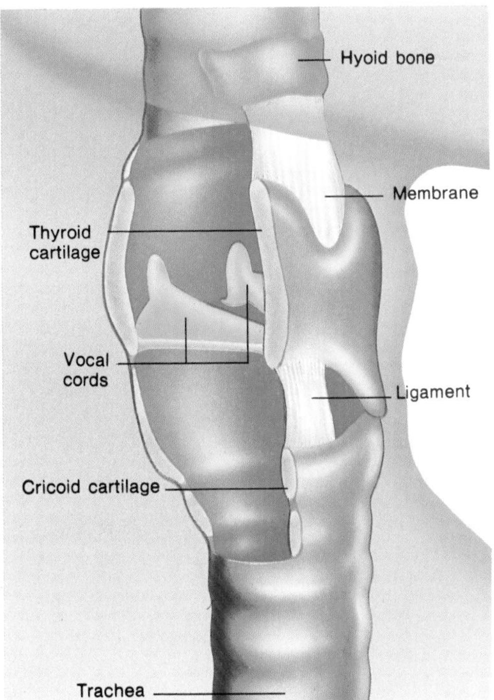

The larynx, or voice box, is an enlargement of the trachea (windpipe), partly closed by the vocal cords. Inflammation of the larynx—laryngitis—often spreads from the throat and causes the vocal cords to become swollen, usually resulting in hoarseness or even complete loss of voice. In an emergency, blockage of the upper larynx by swollen membranes in diphtheria or moniliasis (thrush) may be relieved by a tracheostomy, in which a small surgical incision is made in the windpipe below the voice box.

Heart, blood, and circulatory disorders

Arterial disease, and in particular arteriosclerosis, causes more deaths than any other disease in Western countries. The most common heart disease is actually due to diseased coronary arteries rather than to heart tissue itself. Damage or degeneration of these arteries reduces the blood supply to heart muscle, which ceases to function as a result. Other disorders can affect the rhythm of the heart, the valves, or the muscle directly. The heart can also be affected by general infections such as rheumatic fever, by cancer, usually as a secondary rather than a primary site, and by disorders such as high blood pressure (hypertension), which in turn may result from external factors such as smoking, lack of exercise, and fatty diet.

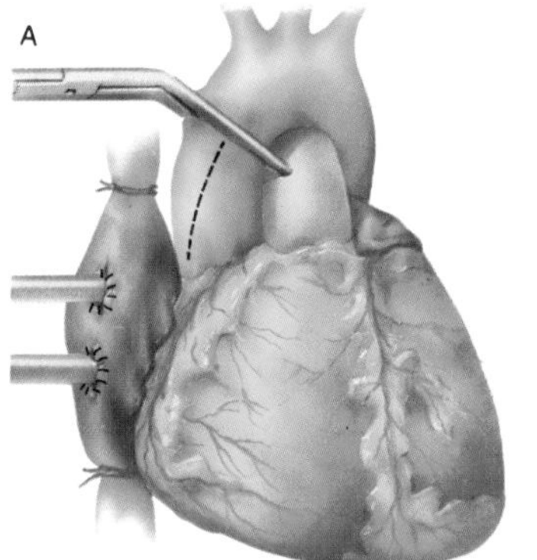

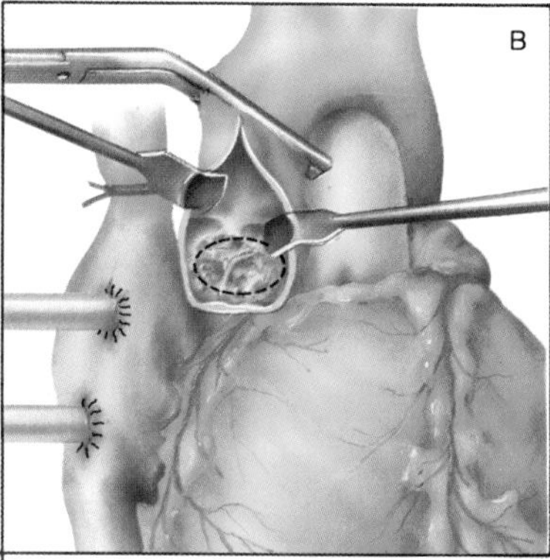

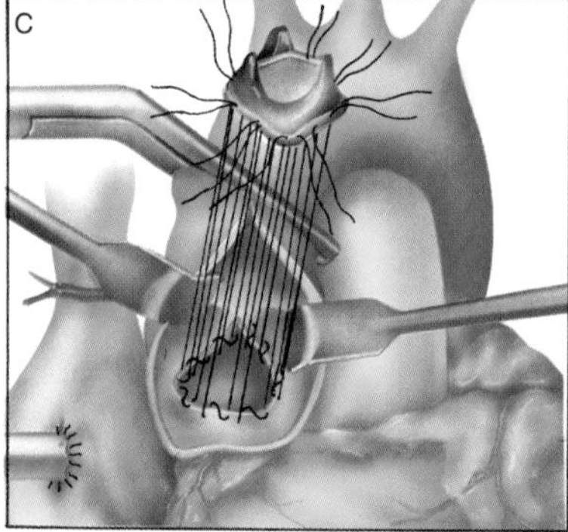

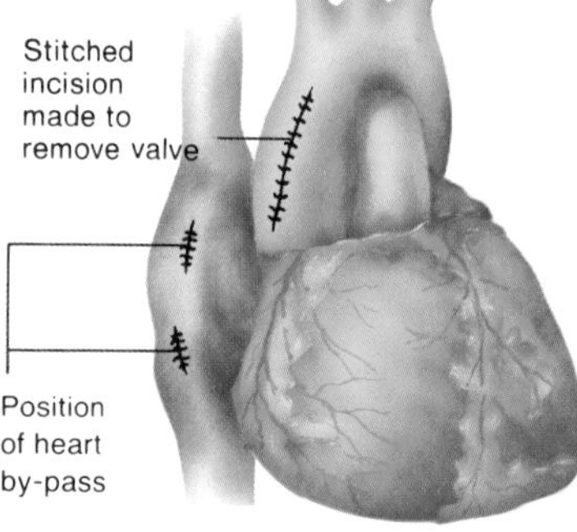

Valvular heart disease may be treated by an operation to replace the disordered valve with an artificial one. First the patient's heart is by-passed by a heart-lung machine (A), the aorta clamped, and an incision made (B) to expose the diseased valve, which is removed. The replacement is lined up with long stitches (C), which are then drawn tight. Finally all incisions are closed (D). The photograph *(right)* shows an artificial heart valve stitched into its final position.

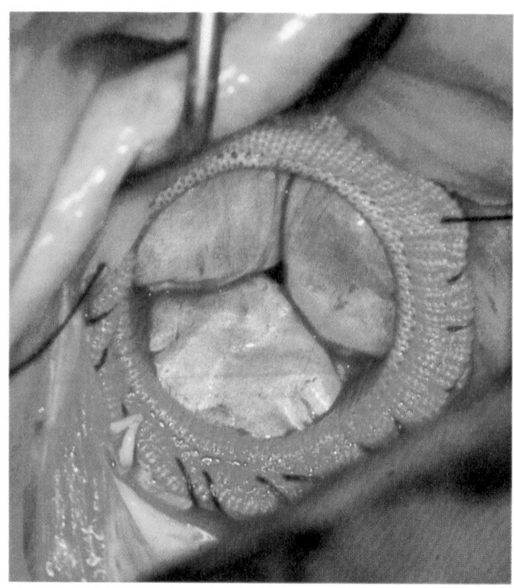

Over the past 30 years, the treatment of heart disease by surgery has advanced astonishingly. The use of heart-lung machines has enabled the heart to be stopped during operations. Implantation of artificial pacemakers and valves is now routine. Even heart transplant operations are becoming more successful, although all the problems have not yet been solved.

Arteriosclerosis

Arterial disorders are particularly dangerous because they affect the blood flow and so can cause damage to the heart, brain, and other parts of the body. With advancing years arteries and their walls become thickened (arteriosclerosis), and fatty material is laid down in the lining (atheroma), narrowing the vessel. Symptoms are unusual before middle age, though studies on American soldiers killed in Vietnam showed the presence of the disease as early as the late teens.

Several factors significantly increase the risk of developing arterial disease: smoking, high blood pressure, the amount of fats (lipids) in the bloodstream, diabetes, and aging. Diet can also affect blood pressure and blood lipid content.

If the surface of an atheromatous plaque is ulcerated, continuous healing and scarring tends to produce an ever-constricting arterial "bottleneck." Partial blockage in the flow of blood causes symptoms of ischemia (reduced local circulation) in the part of the body supplied by the affected arteries. Symptoms vary accordingly, but in the leg, for example, calf muscle pain may be caused by brief exercise and relieved by resting. If coronary arteries are affected, the symptom is chest pain (angina pectoris), which is particularly likely to occur when walking uphill in cold weather. An atheroma that causes ischemia in a kidney, in contrast, results in increased blood pressure.

Thrombosis

As the ulcerated plaque heals, local blood clotting may occur. If the clot (thrombus) blocks the artery completely, the effects are likely to be immediate and dramatic. In the heart, such blockage (occlusion) prevents blood reaching heart muscles, causing a heart attack (myocardial infarction). Unless the blood flow can be restarted quickly, the muscle dies. In the brain, arterial occlusion results in a type of stroke known as a cerebral infarct. In the legs, total loss of blood supply causes gangrene as tissue dies.

Even if such a clot does not block the artery completely, part of it (an embolus) may break off, travel in the circulation, and lodge in smaller arteries. Blockage may last for a short time only before the clot is broken down. If such a vessel is one of the network supplying the brain, short-lived symptoms, such as loss of consciousness, limb weakness, or difficulty with speech, may occur. This is described as a transient ischemic attack (TIA).

Aneurysms

Progressive damage to an artery wall can lead to weak points where the vessel wall bulges, producing an aneurysm. The aorta is commonly affected, and if so, may rupture, causing catastrophic hemorrhage. Aneurysms in cerebral vessels compress the surrounding brain tissue, producing various symptoms according to the part of the brain that is affected.

Treatment of arterial disease

The treatment of arterial disease is divided into prevention of clinical symptoms by slowing the progress of the disease, and repair of damaged vessels after symptoms have developed. Arterial damage can probably be minimized if the risk factors can be controlled by not smoking; by avoiding certain fats (particularly animal fats) in the diet; by treating hypertension; through weight loss; and by reduced salt content in the diet. Psychodynamic methods such as biofeedback, meditation, or other means of reducing stress may also be useful, or drug treatment may be necessary.

Exercise, for instance jogging, cycling, or cross-country skiing, improves the blood supply to the heart and muscles, reducing the risk of damage from occlusion of a single artery. People who exercise regularly tend to reduce or avoid smoking and lose excess weight, thereby lowering blood lipid levels and blood pressure.

Because many of the adverse effects of arterial diseases are related to thrombosis, there is great interest in the possibility that agents that inhibit clotting may reduce the progression of the disease. For instance, aspirin in low doses can inhibit platelet aggregation (stickiness), which is part of the clotting process.

Primarily, however, treatment for arterial disease is surgical. Usually, an occluded artery is opened and the atheromatous area is removed. The arteries commonly treated in this way are the carotid arteries in the neck, which supply the brain, and the femoral arteries, which supply the legs.

Diseases of the coronary arteries may be treated either by surgery or with drugs, depending on the exact sites of obstruction and the individual patient's symptoms. The most common surgical procedure is the coronary artery by-pass graft, in which segments of vein taken from the legs are connected to the aorta and the coronary artery to by-pass the area of occlusion. Surgery is also sometimes required to repair areas of dead muscle after myocardial infarction, especially when the muscular wall (septum) between left and right ventricles has ruptured, or when the muscle controlling the mitral valve is torn.

Two new forms of therapy for coronary artery disease have been developed recently. One employs a thin tube (catheter), which is passed along a coronary artery until a narrowed segment is reached; a balloon on the end of the catheter is then inflated to dilate the constriction. In the other, used if a coronary artery has been obstructed very recently by thrombosis, a clot-dissolving enzyme can be injected into the arteries using a catheter. If this is done within a few hours of coronary thrombosis, heart muscle death can be prevented.

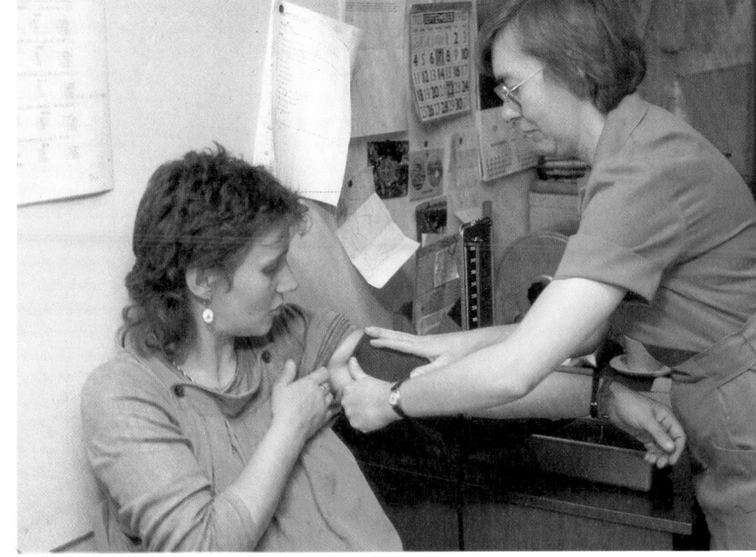

Blood pressure—or, more precisely, the pressure in an artery when the heart muscle contracts (the systolic pressure) and the pressure when it relaxes (the diastolic pressure)—is a useful diagnostic measurement for a physician, shown here measuring the blood pressure of a pregnant woman. High blood pressure, above $\frac{145}{90}$, is called hypertension and generally requires treatment. Low blood pressure (hypotension), below $\frac{100}{60}$, may be a symptom of shock or some other underlying disorder of the circulation.

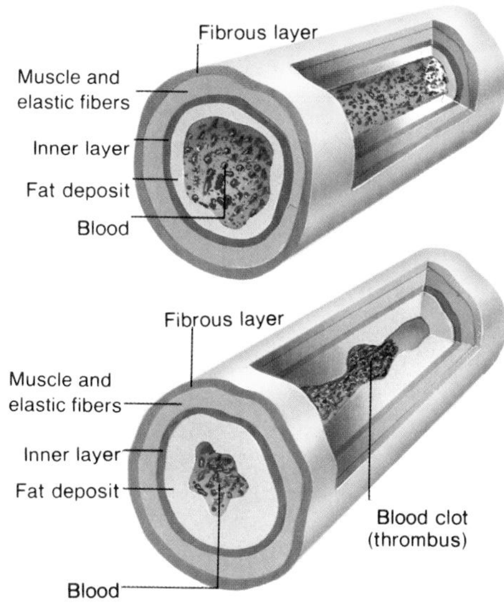

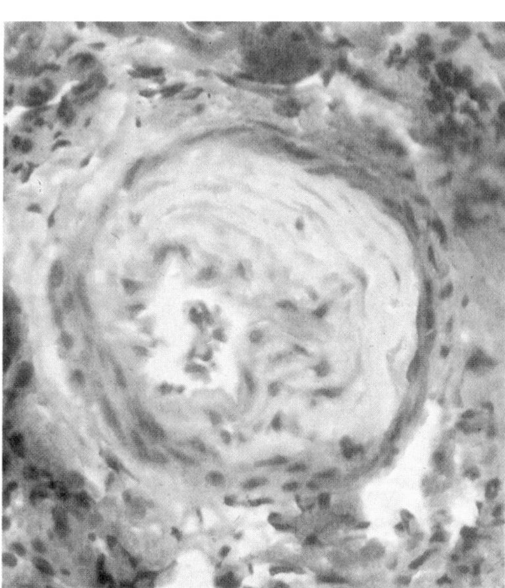

Arteriosclerosis is a disorder in which fatty deposits accumulate in an artery, narrowing it and restricting the flow of blood. The artery also loses its elasticity and suppleness. The diagram shows sections of normal and sclerotic arteries. Severe arteriosclerosis may so narrow a vessel that a blood clot forms. The photograph shows a section of an affected coronary artery that carries blood to the muscles of the heart itself.

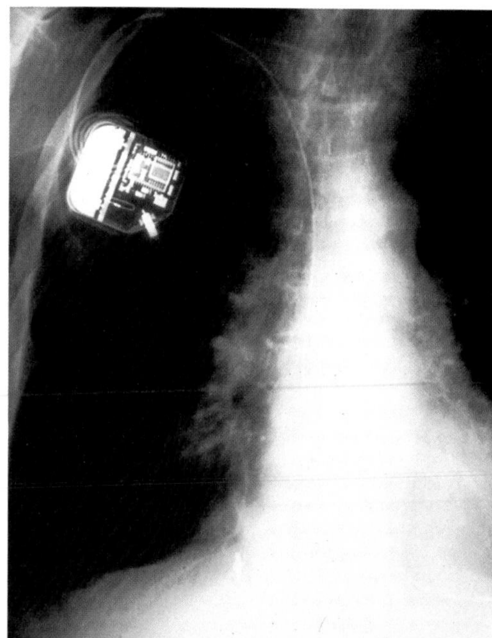

An artificial pacemaker can be connected to the heart of a patient to restore correct rhythmic beating when the natural pacemaker is deficient. The X ray *(right)* shows a pacemaker implanted near the shoulder and connected to the heart along a vein. The child *(below)* has a rechargeable pacemaker that can be reactivated externally, without the need for regular operations to replace the pacemaker's batteries.

Venous thrombosis

Blood may clot in veins because of damage to the vein wall, poor blood flow, or abnormally thick blood. It is more common in women than men, and particularly in those taking the contraceptive pill. The vein affected is almost always in a leg, which becomes red, swollen, and painful. Treatment is with anticoagulants, especially heparin. In some cases, part of the clot breaks loose and travels to the lungs, where it obstructs the blood flow. This is called pulmonary embolus and is also treated with anticoagulants. If the clot is large enough to block the main pulmonary vessels, the condition can be fatal.

Varicose veins

Varicose veins also occur most commonly in the legs. They are dilated veins that form when the valves that normally control the pressure in the vessel are damaged. This may be due to obstruction of the veins during pregnancy, trauma, or gradual deterioration through aging. In the elderly, damaged veins may lead to the formation of varicose ulcers, especially around the ankles.

Treatment may be with elastic stockings, which help compress the vessels; with injections to thrombose small veins leading into the varicosed ones, in order to reduce the blood flow through them; or by surgical removal (stripping) of the affected vessels.

Heart diseases and disorders

Congestive heart failure occurs when the heart muscle cannot pump enough blood for the body's needs. This is usually caused by the gradual replacement of heart muscle tissue by fibrosis. The condition can be partially relieved by drugs, such as digitalis, which strengthen the remaining muscle fibers, and by diuretics, which reduce the accumulation of blood.

The rhythm of the heart may be abnormal in many ways. The most extreme occurs when

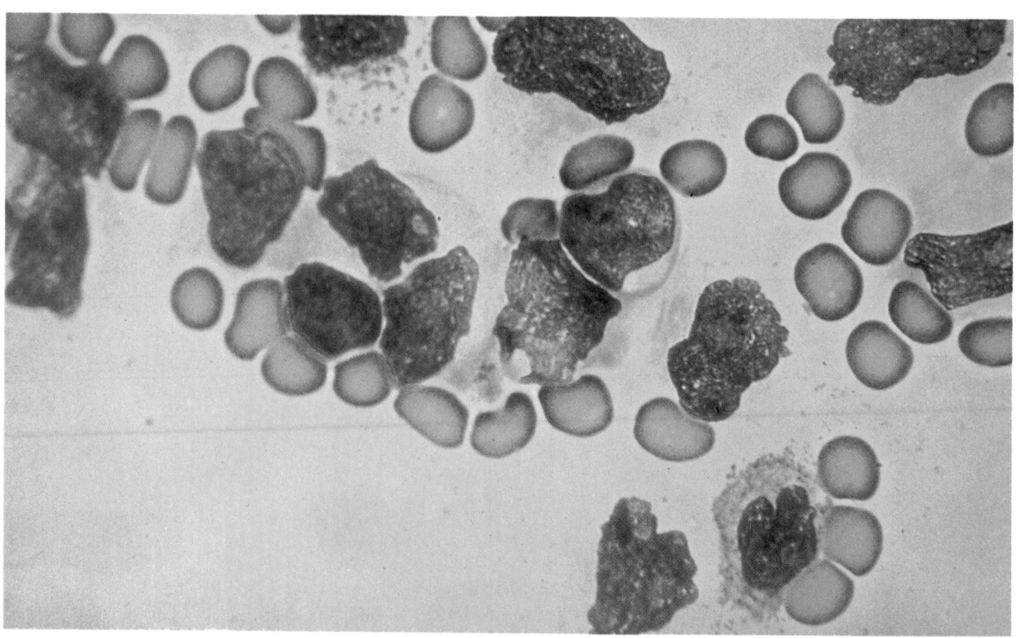

Fast-growing and malignant, leukemia cells are stained purple here so that they show up in a sample of blood from a patient with this pervasive form of cancer, which can spread through the circulatory system. There are various types of leukemia, most of which originate in the bone marrow and other blood-forming tissues. Some respond to chemotherapy using drugs that selectively destroy the cancerous cells. Exposure to radioactivity or X rays has been identified as a possible cause.

the muscle contracts in a completely uncoordinated way (fibrillation). The patient will die within minutes unless cardiac massage or electric shock (cardioversion) is applied. Pacemakers implanted surgically and a variety of drugs may control other arrhythmias.

Heart valves may be damaged by rheumatic fever or by a process similar to arteriosclerosis that affects them directly. In either case, the valve may become too small (stenosis) or leaky (regurgitant). Treatment is to replace the diseased valve with an artificial one by surgery. Some congenital abnormalities may also need surgical treatment.

Blood diseases and disorders

The red cells in the blood carry oxygen; a deficiency of red cells (anemia) produces symptoms such as fatigue and lethargy because insufficient oxygen reaches the tissues. Dietary deficiencies of iron, vitamin B_{12}, or folic acid are the commonest causes. Anemia is especially common during pregnancy, because the fetus uses the mother's reserves. It can also occur as a result of prolonged blood loss, commonly a result of a stomach ulcer or very heavy menstruation, or as a symptom of certain cancers of the digestive tract. Treatment is to replace the missing dietary factor or to treat the cause of blood loss.

An excess of red blood cells (polycythemia) makes the blood thicker than normal and therefore less able to flow through smaller blood vessels. The disease, particularly common in smokers, increases susceptibility to strokes, transient ischemic attacks, and venous thrombosis.

White blood cells are part of the body's defense mechanism and increase in number during infections. White-cell deficiency is rare, but is found in patients treated with cytotoxic drugs against cancer, or following adverse drug reactions. Abnormal white cell production occurs in leukemia, a form of cancer affecting white blood cells.

Infection of the blood is called septicemia, and generally spreads from a local infection such as an abscess or a wound. Treatment is with antibiotics.

Although blood required for transfusion is kept sterile, certain viral or viruslike infections are transmitted by transfused blood nevertheless. At least two types of hepatitis can be transmitted in this way. So can AIDS (acquired immune deficiency syndrome), which can also be transmitted by means of body fluids, such as semen. In AIDS, the balance of different types of white cells in the body is altered, leaving the individual susceptible to unusual infections and certain rare cancers.

Once very rare in America, malaria is now becoming more common as increasing numbers of people travel abroad. It is a blood disorder caused by a parasite that enters the blood from a mosquito bite. The parasite breeds in red blood cells, which then burst to release the offspring, causing symptoms of fever, shivering, and aches. Various drugs are used to prevent the disease but resistant forms are becoming more common.

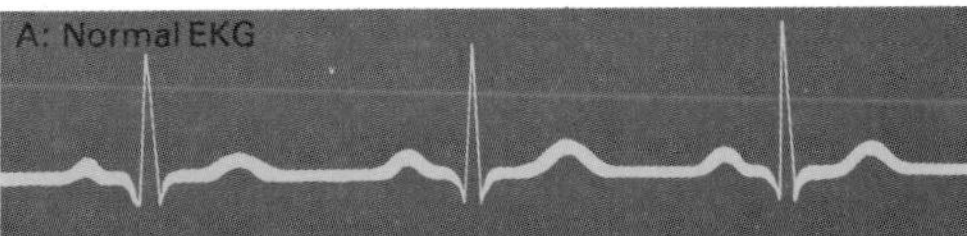

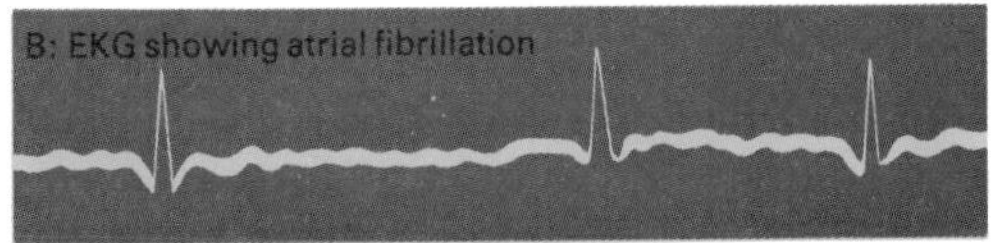

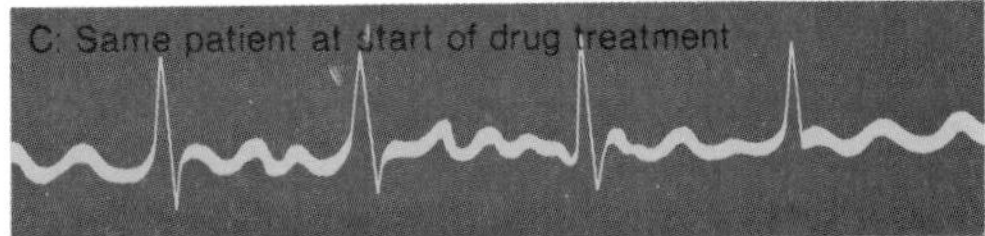

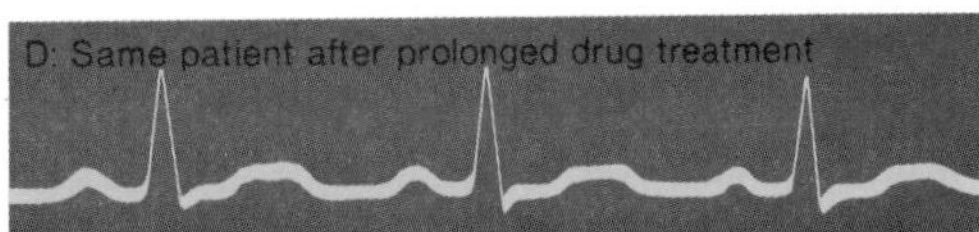

An electrocardiogram (EKG), generated as a graph by a chart recorder or displayed on a cathode-ray tube, is a simple, painless but extremely useful diagnostic device for a cardiologist. Its purpose is to record the electrical activity of the heart, which produces a characteristic trace on the EKG; the instrument above is monitoring the heartbeats of a premature baby. The four EKG traces illustrated *(left)* show (A) a normal heartbeat; (B) that of a patient with a fluttering beat (atrial fibrillation); (C) the same person's EKG after beginning drug treatment; and (D) after prolonged treatment, with a nearly normal EKG.

Fact entries

Leukemia is a cancer affecting white cells in blood or bone marrow. There are many different types, broadly categorized into acute and chronic forms. Probable causes include exposure to radiation, although no actual causes have been established.

Acute lymphoblastic leukemia is the commonest form of cancer in children. It responds well to chemotherapy and at least 50 per cent of cases are curable. Treatment always includes irradiation of the head and spine to kill tumor cells in the nervous system. If chemotherapy fails, bone marrow transplantation may be beneficial. Symptoms of acute lymphoblastic leukemia are high fever with a severe throat infection; there may also be nosebleeds, pain in the joints, lethargy, and increasing weakness.

Acute myeloid leukemia usually affects adults and is less responsive to chemotherapy than acute lymphoblastic leukemia. Bone marrow transplantation, aided by the drug cyclosporin A, is now an important treatment.

Chronic myeloid leukemia can occur at any time in adult life. The development of the disease is generally slow and controllable, though ultimately, in two out of three patients, this is followed by a rapid and fatal crisis.

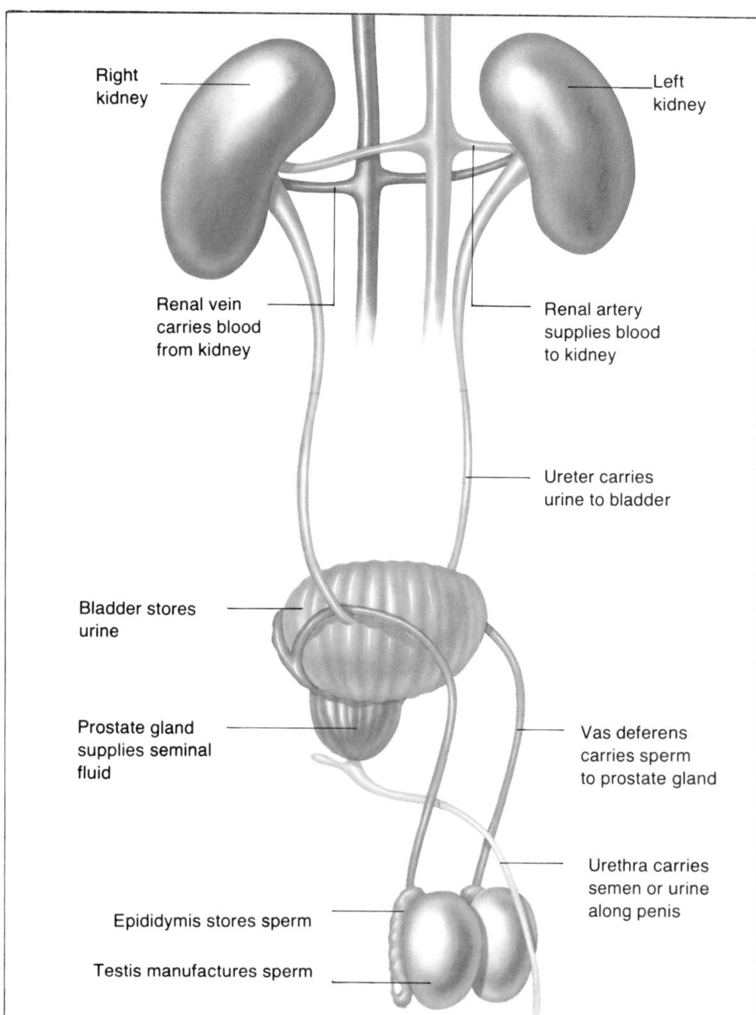

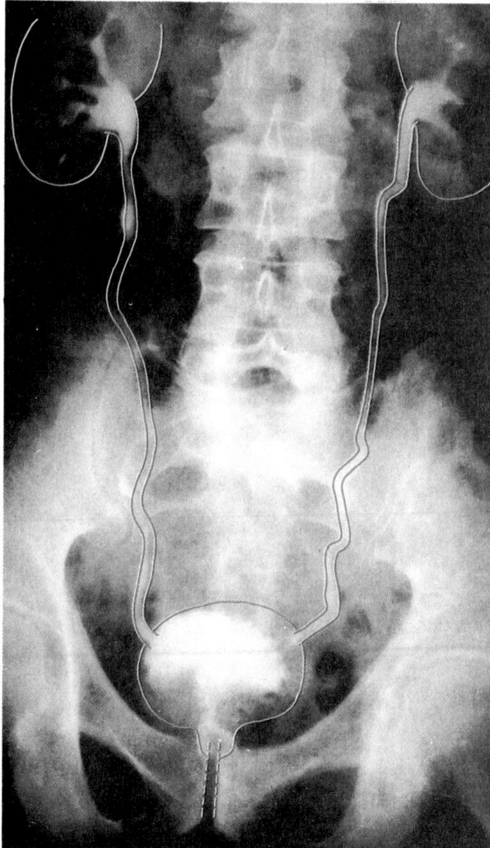

The male urinary system is more complicated than that of a female because of its conjunction below the bladder with the ducts that carry sperm and semen. In the photograph the system has been made opaque to X rays by injecting an iodine compound into the bloodstream. From where blood is filtered by the kidneys at the top, urine flows down the two ureters to be stored in the bladder. From there it should flow along the urethra, but this man has an enlarged prostate gland (immediately below the bladder) which constricts the urethra and blocks the passage of urine. The condition requires urgent treatment, which usually takes the form of surgery to remove the prostate.

Urogenital disorders

The urinary and reproductive systems develop in parallel in the fetus; the genitalia also have both reproductive and urinary functions. For these reasons, diseases of both systems are treated as urogenital disorders.

Kidney disorders

Kidneys may fail for many reasons, the commonest being complications of nephritis, infection, hypertension, and diabetes. Early diagnosis and treatment are important to prevent the development of renal failure. Infection is particularly common in children and pregnant women and must be treated vigorously with antibiotics.

Renal failure may be either acute or chronic. Acute renal failure is a temporary condition that can result from shock, poisoning, or infection. While the cause is being treated, the patient may need dialysis to remove toxic waste. Chronic renal failure requires regular dialysis with an artificial kidney machine or the surgical insertion of a donated transplant.

Stones (calculi) in the kidney may block the urine flow and cause acute pain. Their presence may be indicated by blood in the urine (hematuria). Stones can be removed from the kidney by surgery (lithectomy) or, once they move into the bladder, by crushing. Once done by physically using an endoscope, modern technology has now introduced lithotripsy, which shatters a calculus by focusing ultrasound on it from outside the body.

Renal insufficiency is usually investigated by ultrasonic scanning and by injecting a radiopaque substance such as iodine into the bloodstream. An X ray taken when the substance is passing through the kidneys reveals their internal silhouette and shows how well they are working. Dietary measures are important in the treatment of kidney disorders—particularly to limit the intake of water, salts, and protein. It is also important to treat hypertension, which may cause either renal failure or be caused by it.

Bladder disorders

Infection of the bladder is particularly likely to affect women, because the female urethra is short. The main symptoms of bladder inflammation (cystitis) are frequent and painful urination. Treatment involves drinking large quantities of fluid to flush out the bladder and following a course of antibiotics.

A particularly troublesome form of cystitis, often called "honeymoon cystitis," is caused by the bacteria introduced into the urethra during intercourse.

Bladder cancer is one of the best-documented examples of an environmental cause of cancer. The disease is much more common in petrochemical and rubber workers than in the rest of the population. It is also more common in cigarette smokers. The main symptom is blood in the urine (hematuria). Bladder cancer often takes a very slow course and may be controlled for years if monitored by regular cystoscopic examinations.

Prostate disorders

Enlargement (hyperplasia) of the prostate is part of the male aging process. Surgical treatment may be required if the enlarged gland prevents the normal passage of urine.

Cancer of the prostate, which is common among elderly men, is now generally treated by the oral administration of estrogen, combined with surgery as necessary. Treatment may alter the body's hormonal balance but effectively prohibits further cancerous growth.

Sexually transmitted disease (STD)

STD, or venereal disease (VD), describes a large and diverse group of disorders with little in common except the way in which they are spread and the parts of the body affected. Increased sexual freedom over the past 50 years has led to an increase of the three major forms: nonspecific urethritis, gonorrhea, and syphilis.

Nonspecific urethritis (NSU) is an infection caused by a variety of organisms. One increasingly common form (chlamydia) is smaller than a bacterium, but larger than a virus. The disease causes pain on urination and, in men, a discharge from the penis. It may be difficult to treat because it does not always respond to antibiotics.

The main symptoms of gonorrhea are genital irritation and discharge. Treatment is with antibiotics, although resistant strains of the infection are an increasing problem.

Gonorrhea and NSU often produce no symptoms in women, so contact tracing is important both for their treatment and to prevent further spread.

Syphilis is a more serious disease, with a number of specific stages; the first is a sort of ulcer (a chancre), and the last can affect all parts of the body and may cause death. In the early stages, the development of the disease may be prevented by the use of antibiotics, normally penicillin.

Two other diseases associated with sexual intercourse—though neither is exclusively transmitted by this means—are herpes and acquired immune deficiency syndrome (AIDS).

Herpes is caused by a virus almost identical to the one that causes cold sores, *Herpes simplex.* In both cold sores and genital herpes, the symptoms—small painful blisters at the affected site—appear periodically, and are difficult to treat definitively, although some new antiviral drugs seem to show signs of being successful.

AIDS is a condition that occurs particularly among bisexuals, intravenous drug users, and homosexual men and appears to be spread by blood and body fluids such as semen. In AIDS, the body's defense mechanisms are destroyed so that other infections and certain cancers find no natural resistance. At present, there is no consistently successful form of treatment.

STD's affect homosexuals as readily as heterosexuals, although the lesions occur in different places. Both AIDS and hepatitis B can be transmitted as STD's by homosexuals, although neither is exclusively a sexually transmitted disease.

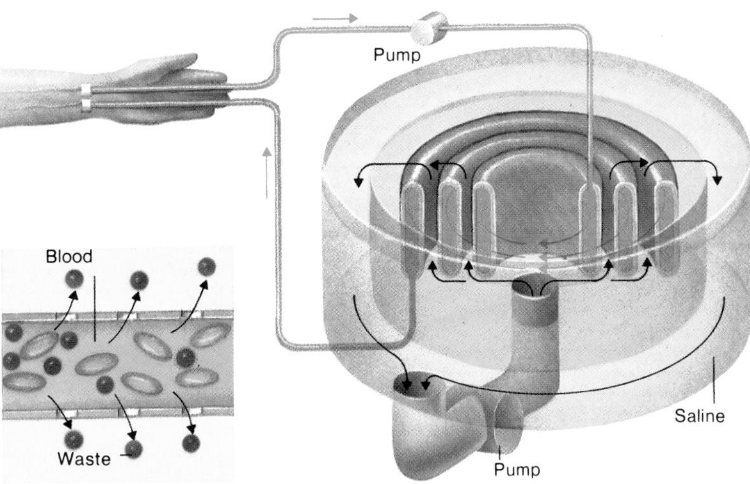

A dialysis machine removes waste products from a patient's blood and so acts as an artificial kidney. In this design, blood from an artery is pumped through a coil of thin plastic membrane, which is bathed in a saline fluid. The waste materials pass through microscopic holes in the membrane, and the "cleaned" blood returns to the patient via a vein.

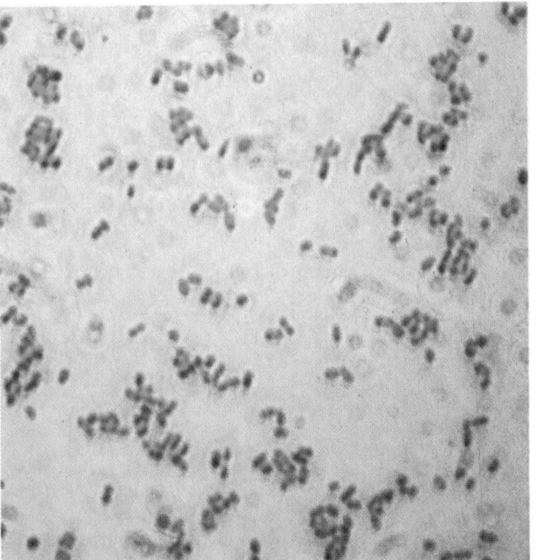

Gonorrhea is a highly infectious disease transmitted by sexual contact. It is caused by the gonococcus bacterium *Neisseria gonorrhoeae,* shown stained red in this photograph. It responds to prompt treatment with antibiotic drugs, but may remain undetected in females, in whom it produces few symptoms. Untreated, it can lead to sterility, and blindness in babies born to an infected mother.

Fact entries

Renal failure, if complete, is fatal unless treated either by artificial dialysis or by transplantation of a healthy kidney from a donor.

A kidney dialysis machine washes toxic substances from the body by bringing a chemical solution (dialysate) into close contact with body fluids so that excretory products pass from the latter into the former. There are two types of dialysis. In hemodialysis, blood is diverted from the body through a machine (artificial kidney), which contains dialyzing fluid separated from the blood by a membrane that acts as a filter. Excretory products cross this membrane and are removed. In peritoneal dialysis, the dialysate is washed in and out of the peritoneal cavity.

Transplantation is the surgical insertion of a kidney donated by another person. The tissue types of the donor must be matched with those of the recipient as closely as possible, and drugs given after the transplant to prevent the donated kidney from being rejected by the recipient's immune system. Such immunosuppressive treatment may have to be continued for several years after transplantation, until the patient may be advised that rejection has become extremely unlikely.

Obstetrics and gynecology

Obstetrics is the branch of medicine concerned with pregnancy and childbirth. Because most pregnancies are not problematic, the main role of an obstetrician is to monitor the progress of mother and fetus and to assist at the birth. Gynecology is concerned with treatment of disorders of the female sex and reproductive organs.

Gynecological disorders

Abnormalities of the menstrual cycle include amenorrhea (absence of periods); dysmenorrhea (painful periods); menorrhagia (heavy bleeding); irregular periods; and premenstrual syndrome (PMS), also known as premenstrual tension (PMT).

A pelvic examination reveals most abnormalities of vagina, uterus, and ovaries. Blood tests reveal hormonal abnormalities. In some cases, an operation called dilatation and curettage (D and C) is performed under general anesthetic: the cervix is dilated and scrapings of the womb lining are taken for examination to detect any abnormalities, such as tumor, fibroids, or polyps. Polyps can be removed in the same operation.

A hysterectomy (surgical removal of the uterus) may be performed if the womb is the site of a cancerous growth, if fibroids (benign tumors) are growing in the uterine muscle, or to treat otherwise uncontrollably heavy periods.

Cancer of the cervix of the uterus is among the easiest neoplasm (tumor) to detect, by means of a cervical smear test. This involves examining microscopic cells scraped from the cervix for precancerous cells. If present, precancerous tissue can be removed—in some operations the affected site is cauterized using a laser—to prevent its development into malignant cancerous tissue.

The commonest malignant tumor in women affects the breast. Usually breast cancer is first evident as a small, hard, painless lump. To treat it, the lump and the surrounding tissue must be removed. In certain cases, this extends to removal of the whole breast (mastectomy). Because the spread of the disease can be rapid and extensive, surgery may be followed by drug and radiation therapy. Eighty per cent of women in whom the disease is treated early are perfectly well five years after treatment. Cysts are another common cause of breast lumps. These are harmless, but must be distinguished from potentially dangerous growths by medical examination.

Infertility

Male infertility is usually caused by absent or decreased numbers of sperm in the semen, or by abnormalities in the sperm. Infertility in a woman may be hormonal or physical. The most common cause of the latter occurs if the Fallopian tubes are scarred or blocked, usually as a result of infection, which prevents the ovum passing to the uterus. Polyps or fibroids in the womb may also cause infertility by preventing implantation. The use of "fertility drugs," which stimulate ovulation, may cure infertility. Alternatively, some cases of infertility

A common complication of pregnancy is a breech birth (A), in which the baby is born buttocks first, rather than head first. About 1 in 80 pregnancies results in twins, of which there are two types. In identical, or maternal, twins (B and *right*) both babies derive from a single egg and share the same placenta in the mother's womb. Nonidentical, or fraternal, twins (C) originate from two separate eggs and each has its own placenta. Nearly all twins are born normally.

A

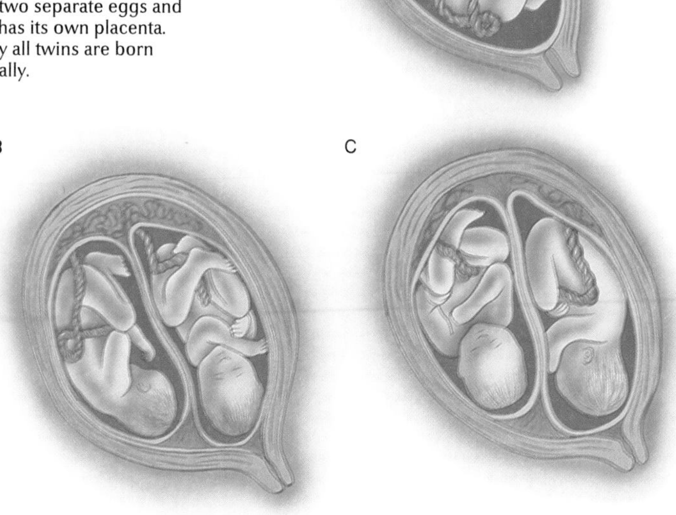

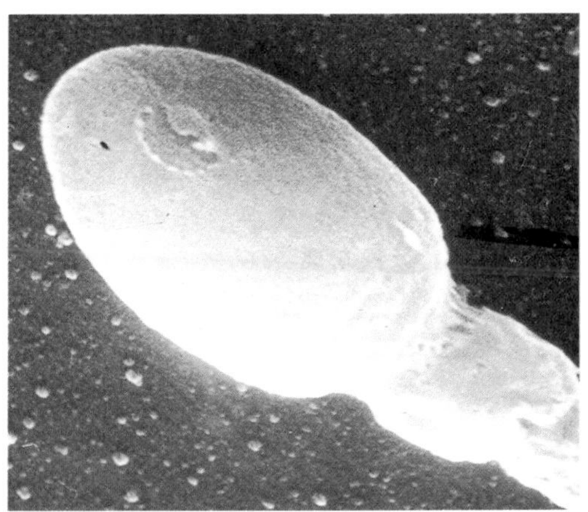

Infertility is a problem that faces many couples who want to have children. Usually it is caused by faulty ovulation or imbalances in the complex cycle of hormonal changes in the woman. It can also occur if the man produces dead, unhealthy, or insufficient sperm. These two photographs show a healthy *(left)* and an unhealthy sperm.

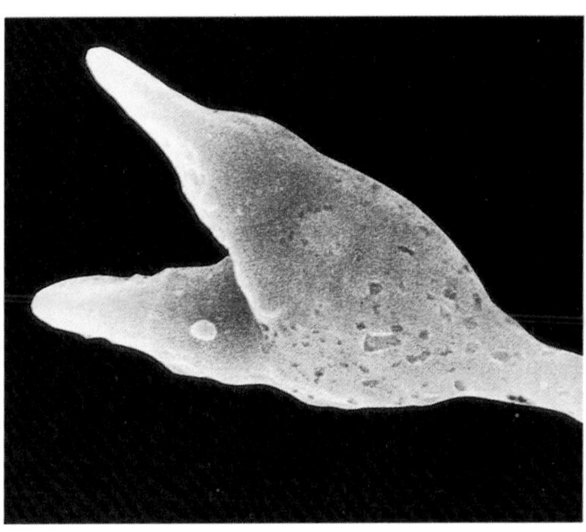

can be treated by removing an ovum and fertilizing it outside the body, then implanting it when the developing embryo is viable. This is the technique described popularly as creating "test-tube babies."

Prenatal screening

During pregnancy, regular visits to a prenatal clinic monitor weight gain, blood pressure, and ankle edema (swelling). Urine is tested for sugar, which may indicate diabetes, and for protein, which may suggest infection or pre-eclampsia. The top of the uterus (fundal height) is regularly checked against the expected size, and if there is a rapid increase, an examination using ultrasound may detect twins or an excess of fluid. This technique is harmless to mother and baby.

Blood is tested for Rhesus factor incompatibility and immunity to various viral infections, including rubella (German measles). The latter is ordinarily a mild infection, but if a woman contracts it in the first four months of pregnancy, fetal abnormalities, such as deafness or blindness, can occur. Further monitoring includes tests for anemia and syphilis. A test for the presence of alphafetoprotein is usually also carried out to detect spina bifida. Amniocentesis—in which a small amount of amniotic fluid is taken from the sac surrounding the fetus—may be carried out whether or not there are signs of fetal abnormality. Cells in the fluid may indicate the possibility of hemolytic disease (from an untreated Rhesus negative mother), and chromosomal abnormalities such as Down's syndrome (mongolism).

Other aspects of pregnancy

Iron and folate tablets are commonly prescribed for the mother, but other drugs should not be taken without medical supervision. Sometimes a miscarriage (spontaneous abortion) occurs for no apparent reason, although it may be a reaction to fetal abnormality or placental insufficiency.

An ectopic pregnancy occurs when a fertilized ovum implants outside the uterus, usually in a Fallopian tube. At about 10 weeks, the tube ruptures and an emergency operation must be performed.

Complications of childbirth

During labor, the child is at risk from hypoxia (shortage of oxygen), and the baby's heart rate is usually monitored to assess this risk. If there is severe fetal distress, or for certain other reasons, such as a misplaced placenta, or if the mother is ill, a Caesarean section may be performed as an emergency. In this, an incision is made in the abdomen and the baby is delivered through the lower section of the womb. Fortunately, however, such complications are rare.

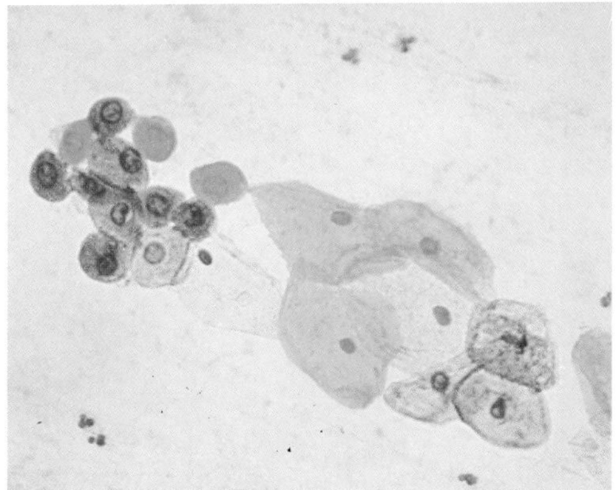

A cervical smear test to detect the possible presence of precancerous cells is carried out on a sample of tissue from the neck of the womb. The cells in the sample are stained and examined using a microscope; a healthy sample has the appearance shown here. The presence of abnormal but precancerous cells allows the physician to begin treatment—with drugs or minor surgery—before the onset of a malignant cancer.

Fact entries

Rhesus factor incompatibility occurs if a woman with Rhesus negative (Rh−) blood with a Rhesus positive (Rh+) partner conceives a Rh+ baby. In this circumstance, the mother's blood creates antibodies to kill the alien red blood cells that enter the bloodstream across the placenta toward the end of the pregnancy. No problem affects the first Rh+ child, but if another Rh+ child is conceived, maternal antibodies crossing into the fetal blood react against fetal blood cells and destroy them, causing hemolytic disease. To prevent this happening, antibodies are injected immediately after the first child is born, so that these antibodies destroy any fetal Rh+ blood cells before the mother can produce antibodies of her own.

Preeclampsia is a complication of pregnancy in which the mother's body retains fluid. The cause is unknown. If unchecked, it can lead to the death of the fetus. Treatment consists of bed rest and diuretics. If ineffective, labor is generally induced.

Gastrointestinal and liver disorders

Most of the gastrointestinal tract is packed in the abdomen like convoluted plumbing. For clarity, it has been separated and extended in the diagram *(below right)*.

In present-day Western society, diet and the consumption of alcohol are the commonest direct or indirect causes of most disorders of the gastrointestinal tract and the liver. Almost all gastrointestinal infections are acquired in this way, as are some forms of hepatitis.

The esophagus, stomach, and duodenum

Many disorders of the upper gastrointestinal tract are caused by acids produced by the stomach in abnormal amounts or locations. These disorders often share a common symptom: a burning pain in the lower chest (heartburn).

Duodenal ulcers are thought to be at least partly caused by excess acid. They and stomach ulcers may require surgery, especially if erosion reaches an artery and causes hemorrhage. Cancer of the stomach is becoming less common in the U.S., possibly due to changes in diet. Surgical removal provides the only possibility of cure, but unfortunately this cancer has often spread by the time symptoms appear.

Virus infections and the bacterial contamination of food cause inflammation of the stomach and small intestine (gastritis). Symptoms include vomiting and diarrhea, both of which are urgent attempts by the body to expel the noxious agent. Serious bacterial infections include cholera, typhoid, and some forms of dysentery, which are treated with antibiotics. Dehydration due to fluid loss and nonabsorption of fluids by the inflamed intestines must also be treated, sometimes by an intravenous saline drip. Drugs—which the gastrointestinal tract may not be able to absorb in these diseases—are sometimes administered intravenously too.

Celiac disease is an abnormal reaction to the protein gluten, present in wheat; individuals affected have to follow a strict diet avoiding all wheat and wheat-flour products.

Intestinal disorders

Disorders affecting the intestines usually cause either diarrhea, constipation, or failure to absorb nutrients such as vitamins and iron, although a low-fiber diet (such as one low in fresh vegetables) may also be a cause of constipation.

Appendicitis occurs when inflammation develops in the wormlike appendix. Treatment is by surgical removal of the appendix, which is usually necessary to prevent it from bursting and so contaminating the membrane that lines

Hepatitis B, which results in inflammation of the liver and symptoms of jaundice, is caused by a virus, shown here in a false-color electron micrograph. It is highly infectious and is spread by various means, including contaminated hypodermic needles and saliva.

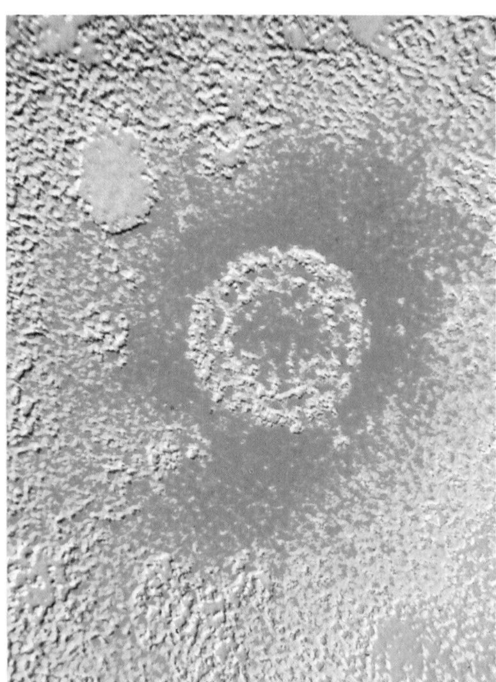

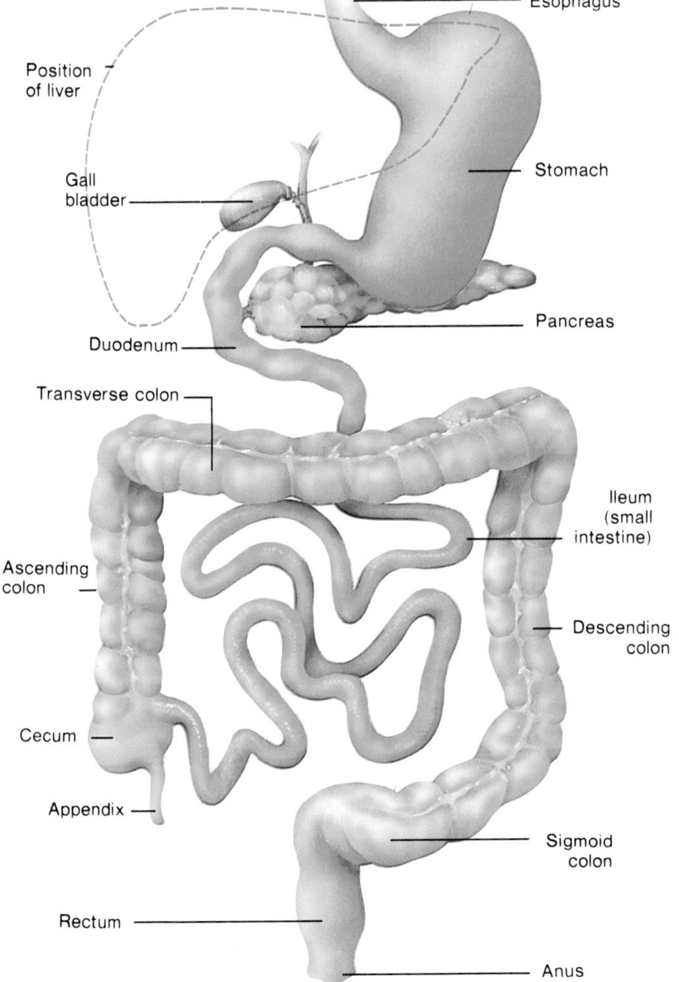

The whole digestive tract *(right)* from esophagus to rectum is susceptible to various disorders, particularly inflammation, resulting in such disorders as gastritis, appendicitis, and colitis. Ulceration and tumors are more serious conditions that can affect the tract.

the abdominal cavity and other abdominal organs.

Crohn's disease and ulcerative colitis are conditions in which parts of the bowel become inflamed and ulcerated. The cause is unknown. Symptoms such as cramping pain and severe diarrhea are treated with drugs, but occasionally surgery is necessary. Irritable bowel syndrome (spastic colon) produces the same symptoms without organic disease.

Hemorrhoids (piles) are dilated veins in the wall of the rectum and anal canal. These may descend through the anus and become trapped there. They are strongly associated with constipation. If the disorder becomes persistent, thrombosing the dilated vein (blocking it, entirely sealing it off) by injection may relieve the symptoms. Surgery may be required. Cancer of the lower bowel (colon and rectum) is common, but can be cured if the growth is removed in its early stages. In some cases, this treatment requires an artificial opening (colostomy) to be made from the colon through the abdominal wall.

The pancreas and gall bladder

These organs produce and store digestive enzymes and bile required for the digestion of fats. The commonest disorder of the pancreas affects the endocrine cells secreting insulin and glucagon, and causes a type of diabetes that is treated as a specialized glandular disorder. Abnormalities in the bile result in gallstones, which in turn may cause inflammation of the gall bladder. The symptoms (abdominal pain and flatulence) are worse after fatty meals. If gallstones block the flow of pancreatic secretions, the pancreas may become inflamed, causing pancreatitis. This can also occur as a result of alcohol abuse. If cancer affects the pancreas, it is usually fatal.

Liver disorders

The liver converts nutrients absorbed from the gastrointestinal tract into products the tissues can use and excretes breakdown products in bile. Any disorder interfering with bile production or excretion may cause jaundice.

At least three major types of viral hepatitis are known. Hepatitis A virus is contracted through contaminated water or food, and the disease is normally self-limiting. Hepatitis B virus and non-A/non-B virus are transmitted in blood or body fluids; they present a small risk of rapid and fatal liver failure, and also a slightly greater risk of persistent infection, which may lead to liver degeneration over several years. Hepatitis may result from alcohol abuse or, rarely, is a complication of drug treatment. Vaccines against hepatitis B virus are also becoming available. Protection against hepatitis B virus, which is particularly common in the tropics, can be achieved by injections of immune globulin, although the effect is only temporary.

Cirrhosis of the liver—in which nodules form on areas of the liver already affected by fibrosis—is generally progressive and results in eventual death, unless the cause can be eliminated. A major cause is alcoholism; others are chronic viral hepatitis and some autoimmune disorders.

Liver cancer is rare in Europe, except in patients with cirrhosis, but is very common in countries where many people suffer chronic hepatitis B infection. The close link between the virus and liver cancer makes possible the prevention of the latter by immunization against hepatitis B.

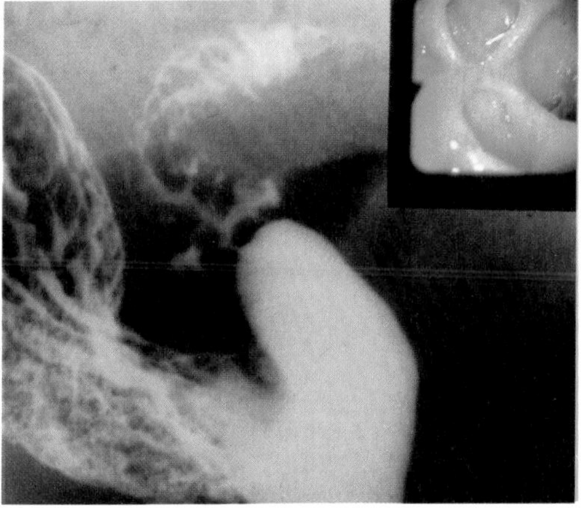

X-ray photography and endoscopy *(see diagram below)* are important diagnostic techniques for examining the gastrointestinal tract. The barium-meal X ray *(left)* and endoscope photograph *(inset)* show fibrosis in the duodenum.

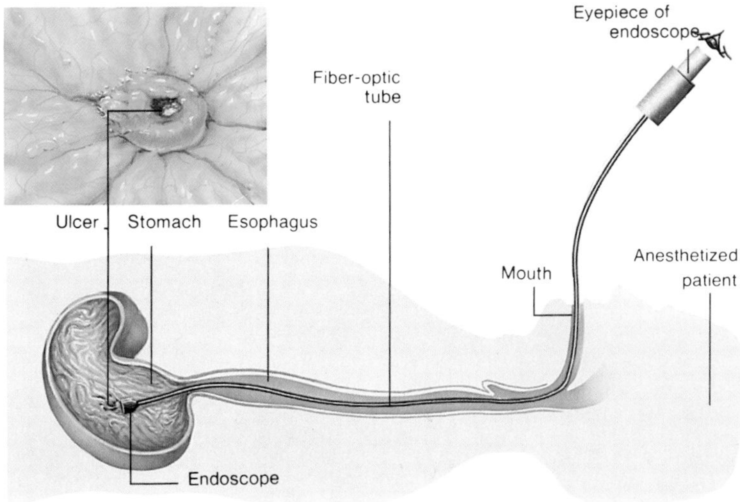

Endoscopy allows a physician to observe directly internal parts of the body—in this illustration an ulcer in the stomach—without cutting through external layers. In some cases, endoscopic surgery can also be performed or tissue samples taken using minute instruments attached to the head of the endoscope.

Fact entries

Jaundice is the yellow coloration of the skin and eyes, which is a common symptom of liver or gall bladder disorders. It is caused by the accumulation in the blood of the yellow bile pigment called bilirubin, which is produced by the liver as one of the products of metabolism. Obstructive jaundice is usually caused by stones in the biliary system or cancer of the pancreas and is treated by removal of the cause, normally by surgery. Hepatocellular jaundice is generally due to a virus infection or an adverse reaction to a drug.

Yellow fever is an acute, infectious, potentially fatal tropical disease that takes its name from the symptoms of jaundice it produces. The disease is caused by a virus transmitted by mosquitoes. Symptoms include fever, vomiting, and hemorrhages, in addition to jaundice. Treatment concentrates on preventing death from dehydration as the disease runs its course. Yellow fever can be prevented by vaccination with a mild form of the virus; protection lasts for ten years. Such immunization is not advised for pregnant women.

Bone, joint, and muscle disorders

Bones and muscles give the body its strength and shape; with joints, they also allow the body to move. Disorders affecting them are usually treated by an orthopedic specialist, though other specialties, such as neurology for neuromuscular disorders, rheumatology for joints, physiotherapy to aid recovery, and alternative treatments, such as osteopathy, may also be used.

Fractures and dislocations

The commonest bone, joint, and muscle disorders are fractures, dislocations, and sprains. In most cases, they are relatively easy to treat, although complications can occur.

Dislocation occurs when the bones at a joint are separated or violently misaligned. Muscles, ligaments, and tendons can be stretched or torn in a dislocation, as well as in injuries such as sprains, where dislocation does not occur.

In all fractures and dislocations, the first treatment is to reset ("reduce") the broken bone or the misaligned joint so that all elements are correctly repositioned. This can be checked by means of X rays. The affected parts are then immobilized while bones, tendons, and ligaments mend. Fractures are usually immobilized by splints, bandages, or plaster of Paris casts. Traction—a way of gently keeping an affected limb extended, using a balanced system of pulleys and weights—may also help to maintain the straightness of a reset bone. In certain cases, internal support is provided by fixing metal pins or plates to the bone. This has the advantage of allowing muscles to be used again as soon as possible, which is important for their healing. Sometimes the pins or plates are removed again at a later date. Some fractures are slow to heal and may be helped by the application of mild electric current to the fractured site. Ultrasound may also be used to speed healing of traumatic damage. It is not known why these last two treatments are effective, however.

Other bone disorders

Bone diseases are uncommon, because bone tissue is well protected from primary infections and because degenerative and deficiency disorders are rare in Western countries.

If bone becomes infected, the most likely disease is osteomyelitis, a bacterial infection of the actual substance of the bone. The infection usually enters through an open fracture or through the bloodstream. The disease most commonly attacks the ends of the long bones of the arm or leg, and is especially likely to affect children. Prompt treatment with antibiotics is almost always effective. Tuberculosis of the bone is a special form of osteomyelitis. It can affect any bone tissue but often involves the spine.

In older people, and especially in women, the bones become more brittle in a disorder called osteoporosis. Hormonal factors—causing bone calcium levels to be reduced—or some deficiency in dietary intake may contribute to the condition, and hormone, vitamin, or calcium supplements may be prescribed in treatment.

A lack of vitamin D, normally obtained in the diet or made by the skin in response to sunlight, disrupts calcium and phosphorus metabolism and causes the bone disease called rickets in children or osteomalacia in adults. It is now rare in developed countries. Treatment consists of adding vitamin D to the diet.

Although a variety of bone tumors occur, statistically they are rare. More commonly, bone cancers result from the spread of cancer cells from elsewhere in the body to form secondary tumors in bones. Of primary bone tumors, the form called an osteosarcoma is most

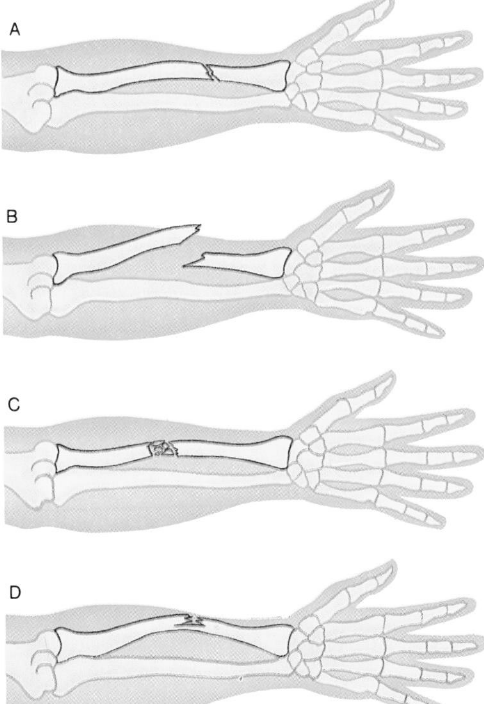

Broken bones are the most frequent condition treated by an orthopedic surgeon. The most common types include (A) a simple or closed fracture; (B) a compound or open fracture, in which the broken bone punctures the skin; (C) a comminuted fracture, in which the bone at the site of the break is in several fragments; and (D) a greenstick fracture, common in children, in which the bone bends and breaks on one side only. Broken limb bones are usually set and kept in a plaster of Paris cast while they heal.

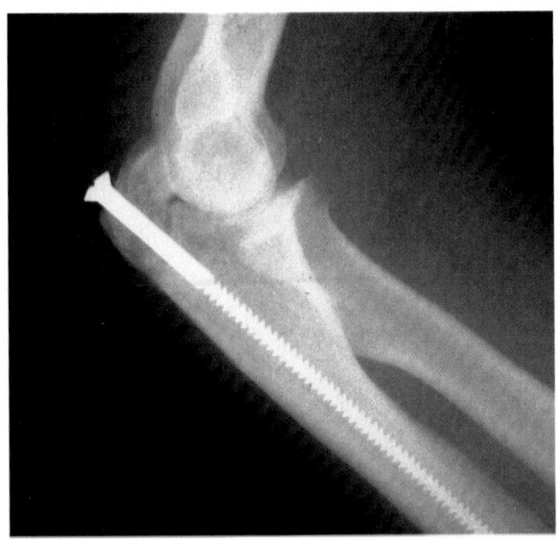

Awkward fractures may require special orthopedic techniques *(far right)*. Here, a broken olecranon bone at the elbow has been fixed back into position with a long metal pin. More sophisticated techniques include the total replacement of a joint, such as the hip or knee, with a metal or plastic substitute.

feared. Commonly occurring in young adults, this requires radical treatment involving drugs, irradiation, or even amputation to prevent its spread.

Disorders of the joints and muscles

Clubfoot, muscular dystrophy, and congenital hip dislocation are all disorders present at birth. Clubfoot, caused by muscular anomalies, can be treated by splinting, physiotherapy or, in some cases, surgery to lengthen tendons that are too short. Muscular dystrophies form a group of inherited, progressive diseases that inhibit muscle function. They affect men more often than women. Congenitally dislocated hips can be treated with splints if diagnosed early enough.

Arthritis is the most common joint disorder. The term—meaning joint inflammation—is applied to rheumatoid arthritis, osteoarthritis, and infective arthritis.

Rheumatoid arthritis is a chronic inflammation of the joints, especially the small ones in the hands and feet. The cause is unknown but may be due to an autoimmune reaction or to an unidentified infection. Symptomatic relief may be achieved with heat treatment, but usually anti-inflammatory drugs such as aspirin are required. Steroids may be necessary in very severe cases. If the disease progresses to permanent joint destruction, the damaged bone ends can be removed and replaced by artificial joints, restoring movements to an otherwise uselessly stiff or deformed hand. Physiotherapy works well in less severe cases.

Osteoarthritis is a degenerative disorder that tends to affect the elderly, usually in the larger joints, such as those of the hip and spine; it may also affect younger patients after trauma.

Treatment for all forms of arthritis involves the use of drugs such as aspirin, which helps to relieve pain and reduce inflammation. In severe cases, surgery may be necessary—for example, to replace an osteoarthritic hip.

Backache is probably the single most common source of discomfort in Western countries. Causes range from minor muscle or ligament strain to serious problems, such as a slipped disk (properly known as a herniated or prolapsed intervertebral disk) or secondary deposits of cancer. Serious disorders may need surgical correction to prevent permanent damage to the spinal cord and nerves. Less dangerous causes of backache can be relieved by relaxation, ultrasound treatment, acupuncture, or osteopathy (spinal manipulation). Since a significant component of pain is psychological, any therapy that concentrates on providing mental relaxation is also likely to relieve symptoms.

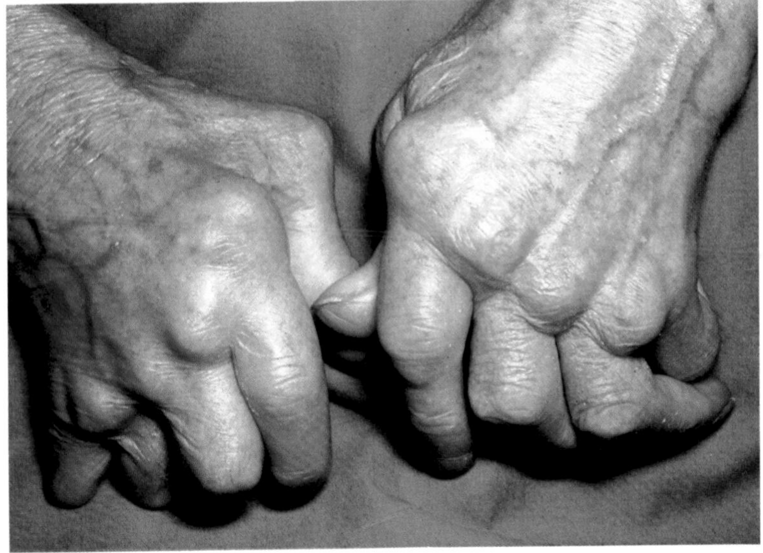

Rheumatoid arthritis is a degenerative disorder of the joints often accompanied by inflammation and swelling.

Artificial limbs

Some amputated limbs can be repaired using microsurgical techniques to re-implant severed muscles, ligaments, blood vessels, and nerves. In other cases, it is necessary to replace a limb with an artificial one (prosthesis). The simplest (such as the traditional wooden leg) provide balance but little else. More sophisticated prostheses aim to replace the limb's function, and some now available have all the appearance of normal flesh. Furthermore, recent advances in microelectronics make it possible to build artificial hands that respond to the nerve impulses and muscle contractions of the remaining forearm, facilitating movements such as grasping.

Types of muscular dystrophy

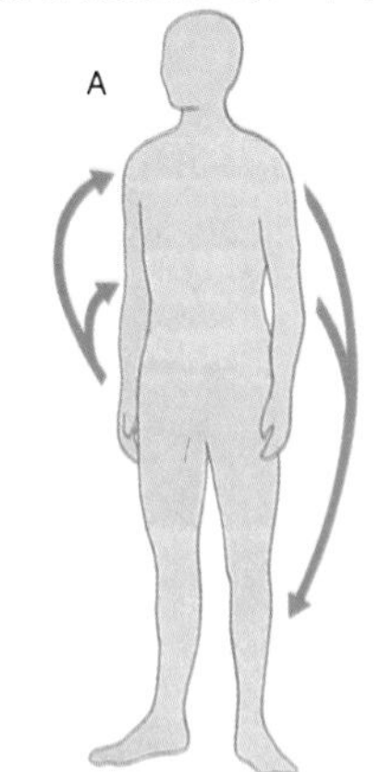

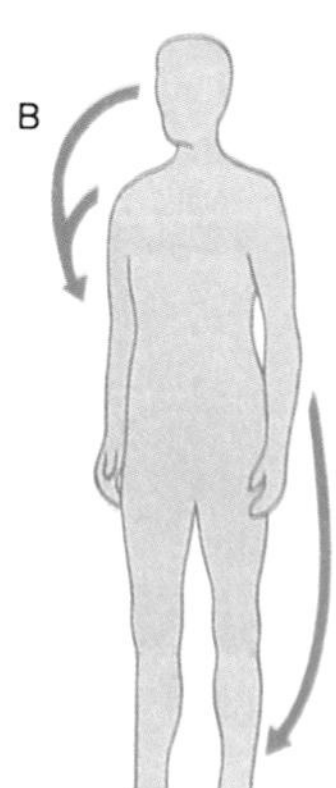

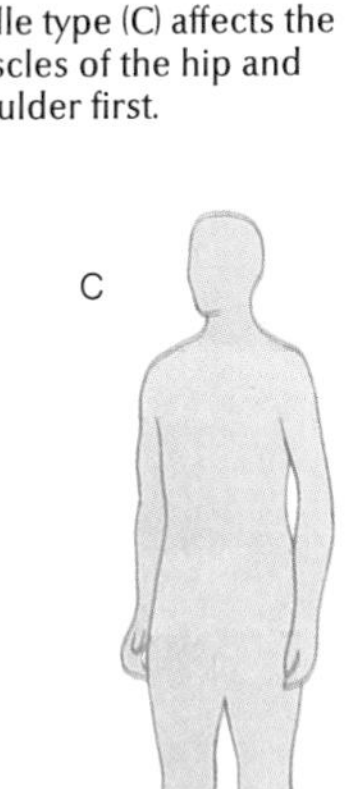

Muscular dystrophy involves progressive degeneration of the muscles. The Duchenne type (A) affects the pelvis first, then the trunk, shoulders, and limbs. The facio-scapulo-humeral type (B) progresses from the face and shoulders to the trunk and limbs. The limb-girdle type (C) affects the muscles of the hip and shoulder first.

Fact entries

Fractures are of various types. Complete breaks can be straight across the bone (transverse fracture), at an angle (oblique fracture), or twisted (spiral fracture). If the bone breaks or splinters with more than one fracture line, it is called a comminuted fracture. And an injury that bends the bone without breaking right through it is called a greenstick fracture. This is particularly likely to affect the pliable bones of children. In a hairline fracture, a bone cracks without breaking completely. A bone may also be indented or crushed. When a bone breaks, the sharp, broken edge may damage nearby tissues, particularly nerves or blood vessels, and when this occurs, it is described as a complicated fracture. It may, alternatively, pierce the skin, in which case it is called a compound fracture. Or it may be forced into another bone, which creates an impacted fracture. Usually, however, none of these occurs, and the commonest fractures are called simple, or closed.

Glandular disorders

Type I (juvenile) diabetes mellitus is caused by the failure of endocrine cells in the pancreas to produce insulin. The pancreas also produces digestive juices, which pour into the duodenum through the pancreatic duct, but between the groups of cells (acini) that produce the pancreatic juice are groups of hormone-producing cells. The groups of cells are called the islets of Langerhans. Alpha islet cells produce glucagon, which is involved in the breakdown of glycogen and so in raising blood glucose levels. Beta islet cells produce insulin, which is needed for the metabolism of glucose. If insufficient or no insulin is produced, glucose levels rise and the symptoms of diabetes mellitus result.

Glands are organs, or collections of cells, which manufacture chemical compounds essential to the body's functioning. There are two kinds—the ductless, or endocrine glands, which release hormones directly into the bloodstream, and the exocrine glands, which release their secretions via ducts or tubes to a particular part of the body, such as the hair, skin, eyes, or alimentary canal.

There are countless exocrine glands throughout the body, from the mucosal glands of the nose to the digestive glands of the alimentary canal and the sweat glands of the skin. There are also several larger, complete collections of exocrine glands—the salivary glands, the thymus, the pancreas, and the prostate among them. The ones most commonly affected by illness are the salivary glands, for example in mumps, which primarily affects the parotid gland, and the prostate, a gland found at the base of the bladder in men that can become inflamed, particularly in older adults.

There are six main endocrine glands—the pituitary, thyroid, parathyroid, pancreas, adrenal, and sex glands (ovaries or testes)—and the term glandular disorders refers most commonly to these.

Pituitary disorders

The activity of several endocrine glands is controlled by the pituitary gland. Specifically, the anterior pituitary gland, stimulated by the hypothalamus, produces trophic hormones that act upon the thyroid gland, adrenal glands, and sex glands. It also produces the growth hormones.

Overproduction of growth hormones may cause gigantism or acromegaly (enlargement and distortion of the bones); underproduction may result in dwarfism, or restricted growth. Excessive secretion of the hormone adrenocorticotropin (ACTH) affects the adrenal glands, causing excessive steroid production. This may cause disorders such as Cushing's syndrome, which is characterized by abnormal fat deposits, high blood pressure, wasting of the muscles, fullness of the face, and various abnormalities of the body chemistry.

Panhypopituitarism, or overall loss of anterior pituitary function—usually the result of a tumor, a cyst, or necrosis of the gland—will be followed by failure of all glands under anterior pituitary control. It can be treated by substitution of the various hormones produced by the target glands.

The posterior pituitary gland produces antidiuretic hormone (ADH), which is responsible for maintaining the correct water balance in the body. Deficiency results in diabetes insipidus. This rare disorder is characterized by the production of excessive, extremely dilute urine, with corresponding dehydration and thirst.

Diabetes

Diabetes mellitus, or sugar diabetes, is the most common endocrine disorder. There are two major types. Type I (juvenile type) is due to deficient insulin production; Type II (Matu-

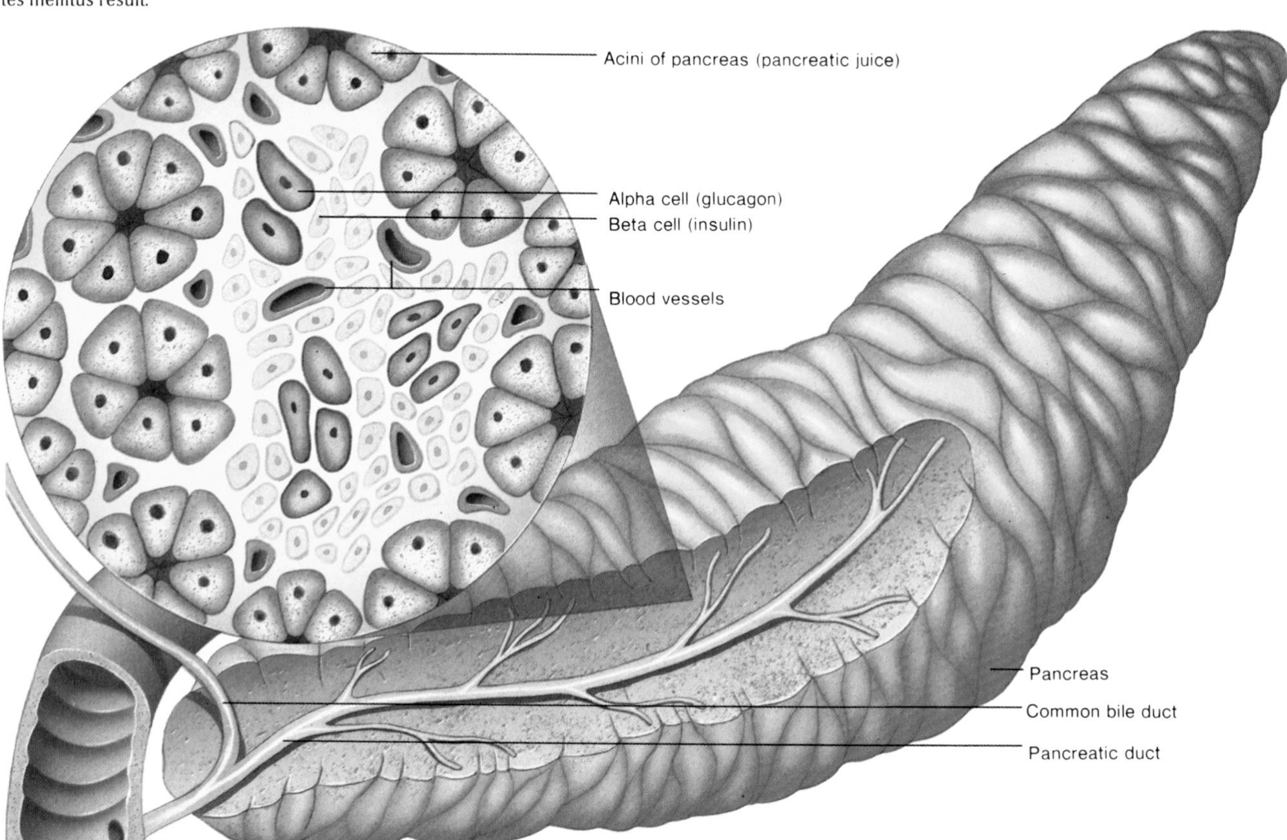

rity onset) is usually due to insensitivity of the body to normal levels of insulin. Insulin itself is produced by clumps of cells called the islets of Langerhans situated within the pancreas. If they fail to produce insulin, the body cannot make proper use of sugar and starch in the diet. Instead of being used by the body to produce energy, glucose and other sugars accumulate in the blood and are excreted as waste in urine. This is associated with severe thirst and weight loss, while the high blood sugar level encourages infection. If untreated, diabetes can produce a number of other symptoms, such as drowsiness, and can lead eventually to coma and cardiac failure.

Diabetes is a common disorder, affecting some two per cent of the population. All diabetics need treatment to reduce the sugar content of their blood and urine and reduce the risk of associated disorders, such as cataracts or arteriosclerosis. Type II diabetes can sometimes be treated by a special diet or by tablets taken orally. Type I diabetes is usually treated only by daily injections of insulin, combined with a controlled diet.

Overproduction of insulin, in contrast, is quite rare and is caused by an insulinoma, or insulin-producing tumor, of the pancreas.

Thyroid disorders

The thyroid gland affects the metabolism of practically all the body tissues. It is unique among the glands in that it requires iodine obtained from the diet to make its principal hormone, thyroxine, in a process controlled by the pituitary. Healthy thyroid function therefore requires an adequate supply of iodine, a normal pituitary gland, and normal pathways of hormone synthesis and release from the thyroid.

Hyperthyroidism, or excessive production of thyroid hormones, also known as thyrotoxicosis, or Graves' disease, may be caused by a benign tumor (adenoma). More commonly, it is a result of an overactive thyroid. Symptoms include weight loss, flushed skin, thirst, tension, and anxiety. Body processes speed up, the thyroid enlarges, and the eyes protrude. Treatment may involve drugs or surgical removal of part of the thyroid.

Hypothyroidism (thyroid deficiency) may develop for a number of reasons, or it may be congenital. Once known as cretinism, the congenital form occurs when a child is born with a deficient thyroid or with no thyroid at all. Or it may develop in adulthood if the pituitary ceases to function normally. Most commonly, the thyroid is attacked by an autoimmune process that slowly destroys the gland and so causes hormone levels to drop, leading to progressive illness. Thyroid deficiency produces a low metabolic rate, giving symptoms such as fatigue, lethargy, depression, slurred speech, and a changed physical appearance as the skin becomes dry and puffy, and the weight increases. Treatment depends on early diagnosis and involves replacement doses of thyroxine.

An enlarged thyroid is known as a goiter. It may be caused by iodine deficiency or excessive production by the pituitary of thyroid-stimulating hormone (TSH).

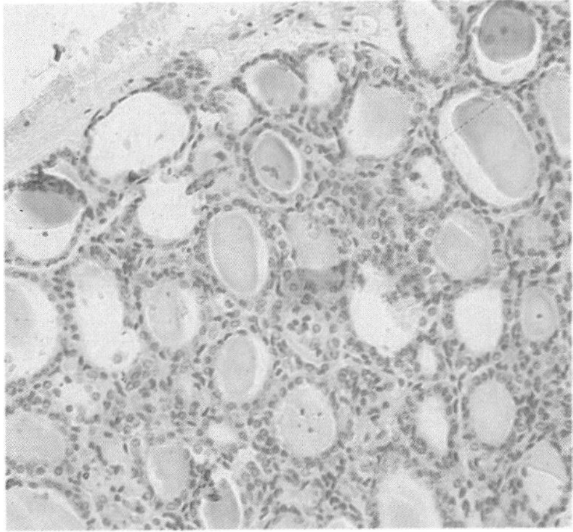

The thyroid gland contains cells that produce thyroxine, which collects in follicles between the cells. This microscopic section of thyroid tissue shows normal cells and follicles.

Goiter is a glandular disorder in which the thyroid gland, situated at the front of the neck, is abnormally enlarged.

Mumps *(below)* is an infection of the salivary glands, particularly the parotid gland, which causes them to swell. The salivary glands are paired, one of each pair being on either side of the face. All secrete salivary juices into the mouth cavity.

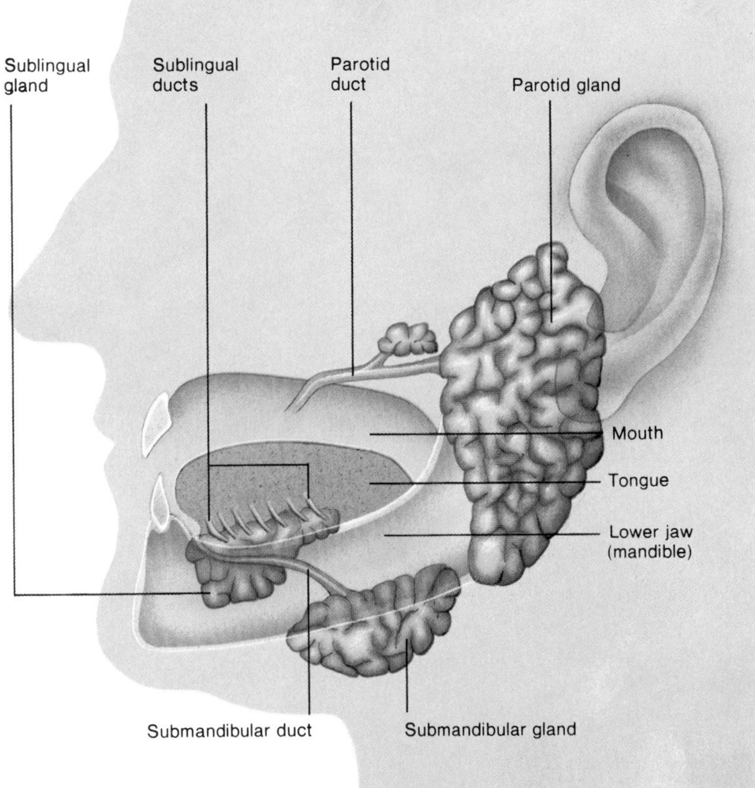

Ophthalmics

The eyes are complex and delicate organs. They have their own external and internal muscles to move the eyeball and change the shape of the lens, and they are supplied by several cranial nerves—the optic nerve for sight, and the oculomotor, trochlear, and abducens nerves for eye movement. They also make use of several specialized types of tissue, notably in the cornea, lens, and retina.

We rely on good eyesight for most of our waking lives. It is the primary sense for perception of events and is important in almost all physical coordination. For most people, even a slight problem with their sight can cause considerable irritation or distress—although in fact it is also true that people adapt to small defects remarkably quickly.

Some babies are born with minor eyesight disorders, such as color blindness (which is hereditary) or a squint (strabismus). The former cannot be cured but the latter can usually be corrected by an operation. Other defects develop through later life, and by about the age of 40 or 50, many adults need to wear corrective lenses for some minor or major problem concerning their eyes.

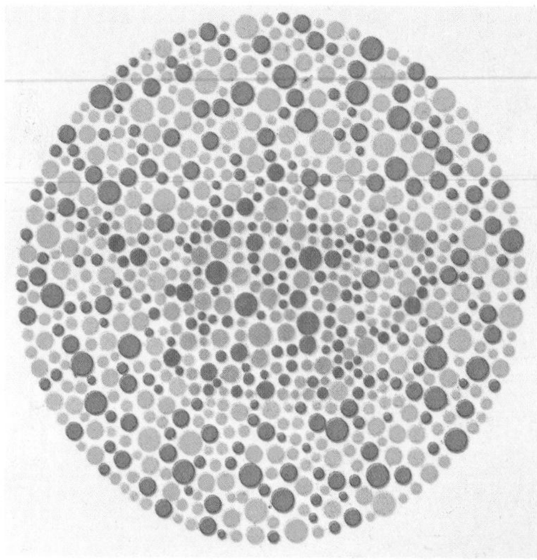

Color blindness can be assessed by a series of tests, one of which is a confusion chart, shown here. Under controlled lighting, a person with normal color vision sees a teapot in the pattern of dots. A person with color-defective vision sees only a cup.

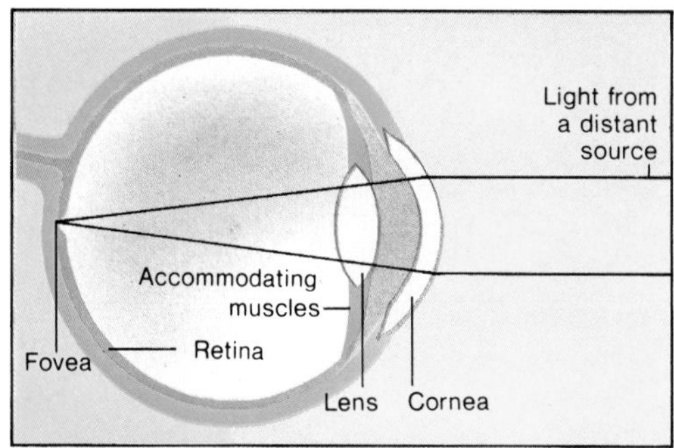

Normal eyes focus light from a distant source precisely on to the fovea of the retina.

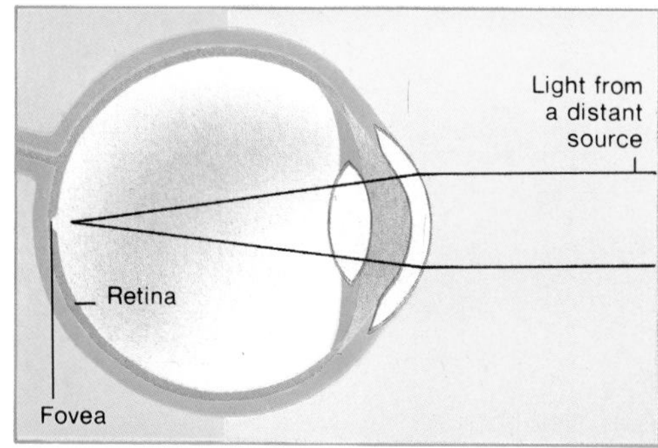

Nearsighted (myopic) eyes cannot focus light precisely from a distant source because the focal point is in front of the retina. They can focus light from a near source, however. The eyeball of a nearsighted person is slightly elongated.

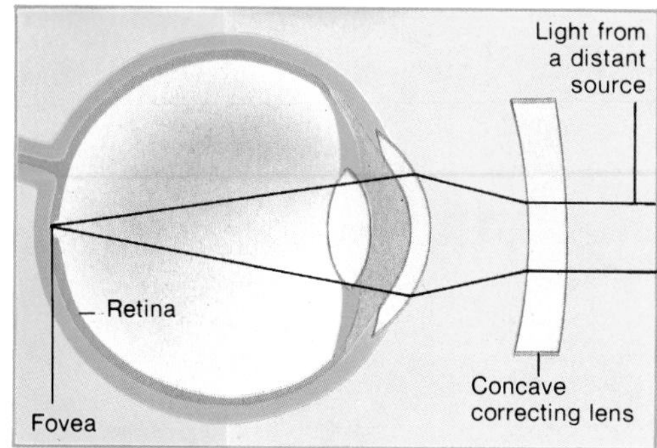

Correction of nearsightedness requires a concave (diverging) lens to be placed between a distant light source and the eye.

Focusing problems

The most common eyesight defects involve a difficulty in focusing on objects sharply. Myopia (nearsightedness) occurs when the eyeball is elongated from front to back. Instead of forming precisely on the fovea of the retina, focal images form slightly in front of it, causing distant objects to appear blurred. Near objects, however, can be seen distinctly.

Hyperopia (farsightedness) is the opposite problem. In this condition, the eyeball is shorter than normal from front to back. The focal point of images is beyond the retina, so near objects appear blurred, whereas distant objects can be seen clearly.

Presbyopia is an age-related disorder in which the lens of the eye gradually loses some of its elasticity, making focusing more difficult.

Astigmatism is a condition in which the cornea, at the front of the eyeball, is unevenly curved. Images are slightly distorted in particular regions, because some of the incoming rays of light are bent more than others.

All these focusing defects can tire and strain the eyes, because the eyes adjust constantly in an attempt to refocus and correct the problem. Eyestrain and headaches are common symptoms of focusing problems that need treatment.

Other eyesight problems

Many other difficulties, not related to focusing, can also affect the eyesight. Problems occasionally occur with the retina of the eye, for example, if it becomes partly or completely detached from the underlying tissue, perhaps as a result of an accident. This damage can repair itself in some cases, but in others must be repaired by surgery. Techniques using a laser to fix the retina back in place are used increasingly in this operation.

A cataract is a disorder in which the lens of the eye gradually becomes more and more opaque, eventually causing almost total loss of detailed vision. Surgery can often provide effective treatment of this disorder, especially cryosurgery, in which the lens is frozen so that the cataract can be removed. The disorder may also require the lens to be removed totally, in which case artificial lenses must be worn after the operation to compensate for the loss of the natural lens.

Other conditions that can affect the eyesight include migraine headaches, which often produce blurred, narrowed, or distorted vision; albinism, an inherited condition in which the normal pigment of the eye is missing (often associated with photophobia, an excessive sensitivity to light); glaucoma, when increased pressure within the eyeball causes objects to appear slightly blurred, as if they have halos around them (this can permanently damage the optic nerve if untreated); and color blindness, or color-deficient vision, an inherited disorder affecting roughly 8 per cent of men and 5 per cent of women, which is characterized by an inability—to a greater or lesser degree—to identify one or more of the primary colors. Some infections, such as conjunctivitis, can also have an adverse effect on eyesight.

Testing the sight

Problems such as defective vision, a squint, or color blindness are noticed most often in childhood. Accurate diagnosis of these and other defects usually requires a full eye test with an optician or ophthalmologist, who tests each eye separately to see if it has any focusing problems. The eyes are also examined with an ophthalmoscope for any possible damage to the retina. The patient is asked whether he or she feels any strain, headaches, or pain associated with the eyesight, in normal or unusual light conditions. The ophthalmologist then tries several different sample lenses in front of each eye to see which one produces the sharpest image. From these experiments, most eyesight disorders can be identified, and corrective lenses can be prescribed.

Corrective lenses

Corrective lenses can be worn either as glasses or as contact lenses. Glasses can be more comfortable to wear because the lenses do not come into contact with the eyes; they also carry less risk of infection. In addition, bifocal or trifocal lenses can be fitted in glasses to avoid the need to use different lenses for different activities.

Contact lenses give a more accurate image of objects, however, because they work closer to the natural eye lens than do glasses. They also tend to be preferred by people who find glasses embarrassing or inconvenient. New users have to accustom themselves gradually to wearing contact lenses all day, because at first they feel like any other foreign body in the eye; however, once they are in place, accustomed wearers find them almost unnoticeable.

Many types of contact lenses are made: some are small and hard and have to be taken out before sleeping; others are large and soft and can be left in at night. All types have to be cleaned regularly and scrupulously. The ophthalmologist usually gives advice on the best kind of lenses to suit an individual's needs, preferences, and life style.

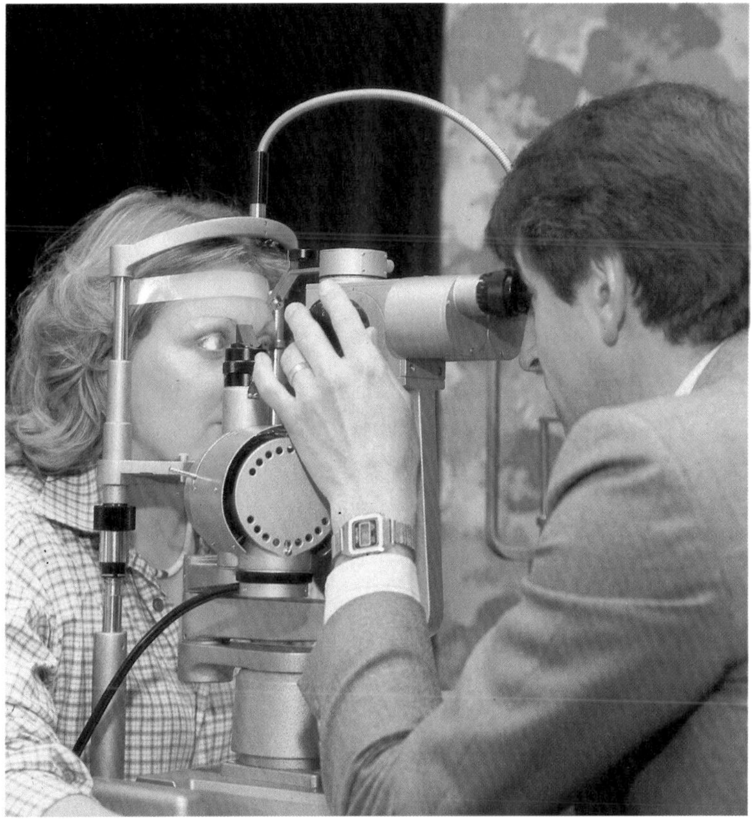

An ophthalmoscope is used by an optician or ophthalmologist to examine the eyes during an eye test.

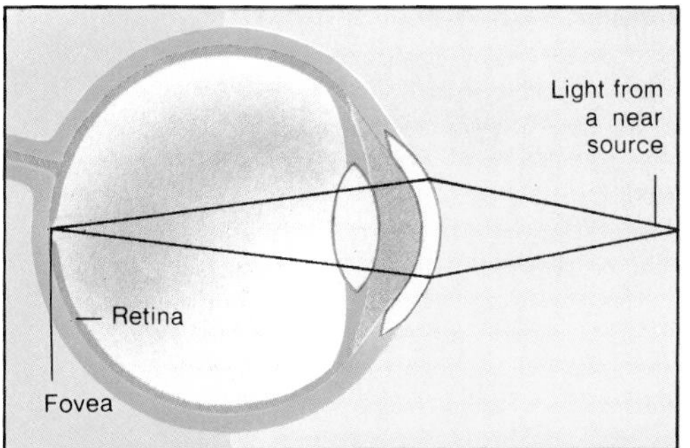

Normal eyes focus light from a nearby source onto the fovea by changing the shape of the lens.

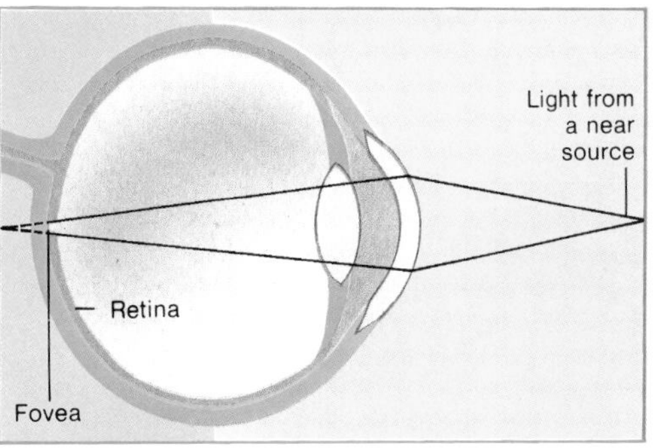

Farsighted (hyperopic) eyes can focus light from a distant source but cannot focus light from a near source, because the focal point of the latter is behind the retina. The eyeball of a farsighted person is slightly shortened.

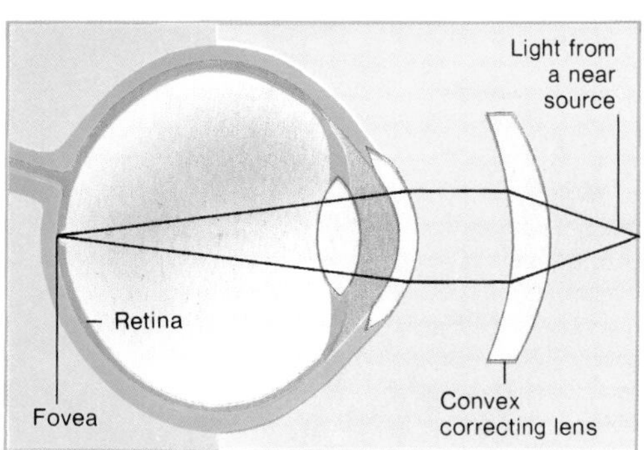

Correction of farsightedness requires a convex (converging) lens to be placed between the nearby light source and the eye.

Dentistry

Dental caries (decay) and gum disease are among the most common disorders of developed societies, and research shows that poor dental hygiene is the prime factor in tooth decay.

Techniques of dentistry are becoming more and more sophisticated, but prevention is both better and cheaper than cure. Habits that encourage good dental hygiene, from attention to diet to regular brushing of the teeth, improve the likelihood of retaining healthy teeth—particularly if these habits are taught to children as the first permanent teeth emerge at about the age of seven.

The teeth

The growth of the 20 first teeth, or milk teeth, begins when a baby is in the womb. Calcium for the formation of the baby's bones and teeth is taken from the mother's own supply, so if her diet contains insufficient calcium, the baby's requirements may cause the condition of her own teeth to deteriorate.

Generally, the milk teeth begin to emerge from the gums at about six months after birth, first the front teeth, then those at the sides and the back. Gradually through childhood, these teeth are replaced by a set of 32 permanent teeth. The permanent molars do not replace primary teeth; they erupt into spaces provided by the growth of the jaw. The back molars, known as the wisdom teeth, are the last to emerge.

Each tooth consists of a crown (the visible part) and the root, which anchors it in sockets in the jaw. A tooth consists mainly of hard dentin. The crown is coated with even harder enamel, while the root is covered with cementum to help anchor it in the jaw. Inside each tooth is a cavity full of pulp, carrying nerves and the tooth's blood and lymph supply. Decay usually begins at the enamel and eats through the dentin to the pulp. When decay reaches the pulp, pain and inflammation follow, and the tooth may die.

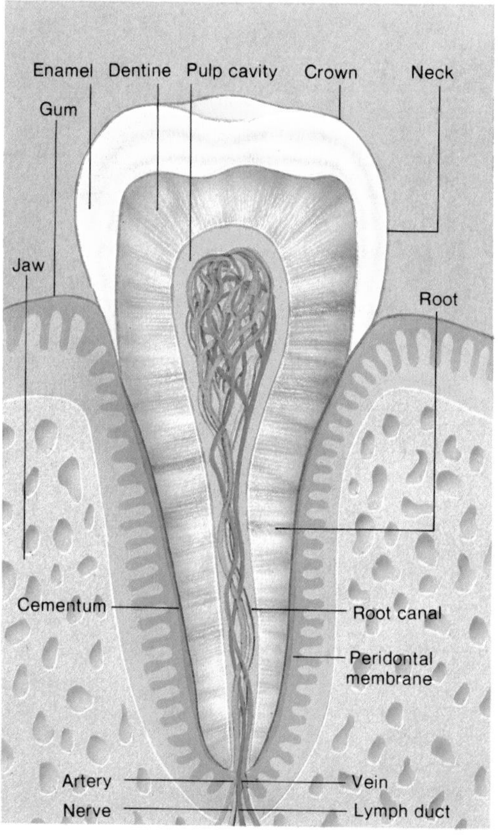

A tooth consists mainly of hard dentin, which is covered on the tooth's crown and neck by even harder enamel. At the center of a tooth is the pulp cavity, which contains the tooth's blood, nerve, and lymph supply. The root of a tooth, covered by cementum, is embedded in a socket in the jaw. The peridontal membrane, an extension of the gum, lies between the cementum and the bone.

Treating decay

Decay is caused by the corrosive action of the acid in plaque, a sticky substance that forms from minute food particles and adheres to the enamel surface of the teeth. The first step in treating early decay is to drill out the decayed matter and to replace it with a hard substance (filling) so that decay does not recur.

The usual technique is to create a clean cavity with a high-speed drill, then to fill this cavity with amalgam (a mixture of silver, tin, copper, zinc, and mercury) in the back teeth, or a white resin for the front teeth. Each cavity is first lined with an insulating material to protect the sensitive pulp from temperature changes that are easily transmitted by the metallic amalgam. If the decay has reached the pulp, the pulp cavity can be cleaned out and then filled with a sterile substance to save the tooth. This is called root canal therapy. Badly decayed teeth, once they have been repaired, can be capped (rebuilt) with gold or porcelain crowns to restore the tooth's function and aesthetics. Cosmetic dentistry can also be done to change teeth that are damaged or discolored.

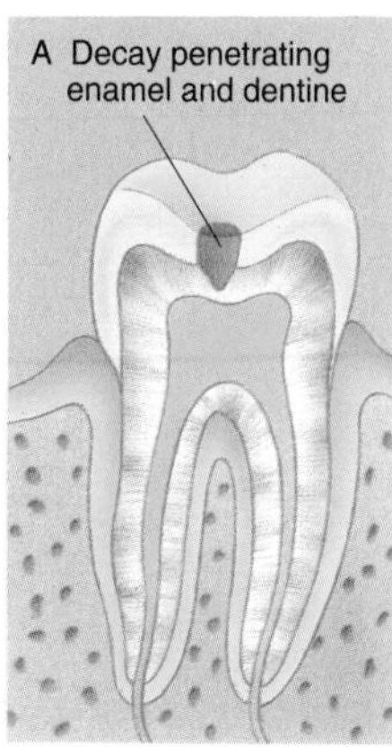

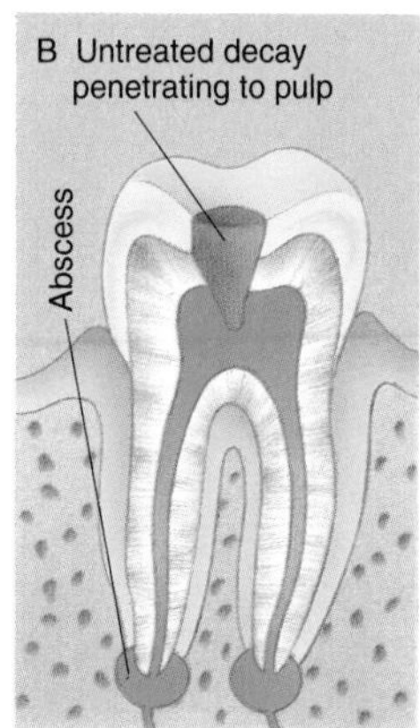

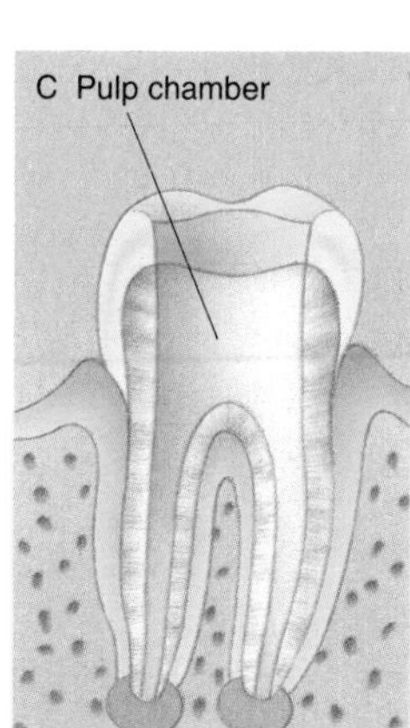

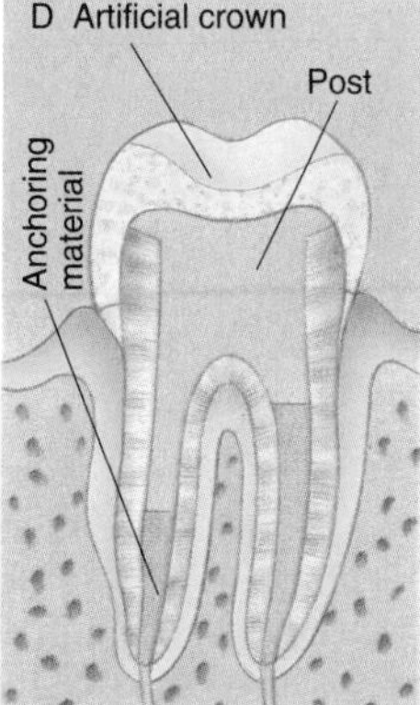

Tooth decay usually starts (A) at the chewing surface. Abscess and inflammation of pulp (B) occur if initial decay is not prevented and the pulp is penetrated. The tooth must then be treated with root canal therapy (C) in which the pulp is removed and the pulp chamber is cleaned and smoothed. Insertion of anchoring material and a post into the treated tooth (D) may then be necessary to hold the artificial crown in place.

This is done using bonding, plastic or porcelain facings, or crowns.

Extraction

Badly decayed teeth can cause extremely painful abscesses in the gums; if root canal therapy is not indicated, the tooth may need to be removed to cure the abscess. But extraction may be necessary even when the teeth are healthy. The usual reason for this is overcrowding in the mouth. Wisdom teeth that do not emerge normally should also be removed to allow the other teeth to grow properly. Extractions can be done under local anesthesia, which blocks the nerves of the teeth and jaw, or under general anesthesia, which causes temporary unconsciousness.

Replacement teeth

False teeth can be made to fill the gaps left by an extraction. A single tooth can be screwed into the jaw (implant) or attached to adjacent teeth (fixed bridge). Two or more teeth can be attached to a plastic or metal or plastic plate which fits in the mouth (partial removable denture). A full set of false teeth (full denture) is fabricated to fit the interior of the mouth.

Orthodontics

Orthodontics is the branch of dentistry that is involved in correcting faults in the positioning of the teeth. Many people's permanent teeth emerge crooked or too crowded, often looking unsightly and also making good dental hygiene difficult.

Some teeth may need to be removed in order to reduce overcrowding in a growing jaw. If this is done, the remaining teeth can then be repositioned gradually with the aid of an adjustable brace, which is either clipped over the teeth or cemented temporarily to their surfaces. A child's teeth can also be pushed out of alignment by habits such as constant thumbsucking or chewing on pencils. In such cases, the habit needs to be stopped before the orthodontic treatment can be effective.

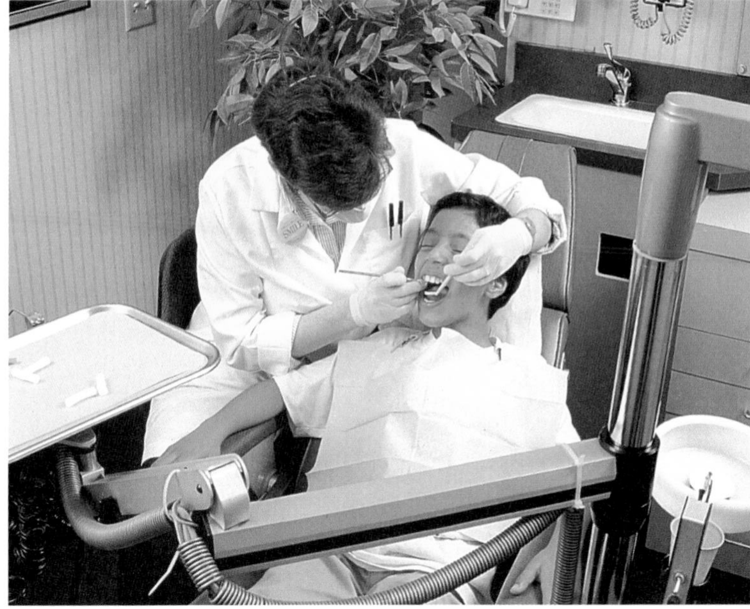

Dental care from an early age helps to ensure that the teeth remain healthy throughout a person's lifetime.

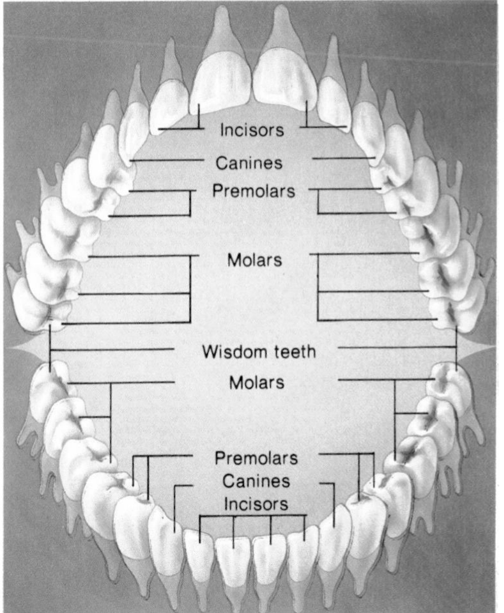

An adult's mouth contains 32 teeth, 16 in the upper jaw and 16 in the lower jaw. The rear molars are also known as wisdom teeth.

Preventive measures

The importance of the prevention of decay is constantly emphasized by dentists. Plaque is formed most readily by sticky, sugary food particles, so it can be minimized by avoiding excess sugar in the diet, and also by avoiding snacks between meals. Cleaning the teeth thoroughly after every meal, using a good-quality brush and proper brushing technique, is also advised by dentists. Dental floss should be used for cleaning between the teeth. Also, some public health authorities add fluoride to the water supplies because it helps reduce the occurrence of tooth decay.

Regular visits to the dentist are essential, so that the teeth can be cleaned and polished, any decay can be detected at the earliest opportunity, and specific advice can be given if necessary. Some dentists also use fissure sealants to smooth out the cracks where plaque can lodge.

AIDS

In the 1980's the AIDS virus became a great medical concern. To eliminate the transmission of the HIV virus, dentists and other health professionals adopted the use of barrier techniques. The use of masks, gloves, and glasses has become common. Also sterilization procedures have become more rigorous. There will certainly be more changes in the future as better methods for infection control are developed.

Nervous system and skin disorders

Herpes simplex virus, shown here in an electron micrograph, causes cold sores, watery blisters that affect the lips. A similar virus, *Herpes zoster,* attacks nerve endings in the skin, causing the acutely painful disorder called shingles.

The brain, central nervous system (CNS), and autonomic nervous system control most body functions. The skin is the body's largest sensory organ and is supplied with local pain and temperature receptors as well as parasympathetic fibers to hair follicles, sweat glands, and blood vessels.

The brain and spinal cord

In order to function, the brain must be supplied with blood. If this supply ceases because of a blood clot (thrombus) blocking a vessel, a stroke occurs. The symptoms may include partial paralysis, numbness, or loss of speech. After a stroke, these usually diminish gradually as other areas of the brain take over some functions of the damaged part. Factors that increase the likelihood of a stroke are constriction in a blood vessel (atheroma), high blood pressure, heart disease, and shock.

Investigation of any brain damage is essential after a stroke. Modern technology utilizes angiograms, ultrasound, and computerized axial tomography (CAT scans, involving computer-enhanced X-ray photography); treatment varies according to the diagnosis. Where muscles and coordination are affected, physiotherapy is almost always necessary.

Symptoms resembling those of a stroke may be caused by accidents to the head, particularly if there is any bleeding in or around the brain. The most obvious symptom is loss of consciousness, though whether this occurs or not, more profound symptoms—loss of memory, disorientation, fainting attacks, and speech or motor defects—may occur later, even after apparent recovery.

The second most common neurological disease is epilepsy, caused by abnormal electrical activity in the brain. Symptoms vary in character and severity and can include twitching, hallucinations, unconsciousness, and convulsions. Treatment is normally by drugs, though these control symptoms rather than cure the condition.

Spinal nerves are susceptible to damage if the bone or cartilage surrounding them shifts awkwardly. This occurs in a herniated disk, in which a damaged intervertebral cartilage disk presses on a spinal nerve. If the sciatic nerve is so trapped, this causes sciatica.

Infections of the brain or spinal cord, such as meningitis or encephalitis, which affect the protective covering membranes (meninges) or the brain itself, are extremely dangerous. Treatment is with antibiotics and must be both rapid and vigorous, as both conditions can cause long-term damage and may be fatal. Poliomyelitis is a virus infection that affects the

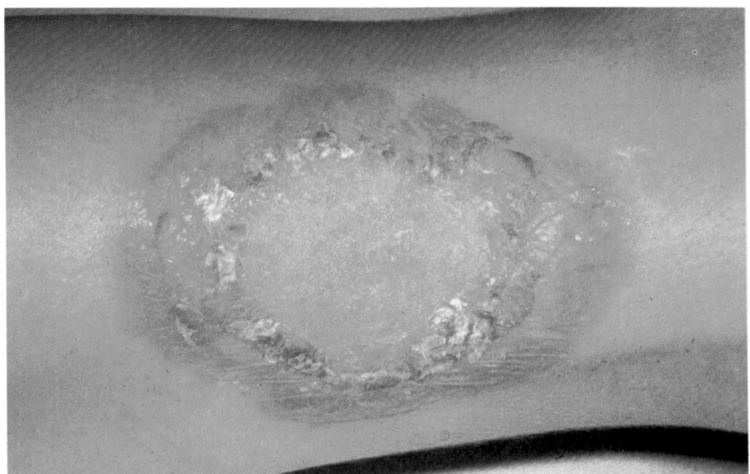

Eczema is inflammation of the skin characterized by an itching red rash, often symptomatic of an allergic reaction. The photograph *(above)* shows a spreading patch of eczema on a child's leg, below the knee. Antihistamines and corticosteroid drugs may be used in treatment, while an attempt is made to eliminate the cause of the allergy.

Permanent paralysis is a possible outcome of some disorders of the nervous system, such as poliomyelitis. These archers suffer from paraplegia (paralysis of the lower half of the body), but ably demonstrate their ability to lead a full and active life.

gray matter of the spinal cord and can cause paralysis. Children can be immunized against the disease, and it is now rare.

Damage to the brain in an accident may cause concussion, or symptoms similar to those of a stroke. Spinal cord damage usually results in paralysis of parts of the body supplied by nerves originating below the point of injury. Peripheral nerves can be cut or crushed, but can grow again. New microsurgical techniques endeavor to join severed nerve sheaths to help this regeneration.

Degeneration of the nervous system

Like other parts of the body, the brain degenerates with increasing age. Ultimately, this may cause senile dementia, which is marked particularly by deterioration in intellectual functions. One form of dementia, called Alzheimer's disease, can occur in middle-aged people as well as in the elderly.

Multiple sclerosis is a degenerative disease of the white matter of the brain and spinal cord. The cause is not known. Symptoms vary according to the parts of the CNS that are affected, but are characterized by various forms of uncoordination. There is no specific treatment, although steroids and ACTH (adrenocorticotropic hormone) may sometimes help.

Infections of the skin

Skin is exposed to a wide variety of damaging agents, including viruses, bacteria, parasites, carcinogens, and even the sun.

Viral infections of the skin include warts and cold sores and are extremely common. Treatment concentrates on alleviating the symptoms, though some antiviral drugs are available. Boils and impetigo, caused by bacteria, are treated with antibiotics. Fungal infections include ringworm, thrush (moniliasis), and athlete's foot, treated with antifungal drugs. The skin may also be attacked by scabies mites, fleas, or lice.

Other skin conditions

Eczema is a type of allergic reaction in which the skin is itchy and inflamed and may flake at the affected patch. Treatment is with soothing creams or, in more serious cases, with ointments containing steroids. Dermatitis is a similar condition, generally caused by a substance such as a metal or a chemical compound, for example, soap that has been in contact with the skin.

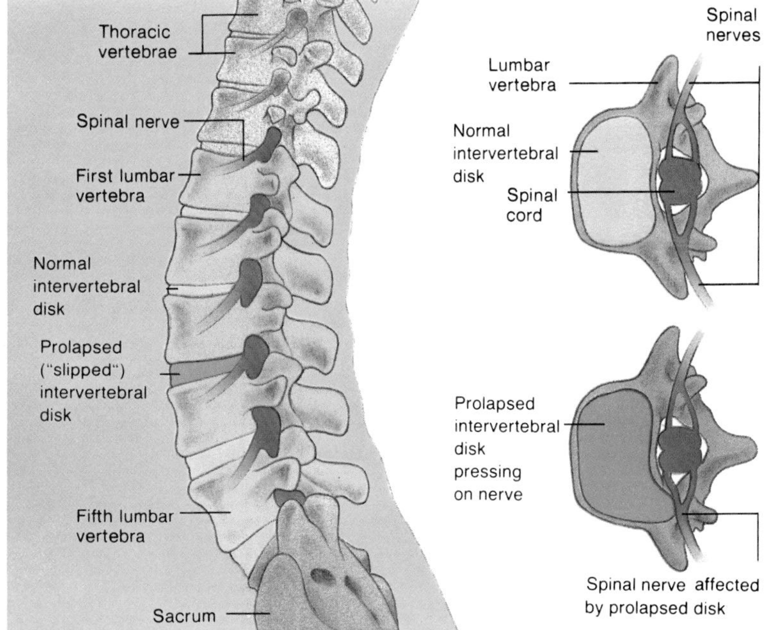

Pain due to pressure on a nerve may be caused by a herniated disk, when an intervertebral disk ruptures or moves out of its normal position between the bones of the spine. The pain is felt in the area served by the nerve; for example, a herniated lumbar disk may give rise to referred pain in the leg.

The cause of acne remains unknown, although hormonal factors appear to be important. In most cases, the condition improves spontaneously. Recently, high doses of vitamin A have been found to be effective in prevention or treatment. Exposure to sunlight may also help.

Psoriasis produces red, scaly lesions, especially over the elbows and knees. Treatment involves the use of ointments that improve the skin's ability to absorb sunlight.

Sunlight has beneficial effects on the skin, notably the production of vitamin D and the reduction of acne. But sunlight is potentially harmful, too. It damages the underlying connective tissue, reducing elasticity, and is a potential cause of all types of skin cancer.

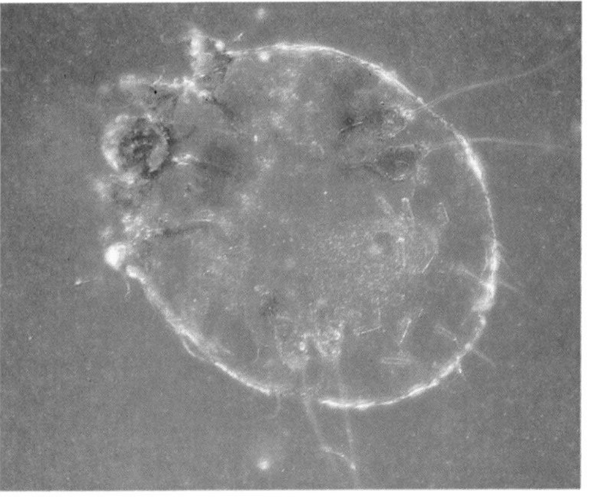

The scabies mite *Sarcoptes scabiei,* a microscopic arachnid animal, burrows into the skin and causes an itching, contagious skin condition that is an allergic reaction to the mite and its eggs. The hands and feet are most usually affected, and treatment is to paint the patient's body with scabicidal chemicals.

Fact entries

Epilepsy is a general term covering several different types of seizures. Seizures used to be described as *petit mal, grand mal,* and psychomotor. But the International Seizure Classification groups and describes seizures according to the area of the brain involved. The two major classes are generalized seizures, which involve all of the brain, and partial seizures, which involve only a part of the brain. Both types are the result of an involuntary discharge of electricity by brain cells. Epilepsy may develop at any age.

Generalized seizures are characterized by momentary periods of unconsciousness, or absence attacks, in which the person appears totally unaware of his or her surroundings. They are most common in children, and tend to disappear in adolescence or early adulthood. Seizures apparently rarely cause any permanent damage.

Generalized tonic-clonic seizures are usually characterized by major convulsions. A seizure is often preceded by a combination of sensations called an aura. These culminate in sudden unconsciousness and often convulsions. Following the seizure, the patient may feel disoriented, and is likely to wish to sleep.

Partial seizures with simple symptoms produce twitching movements of specific muscle groups and sometimes brief visual or auditory hallucinations. With complex symptoms, partial seizures involve impairment of consciousness and may be characterized by purposeless activities or aimless wandering.

Mental disorders

Until the end of the last century, most people thought mental disorder was the same as insanity. This view changed following the careful observations of the German psychiatrist Kraepelin, who established the classification of psychoses and differentiated depression into two categories: endogenous (coming from within) and reactive (having an external or social cause). During this century, a great deal of thought has been devoted to such classification and definition.

Definition of mental disorders

The definition and diagnosis of mental disorders and what is considered to lie within the bounds of normality varies, inevitably, with different cultures. In many non-European cultures in all parts of the world, states of "possession" by spirits, involving trances and hallucinations, are considered normal, while in our society such behavior would almost certainly be seen to indicate some form of mental disorder. Even among Western societies, there is disagreement about the details of what constitutes mental disorder and how it should be classified. The diagnosis of schizophrenia, for instance, is made more frequently in the United States and Canada than in Western Europe, although research indicates that the incidence of the disease is fairly uniform throughout the world.

Despite these arguments about the borderlines between normality and abnormality, there are certain disorders of mind and behavior about which there is general agreement. These include altered states of mind such as abnormal anxiety, depression, or phobias, in which the individual is subject to considerable personal suffering, and aspects of individual behavior that are clearly regarded as disordered by the community as a whole.

Freud and Jung, seated left and right of G. Stanley Hall, their host, visited Clark University, Worcester, Massachusetts in 1909 during their visit to the United States, where their ideas were received with great interest. Their colleagues A. A. Brill, Ernest Jones, and Sandor Ferenczi *(left to right)* stand behind them in this photograph.

Basic concepts

The development of ideas about mental disorder reflects the history of society itself. In the Middle Ages, disordered behavior was usually attributed to witchcraft; in the late nineteenth century, to brain disorder or heredity; and today, there is disagreement between social or psychodynamic and biological psychiatrists about causes of mental disorder, particularly about what is socially or environmentally determined.

One of the major contributions of Sigmund Freud was to show that unconscious factors play a crucial part in determining an individual's behavior. In particular, he established the idea that the unconscious is a reservoir of wishes and fantasies, basically sexual and aggressive (love and hate), and showed how unconscious conflict can give rise to psychopathology. He also supplied the method (psychoanalysis) for further study of the unconscious by later investigators.

In developing his theories about unconscious mental processes, Freud used three concepts termed id, ego, and superego, to denote interacting forces in human behavior. The id is the sum of primitive instinctive forces in an individual, which seek expression constantly through the search for pleasure and the avoidance of pain. The ego is the conscious self that mediates between the primitive id and the third aspect of the mind, the superego, and through this mediation controls behavior. The superego is perhaps best described as the "conscience." It is developed through upbringing and experience, and often conflicts with the instinctual drives of the id. Such conflict is normally resolved by the ego, but if it remains unresolved, neuroses can develop. Freud thought that much neurosis was

Early schools of psychoanalysis, such as those of Jung and Adler, and the Neo-Freudian analysts, such as Klein and Horney, can trace their origins to the work of Freud. The links between Freud and other psychotherapies are more tenuous.

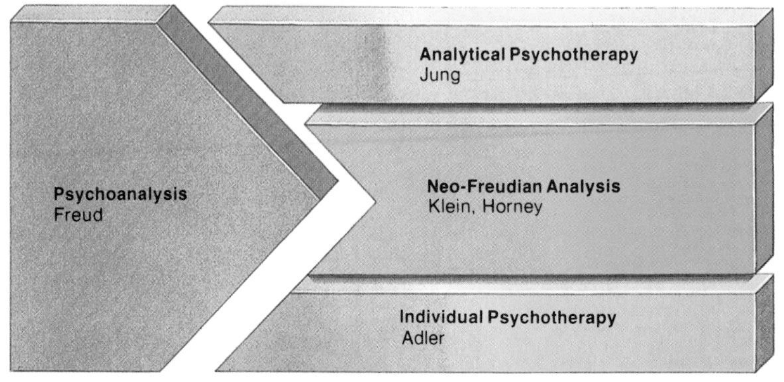

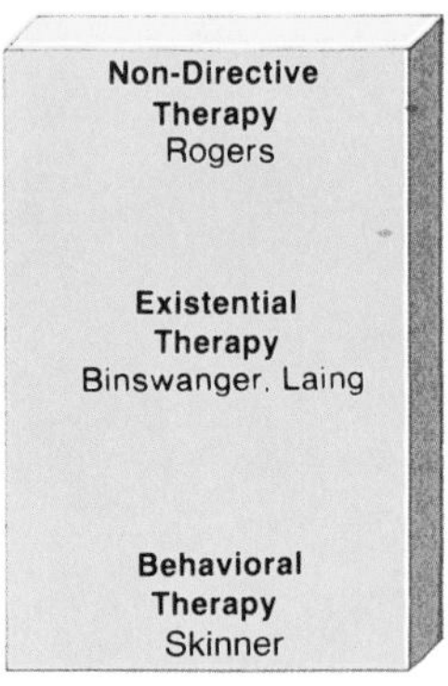

caused by the suppression of the knowledge of sexual events in childhood. Not everyone accepted this emphasis, however. Carl Jung, for example, broke away from Freud's teachings because he was unable to accept that suppression of sexual memories was the primary cause of neurosis. He believed in the notion of a collective unconscious and dwelt more on the psychological present and future (stressing what people were capable of becoming) than on the past. Melanie Klein, who studied under Freud's pupil Sandor Ferenczi, placed the origins of neurosis and mental disturbance earlier in a child's psychic life than Freud proposed, maintaining that the significant period is in the first months and the first two years of childhood.

Classification

Neuroses are distinguished from psychoses because, in the former, contact is maintained with reality, whereas in the latter this contact is lost. The classification of neuroses is somewhat arbitrary, because most patients suffer from more than one classic type. The types serve to identify symptoms, however, and include a form of anxiety, phobias, obsessive or compulsive behavior, hypochondria, hysteria, a form of depression, and neurasthenia or excessive fatigue (which often accompanies depression).

Psychosis, in contrast, describes a mental state with no evident physical cause, in which a person's mental disorder is so great that contact with reality is lost, and delusions and possibly hallucinations occur. Manic-depressive psychosis, paranoia, and schizophrenia are the best-known psychotic syndromes.

Personality disorder, a loose classification, is usually regarded as the third major area of mental disorder. Such disorders range from minor disturbances, such as excessive shyness, irrational mood changes, and mild paranoia, none of which need be debilitating, to compulsive personality traits, often with a deviant sexual focus and extreme antisocial psychopathic behavior.

Superficial similarities between some minor personality disorders—irrational mood changes (cyclothymia) for instance—and psychoses, such as manic-depressive psychosis, emphasize the difficulty of classification. Other difficulties are posed by the question of whether minor sexual disorders, such as impotence or frigidity, and the states of mind associated with alcoholism, drug addiction, and even suicide are mental disorders as such or merely unfortunate aspects of the human condition.

Psychiatric syndromes

In the psychiatric treatment of mental illness, several specific syndromes are of particular concern. Anxiety and depression are prominent among these, because they are the two most common symptoms the psychiatrist is called upon to treat. Anxiety may be neurotic or psychotic. Neurotic anxiety is, perhaps, the commonest neurosis. Psychotic anxiety accompanies schizophrenia or manic-depressive states.

Mental subnormality, or deficiency, de-

Group therapy, with its informal atmosphere, is a valuable form of psychotherapy for people who share a common problem, such as a personality disorder or psychological dependence on drugs or alcohol. Professional organizations that help people to overcome alcoholism or compulsive gambling, for example, commonly use group therapeutic techniques. The therapist may initiate the discussion, but then often takes a more passive role, allowing the group members to talk among themselves.

Art therapy encourages people to express their inner thoughts and feelings through drawings and paintings, and may help to reveal repressed or unconscious aspects that contribute to a mental disorder.

Manic-depressive psychosis is a severe mental disorder that affects up to one person in every hundred, and is more common in women than in men. It is characterized by extreme swings of mood. In the manic phase *(left)*, the person is overactive and excited, often to the extent of lacking all self-control. In the depressive phase *(right)*, there is a prolonged period of deep depression and melancholia that may be severe enough to be suicidal.

scribes a condition of retarded, incomplete, or abnormal mental development at birth or in early childhood. Treatment is more commonly the concern of educational psychologists than psychiatrists, though where medical therapy is required the responsibilities may overlap.

The most common psychiatric illness in old age, senile dementia, is commonly manifest in childlike, perverse, or destructive behavior. The cause is unknown, but current research suggests it may be related to the pathology of Alzheimer's disease. There is no effective treatment, though research into Alzheimer's disease has recently made some advances.

Other disorders

Alcohol and drug abuse are difficult to classify in psychiatric terms, though both can be seen as attempts to allay or avoid anxiety. There is a possibility that those who become addicted to either have a psychological propensity toward addiction, which may be a neurotic compulsion, a personality disorder, or an indefinable urge toward self-neglect or self-destruction. However, both alcohol and addictive drugs are severely harmful in themselves, and mental disturbance is a frequent result of alcohol or drug abuse.

It is believed that suicide reflects a person's feeling that he or she can no longer go on living with profound and long-standing depression. A distinction is usually made between successful and attempted suicide on the assumption that the latter is a dramatic "cry for help" rather than a serious attempt to die. Treatment of an attempted suicide concentrates on the underlying cause.

Minor sexual disorders can sometimes be treated by psychotherapy or psychoanalysis. More direct or interactive methods, usually described as sex therapy, may be successful.

Disorders in which the mind unconsciously affects the body are termed psychosomatic. In fact, many disorders may have a psychological component, and the term psychosomatic could describe conditions as varied as stress-related eczema and impotence. One serious psychosomatic condition is anorexia nervosa, in which an excessive desire to lose weight results in emaciation; typically, this affects teenage girls.

Modern mental hospitals include a whole range of recreational facilities, many of which acknowledge the therapeutic role of exercise and normal activities in the treatment of mental disorders. The hospital illustrated below has a nine-hole golf course laid out in relaxing country surroundings.

Drug and other medical treatments

Although many mental disorders do not seem to have an obvious physical cause, physical methods seem to be the only successful way to treat them. Drugs in particular are used extensively. Because there is no physical disorder to attack, however, drug treatment tends to concentrate on relieving and controlling symptoms. The main types of drugs used are tranquilizers and antidepressants. Antischizophrenic drugs are powerful tranquillizers, but are regarded as a separate category because of their specific uses in the treatment of schizophrenia. The use of lithium, usually in the form of lithium carbonate, in conjunction with an antidepressant, is sometimes valuable in reducing the mood changes in manic-depressive psychosis.

Two other treatments, electroconvulsive therapy (ECT) and psychosurgery, are sometimes (though ever more rarely) used. ECT induces a modified epileptic seizure in an anesthetized patient by means of electric current, in an attempt to treat severe depression. Psychosurgery involves surgery on part of the brain to prevent the symptoms of chronically depressed or obsessive patients. Both are controversial and are questioned by many psychiatrists on moral and ethical grounds.

The talking cures

Adjuncts to medical treatment are the forms of therapy that attempt to treat the psychological causes rather than the symptoms of mental disorders. Collectively, these forms of treatment are called psychotherapy.

The original "talking cure" was developed by Freud, who gave it the name psychoanalysis to stress its scientific foundation. The science of psychoanalysis has been developed by Freud's successors into a variety of analytic techniques based on the principle of developing a close relationship between patient and analyst, which allows undesirable or abnormal aspects of the patient's mental state to manifest themselves. The origin, nature, and effects of these can then be made clear to the patient by the analyst's explanation.

In an alternative, more specific sense, the term psychotherapy describes modified forms of psychoanalysis in which the patient is seen only once or twice a week, and not necessarily for such an extended period as in psychoanalysis.

There is also a wealth of alternative therapies with different approaches and methods. These include behavior therapy, family therapy, group therapy, and psychodrama. Behavior therapy attempts to modify behavior by psychological conditioning. The technique does not require the patient to understand the cause of his condition. The others use a psychodynamic approach, aiming to involve patients in the process of understanding themselves and coming to terms with their problems, with the guidance of an experienced therapist who directs the course of the treatment.

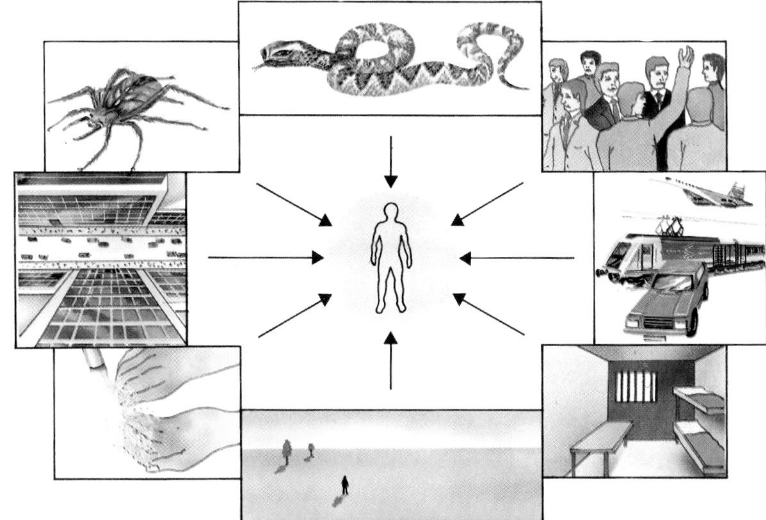

Phobias can be caused by many things, some of which—for instance, modes of transport, crowds of people, or open spaces—give little or no cause for fear in most people. The diagram *(above)* illustrates these and other common phobias.

Anorexia nervosa is a disorder that occurs most frequently in teen-age girls. Their refusal to eat can cause extreme loss of weight and cessation of menstruation. The condition usually needs prolonged psychiatric treatment.

Fact entries

Hall, G. Stanley (1884-1924), American psychologist and teacher who was among the first to link the results of investigations into child psychology with theories about the education of children.

Freud, Sigmund (1856-1939), Austrian physician whose study of mental disorders, particularly neuroses, led him to formulate theories of the unconscious and subconscious mind, which became the basis of the therapeutic technique known as psychoanalysis.

Kraepelin, Emil (1856-1926), German psychiatrist who established the classification of psychoses into schizophrenia (dementia praecox) and manic-depressive psychosis.

Adler, Alfred (1870-1937), Austrian psychiatrist who disputed the Freudian emphasis on sexuality and formulated an alternative theory that the desire for power or success is fundamental in human motivation.

Jung, Carl Gustav (1875-1961), Swiss psychologist and psychiatrist who founded his own school of analytical psychology after disagreement with Freud. Jung's theories centered on the unconscious and spiritual nature of the mind, and emphasized the need for self-discovery in the growth of the personality.

Binswanger, Ludwig (1881-1966), Swiss psychiatrist whose modification of psychotherapy, based on existentialist philosophy, explains certain mental disorders in terms of the patient's distorted image of the self and its relation to the world.

Klein, Melanie (1882-1960), Austrian psychoanalyst whose work on child psychology, particularly in terms of the psychological significance of play in anxiety situations, extended understanding of the processes of childhood development far beyond the Freudian model.

Horney, Karen (1885-1952), American psychoanalyst whose modifications of Freudian theory stress the importance of social and environmental factors in determining personality.

Rogers, Carl Ransom (1902-), American psychotherapist whose "client-centered" therapy stresses the mind's "actualizing tendency" to heal and fulfill its own potential.

Bettelheim, Bruno (1903-), American psychiatrist and educator, renowned for his studies of the psychology and treatment of emotionally disturbed children, with particular regard to social factors.

Skinner, Burrhus Frederic (1904-), American psychologist whose views have had great influence on the techniques of behavior therapy.

Laing, Ronald David (1927-), British psychiatrist whose interpretation and treatment of psychosis, particularly schizophrenia, emphasizes that the stresses in many "normal" social relationships are great enough to be a prime cause of psychotic illness.

Drugs

A physician's task in treating various kinds of ailments and their symptoms has been made much easier in recent years by the availability of a vast armory of drugs. At the same time, the manufacture of drugs has become a full-scale industry with its own research, testing, packaging, marketing, and promotion divisions. Constant research, refinement, and experimentation by the pharmaceutical companies is continually resulting in the production of new or improved drugs. As an overall consequence, drug treatment is becoming more effective all the time.

Although treatment is undoubtedly improving, drugs are also becoming increasingly expensive, and questions about the cost of producing drugs are of great concern to many people. Research and development is often a long and costly process, and even when a new drug is discovered it can be both difficult and expensive to produce. On the other hand, enormous sums are spent in packaging and advertising drug products, so arguments about costs and waste are difficult to resolve.

One point often used to explain the cost of drugs is that every care must be taken to ensure that they are safe to use. Indeed, it has even been argued that so much attention is paid to safety requirements that this actually inhibits research.

Despite such stringent precautions, however, mistakes do occur, and the question of where responsibility lies is also controversial. Some mistakes are particularly horrifying, as in the cases of malformed children born to women who took the drug thalidomide as a sedative while pregnant. Many drugs are extremely potent agents and most can be dangerous if misused. In any case, drugs should be considered only as temporary solutions even to permanent problems. The fact remains, however, that most drugs are taken on prescription to combat pain or disease, and few are abused.

Some antibiotics can be prepared from organic sources, such as mold (one type of which is a source of penicillin) or bacteria—for example, this culture of *Streptomyces lividans.*

Thalidomide is a sedative drug used originally in the 1950's and 1960's, which caused pregnant women who took it to give birth to physically malformed children. These children were not mentally defective, however, and many live normal lives.

Drugs and the physician

A physician, faced with a patient who has described all the perceived symptoms, may decide to prescribe drug treatment. Most physicians are inundated with leaflets, brochures, and free samples from pharmaceutical companies advertising their drugs, and from these and other sources of information the physician has to choose a drug that provides the maximum help. The treatment might have to be effective in more than one way—treating both pain and infection, for example, as well as any other localized or general condition. Alternatively, a combination of drugs might be indicated—and the compatibility of the prescribed drugs has to be ensured. For information on this subject, the physician generally consults one of the large reference works on drugs, commonly known as a *Physician's Desk Reference.* But a physician may use a "trial and error" approach with certain drugs if the symptoms displayed indicate one of several possible causes.

The physician has also to consider possible side effects of drug treatment. A number of useful drugs have known side effects, and a patient should be warned about these in advance. They can vary from comparatively minor effects, such as the tendency of the painkilling drug codeine to cause constipation, to potentially hazardous ones, such as the drowsiness induced by some drugs prescribed to combat travel sickness. The occurrence of side effects is especially serious in some chemotherapy techniques for treating cancer, in which internal tumors are virtually overwhelmed with drugs. The treatment can be very effective, but there may be visible side effects (such as alopecia) that may depress the patient's morale. The physician must therefore consider whether such possible side effects balance or even outweigh the potential benefit derived from the use of the drug, and careful monitoring of a patient's reactions to a drug is therefore essential.

Before contemplating the type of drug to prescribe, the physician must be certain the patient's condition has been diagnosed correctly. Diagnosis must take into account the patient's possible inability to explain exactly what and where the symptoms are, the fact that pain can be "referred" from one location in the body to another, and the fact that to a patient a secondary side effect may assume greater importance than that of a primary symptom. There is also the possibility that the patient really needs no medical treatment at all—that attending the clinic or office is essentially either a cry for social rather than medical help, or the result of genuine hypochondria.

In the latter case, a physician must prescribe a course of "dummy" pills (placebos), which are realistic fakes that may fool the patient but which have no clinical effect. In fact, it is now believed they may have some slight effect—possibly by encouraging the release of the peptides known as endorphins in the body. Unfortunately, however, the introverted personality of a hypochondriac is usually of the type least likely to be affected by such treatment, and placebos seem to work most effectively with stable, extrovert personalities. One survey on the use of placebos provided the interesting statistic that one in three patients who are unaware of being prescribed placebos comes back for more.

Such subtle analysis requires the physician's personal knowledge of the patient. And although such a close acquaintance with every patient may be difficult, particularly in an urban area, a physician has to be quite certain before completing a prescription for a drug that the prescribed drug will produce no allergic effects, nor any side effects with which the patient might be unable to cope satisfactorily. A physician has to be especially vigilant in diagnosis when prescribing drugs that could be abused because extended usage of certain drugs could encourage addiction. This is particularly likely with some stimulants and depressants.

The various forms of prescribed drugs

The form in which pharmaceutical compounds are presented—solid, liquid, or gaseous—depends on the nature of their ingredients and what they are designed to do.

Solid forms include granules, tablets, capsules, and even a type of chewing gum (for weaning smokers off cigarettes). Powders, creams, and ointments are generally designed for external (topical) application. Pessaries and suppositories, which consist of a drug in a soluble base that dissolves in moist conditions and at body temperatures, deliver drugs directly into the vagina and rectum, respectively. Some drugs are designed to be dissolved in water first for easier internal absorption, particularly the proprietary drugs sold as fast-acting painkillers.

Liquid drugs include remedies such as

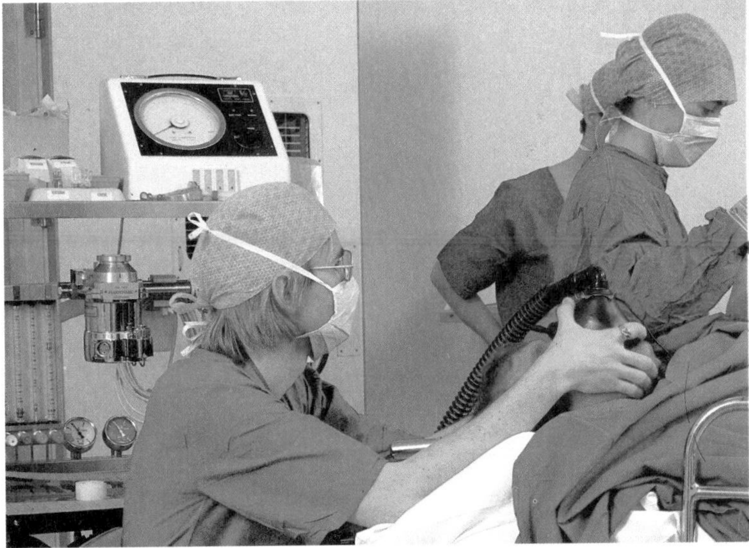

Modern surgery relies to a considerable extent on anesthetic drugs and on the skill of the anesthetist to select the appropriate drug and technique of administration, depending on the type of operation and the patient's age and condition.

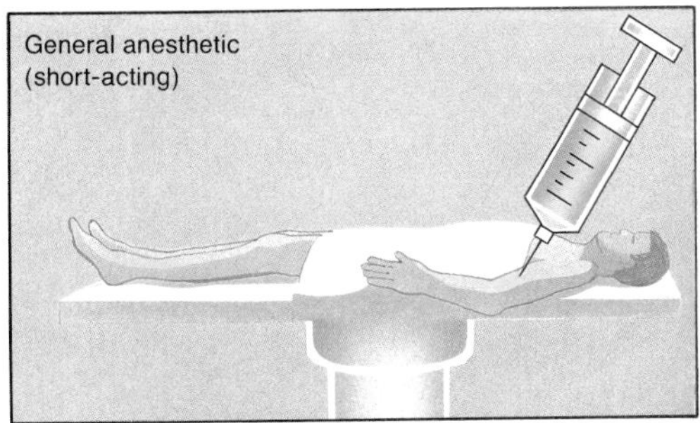

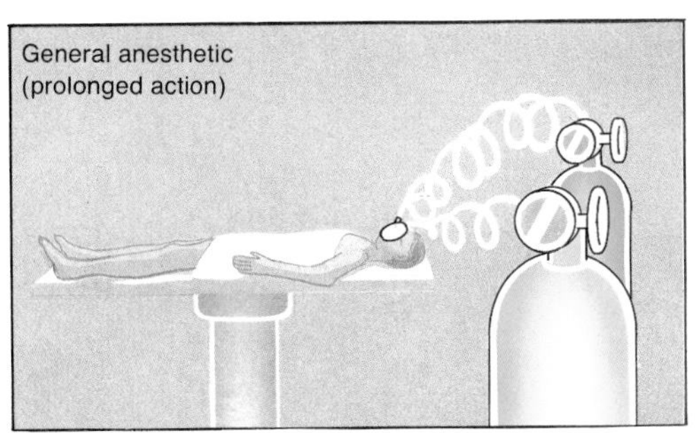

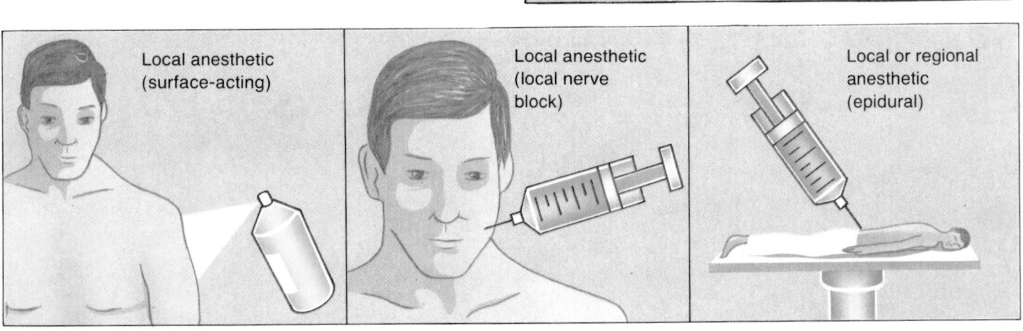

Anesthetics can be classified as general or local, according to their action. General anesthetics affect the whole body and cause complete unconsciousness. Short-acting ones are usually administered by injection; long-acting ones by inhalation. Local anesthetics are intended to anesthetize a specific area of the body. They can be administered by a spray, often used to relieve the pain of a burn, or by injection, which a dentist uses to block nerves to the teeth. A special type of local anesthetic (called epidural) is injected into the fluid around the spinal cord. This anesthetizes parts of the body supplied by lower spinal nerves and is sometimes used to relieve the pain of childbirth.

Drugs can be administered in various forms. The main ones are illustrated here. The symbols below relate to the table of drugs on this and the facing page. The forms illustrated are, in clockwise direction, liquid, spray, liquid for injection, suppositories, hypodermic syringe for injection, tube for cream or lotion, capsules, and tablets.

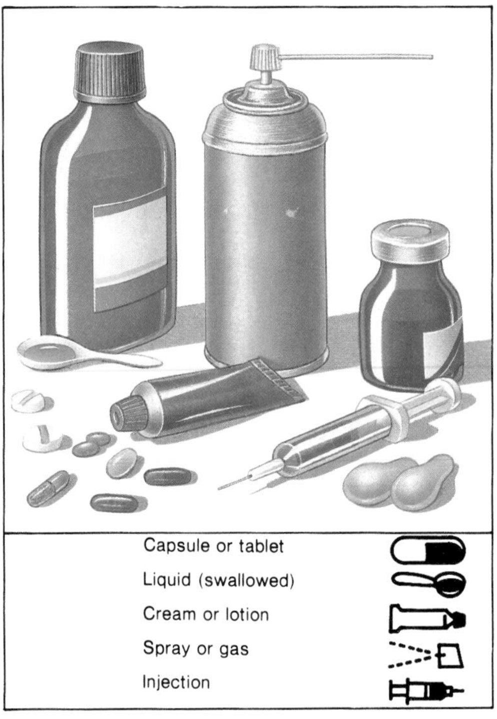

cough mixtures; antibiotic preparations for babies, young children, and elderly people; drugs to counteract gastrointestinal infections; some laxatives; and ulcer-healing preparations. Other liquid drugs are given by injection: under the skin (subcutaneously), into muscle (intramuscularly), or into veins (intravenously). Large volumes of liquid-containing drugs can be administered directly into veins from an intravenous infusion set.

Gaseous drugs include some general anesthetics, inhalations for catarrh and sinusitis, drugs for the heart condition angina pectoris, and some old-fashioned cures, such as smelling salts for fainting attacks. Drugs that relax constricted bronchial passages (bronchodilators) are commonly supplied to a patient in an inhaler (an aerosol or mechanical spray).

Types of drugs

Most types of drugs—including some that occur naturally in the body (such as hormones)—are represented in the table on this page.

Generally, they are intended either to give

Drug group and description	Usual forms	Examples
Analgesics relieve pain (without affecting other sensations)	Capsule or tablet	aspirin, acetaminophen
Anesthetics numb sensation, either generally or locally	Spray or gas; Injection; Capsule or tablet; Cream or lotion	halothane, sodium pentathol, nitrous oxide (general); procaine (local)
Antacids neutralize stomach acid (to relieve indigestion)	Capsule or tablet; Liquid (swallowed)	sodium bicarbonate, aluminum hydroxide
Antiarrhythmics steady irregular and/or fast heartbeat	Capsule or tablet	digoxin
Antibacterial drugs prevent or treat bacterial infection	Capsule or tablet	sulfadiazine
Antibiotics counteract bacterial or fungal infections by preventing the growth of microorganisms	Capsule or tablet; Injection; Liquid (swallowed)	penicillin, ampicillin, tetracyclines, chloramphenicol, griseofulvin
Anticoagulants inhibit the blood-clotting mechanism	Capsule or tablet; Injection	heparin, warfarin
Anticonvulsants control epileptic or other seizures	Capsule or tablet; Injection	phenobarbital, diazepam, ACTH
Antidepressants treat depression	Capsule or tablet	imipramine, phenelzine
Antihistamines counteract allergic and traumatic reactions to histamine release in the body; also used as sedatives and antinauseants	Capsule or tablet; Cream or lotion; Injection	brompheniramine maleate, promethazine
Antimalarial drugs prevent or treat malaria	Capsule or tablet	quinine, mepacrine, chloroquine
Antinauseants counter vomiting (as in travel sickness)	Capsule or tablet; Injection	meclizine, prochlorperazine, trimethobenzamide
Anti-Parkinsonism drugs treat Parkinson's disease	Capsule or tablet	levodopa (l-dopa)
Antipyretics relieve or prevent fever	Capsule or tablet	indomethacin, aspirin
Antirheumatic drugs relieve rheumatic pain	Capsule or tablet	phenylbutazone
Antiserums are used in vaccinations to prevent certain specific disease (and contain antibodies against them)	Injection	diphtheria vaccine
Antispasmodics relax intestinal and bronchial smooth muscle (when they are bronchodilators), to relieve diarrhea or lung congestion	Capsule or tablet; Spray or gas; Injection	ephedrine, theophylline
Antitussives suppress coughing	Capsule or tablet; Liquid (swallowed)	noscarpine, codeine
Antivenins treat bites from venomous animals (such as snakes and spiders)	Injection	specific to animal
Antiviral drugs treat certain virus infections (such as shingles and cold sores)	Capsule or tablet; Cream or lotion	idoxuridine
Chelating agents treat heavy metal poisoning	Capsule or tablet	penicillamine
Contraceptive drugs prevent ovulation in a woman	Capsule or tablet	estrogen-progestogen hormone combinations

protection against disease, as do immunization and vaccination, or to cope with a disease once it is diagnosed, as do antibiotics, for example. In the latter case, drugs may be prescribed to treat the condition either by eradicating the underlying cause, or by suppressing the symptoms. Usually it is the underlying cause that the physician prescribes the drug to attack, but there are certain conditions (such as peptic ulceration and arteriosclerosis) in which the best treatment is to alleviate the symptoms. There are, in any case, many more symptom-suppressing drugs than there are those that attack root causes.

Moreover, some medical conditions caused by environmental circumstances require treatment with chemicals and substances that are not usually considered drugs. Deficiency diseases, for instance, endemic in some parts of the world, are often only temporarily "cured" by administering proteins, vitamins, or any other substances that make up the deficiency. Proteins and vitamins could then quite legitimately be termed drugs.

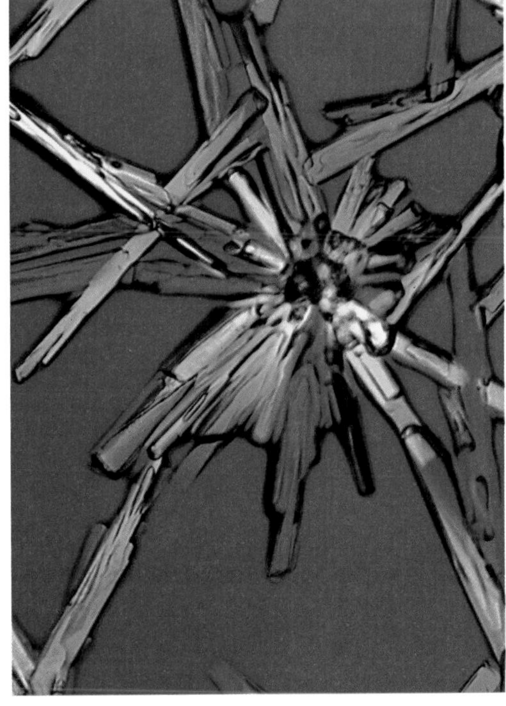

Ampicillin crystals photographed with polarized light testify to the purity of this synthetic antibiotic drug. All drugs have to be produced in a clinically pure form as either a solid or a liquid of known concentration, so that dosages and formulations can be made up accurately.

Drug group and description	Usual forms	Examples
Corticosteroids reduce inflammation and relieve allergic or rheumatic symptoms		hydrocortisone
Cytotoxic drugs destroy or prevent the growth of cancerous cells (also called anticancer or antitumor drugs)		fluorouracil, l-asparaginase
Decongestants relieve wheezing or clear nasal passages		antispasmodics, antihistamines
Diuretics increase the output of urine from the kidneys (to treat edema or glaucoma)		thiazides, caffeine
Emetics promote vomiting		salt solution, ipecac
Globulins (proteins in blood plasma) are used in transfusions and sometimes to confer immunity		fibrinogen
Hallucinogens (psychedelics) produce perceptual distortions and mood changes		LSD, mescaline, phencyclidine
Hormones are natural glandular secretions or synthetic equivalents used to treat a lack or deficiency of the hormone in the body or to moderate hormone balance		anabolic steroids, male sex hormones, female sex hormones
Hypnotics induce sleep or unconsciousness		chloral hydrate, barbiturates
Hypotensives reduce blood pressure or slow heartbeat		thiazides, beta-blockers
Immunosuppressants suppress the body's immune system (generally to avoid rejection of grafts or transplants)		azathioprine, cyclophosphamide, prednisone
Laxatives promote evacuation of the bowels		cascara sagrada, mineral oil
MAO inhibitors are antidepressants, often used to treat mental illness		phenelzine, isocarboxazid
Muscle relaxants relax certain muscles		atropine, scopolamine
Narcotics suppress pain and, in larger doses, produce stupor		morphine, codeine
Sedatives depress brain function and promote sleep; mild sedatives are called tranquilizers		barbiturates
Stimulants raise blood pressure, increase heartbeat and may increase the sense of alertness and/or well-being		amphetamines, caffeine
Vaccines confer immunity from certain specific diseases (and contain weak or dead pathogens that stimulate antibody formation in the body)		measles vaccine
Vasoconstrictors make blood vessels contract		(epinephrine) adrenaline
Vasodilators expand blood vessels		azapetine

Surgery

Surgery is one of the fields of medicine in which great advances are continually being made—stimulated as often by misfortunes, such as accidents and war, as by advances in other areas of medicine and science. New techniques and equipment enable surgeons to undertake remarkable treatments, from transplanting organs, such as the heart or kidney, to replacing a severed limb and restoring its function.

Diagnosis has also been considerably improved, both by refinements in slightly older techniques—such as the electroencephalograph (EEG) and the electrocardiograph (EKG)—and by the invention of new ones—such as the use of ultrasound, or of a computer to interpret X rays in the process known as computerized axial tomography (CAT) scanning.

Surgery itself has undergone remarkable refinement, with the result that many seriously ill or injured people can now be successfully treated, whereas perhaps only ten years ago little or nothing could have been done for them.

New surgical techniques

Among the most important new instruments and techniques available to the surgeon are endoscopy, microsurgery, cryosurgery, laser surgery, and patient monitoring devices.

An endoscope is a device for looking inside a patient's body. Most modern endoscopes employ fiber optics, in which strands of fiber packed together in a long, thin, flexible tube carry light (or an image) from one end of the tube to the other. The tube thus becomes an excellent diagnostic aid if inserted through a bodily orifice (or small surgical incision) to the site of whatever the physician wants to examine. It can also be used as a surgical instrument when the internal end of the tube is fitted with a wire loop or blades, which can cut or cauterize tissue. Stones in the bladder, for instance, can be easily crushed and washed out using this method (litholapaxy), with no need for abdominal surgery. In parts of the body that are particularly difficult to reach, a computer-enhanced image intensifier and a visual display unit (VDU, a television screen) may be used in conjunction with the endoscope so that its pictures are made quite clear.

A VDU attached to a microscope is now commonly used for microsurgery, which deals with the smallest and most sensitive parts of the body, such as individual nerve endings and blood vessels. Using microsurgery, it is possible not only to reattach an accidentally amputated limb, but to reconnect many of the neural pathways and thus enable the patient eventually to regain movement—and even some feeling—in the limb. This is an exceptional use, however; more common areas for microsurgery are the larynx and the ear.

Another modern technique is that of using localized but extreme cold (below −4° F., −20° C) to freeze and thus destroy tissue. This method—called cryosurgery—is not in common use, but is nevertheless occasionally employed in brain surgery, in ophthalmology, and in treating some skin disorders.

Probably the field in which most advances have been made recently uses lasers, which have various surgical applications. Pulsed laser beams can be produced either as an extremely narrow, concentrated ray with a diameter of only a fraction of a millimeter (used as a scalpel), or as a wider, diffuse ray (used to "vaporize" tissue over an area). The laser's main advantages are that it is totally aseptic and that—particularly when it is used as a scalpel—the heat produced cauterizes smaller blood vessels instantly, so that blood loss (and therefore shock) is greatly reduced. Moreover, a laser beam can be used in combination with an endoscope. The overall power of a beam depends on the type of laser. Carbon-dioxide lasers are extremely powerful (and are used mainly for the vaporization of unhealthy tissue). But they need a marker beam from a second laser (usually an argon or neon type) projected along the same path, because they are otherwise invisible. Probably the most common application for lasers in medical practice is to remove unhealthy tissue in a condition known as precancer of the cervix. The best-known use, however, is in "welding" back a detached part of the retina of the eye.

New and improved drugs for use as anesthetics during operations are constantly being discovered. At the same time, refinements are also being made in the equipment used for monitoring the patient's condition during an operation—also the responsibility of the anesthetist. Most operating theaters now have an array of automatic electronic monitoring devices.

Modern surgery

Nearly all parts of the body can be treated surgically; some organs and body systems, however, present the surgeon with special prob-

An operation is conducted in aseptic conditions. All instruments are sterilized and the surgical team wear sterile clothes.

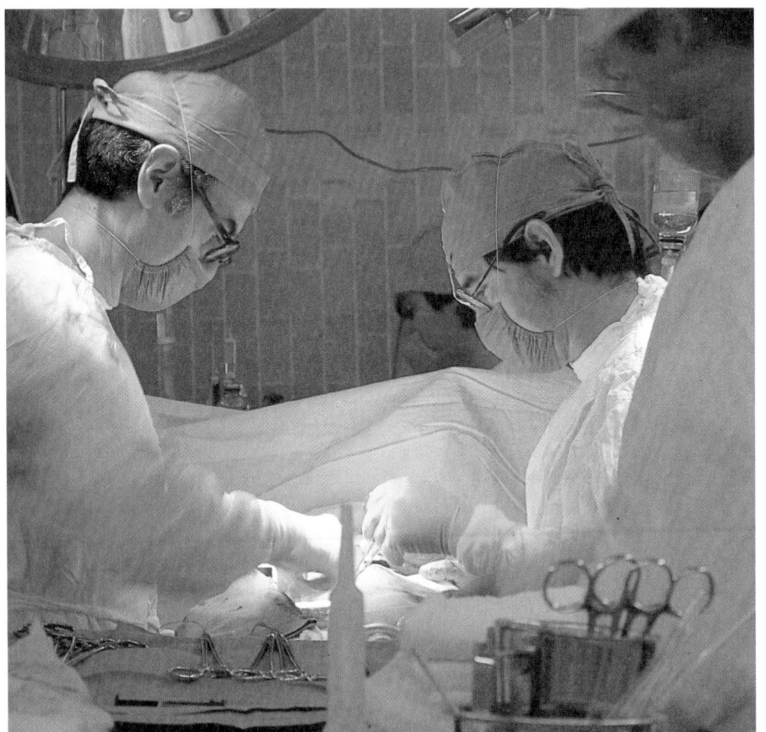

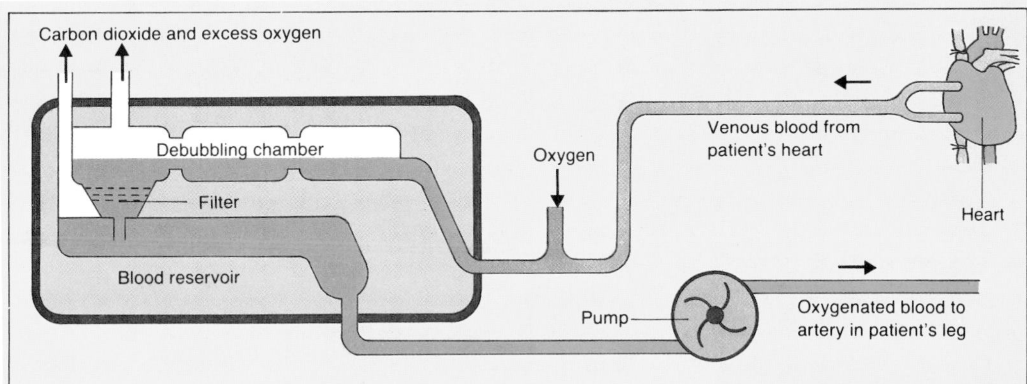

A cardiopulmonary by-pass, commonly known as a heart-lung machine, makes it possible for a surgeon to maintain the blood circulation while a patient's heart is stopped. Venous blood from the patient's heart is oxygenated, displaced carbon dioxide and excess oxygen are removed, and the filtered blood is pumped back into the patient's circulation via an artery in the leg.

lems. Until quite recently, most operations were performed by general surgeons. Even today, although specialization is increasingly important, a general surgeon is the most likely person to deal with appendectomies, gallbladder operations, breast operations, and surgery on the gastrointestinal tract. In some cases, the general surgeon may also be concerned with the removal of benign or malignant growths. In this context, a surgeon may have to decide, during the operation, how much tissue to remove to prevent further spread of cancerous growth.

Specialist surgeons are concerned not only with the appropriate surgical techniques but also with all other aspects of medical care relating to their speciality.

A neurosurgeon, for example, is concerned with operations on the nervous system: the brain, spinal cord, spine, and nerves. Injuries to the brain through accidents are all too frequent; tumors of the brain and spinal cord, and congenital disorders, such as hydrocephalus, are other common problems. Technical advances that have been of particular benefit to neurosurgeons include cryosurgery and laser surgery, both of which may be used in highly specific operations on the brain.

An orthopedic surgeon deals with disorders of the bones and joints. Common operations include the correction of congenital defects, such as clubfoot or scoliosis (curvature of the spine), and the insertion of metal or plastic artificial joints, for example, in the hip. Treatment of fractures is important too, and usually involves returning broken bones to their correct position and fixing them there—using splints or traction—until they have healed. Other orthopedic operations include the treatment of people with herniated disks, accident victims, and patients with bone cancer.

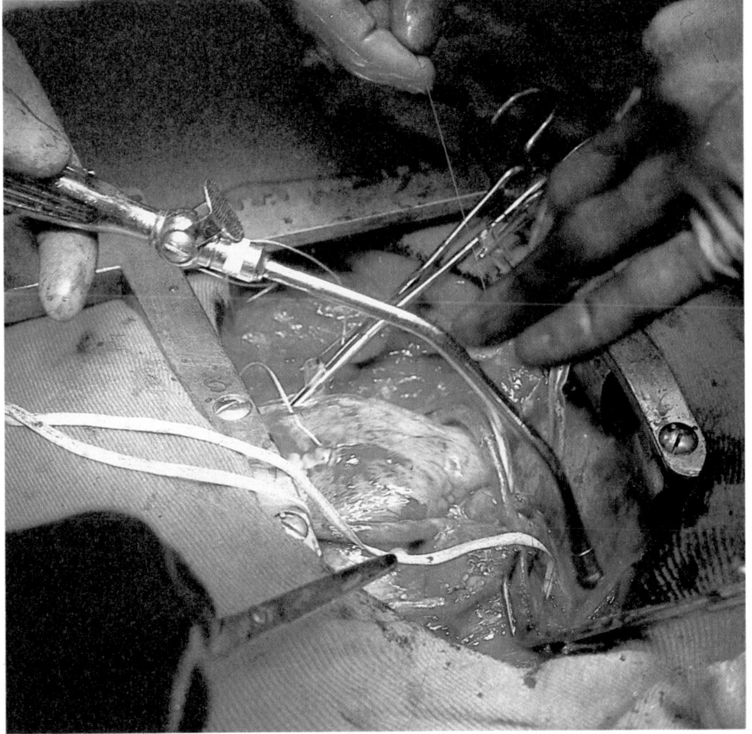

Open-heart surgery, shown below, has become a common technique since the development of the heart-lung machine, which takes over the functions of the patient's heart and lungs so that the operation can be performed with the heart stopped.

Urological surgeons deal with disorders affecting the urinary tract and male reproductive organs. Common problems include prostate disorders, kidney stones and kidney disease, and cancer of the kidneys, bladder, prostate, or testicles.

Obstetricians and gynecologists are concerned with pregnancy, childbirth, and female reproductive problems. Careful monitoring

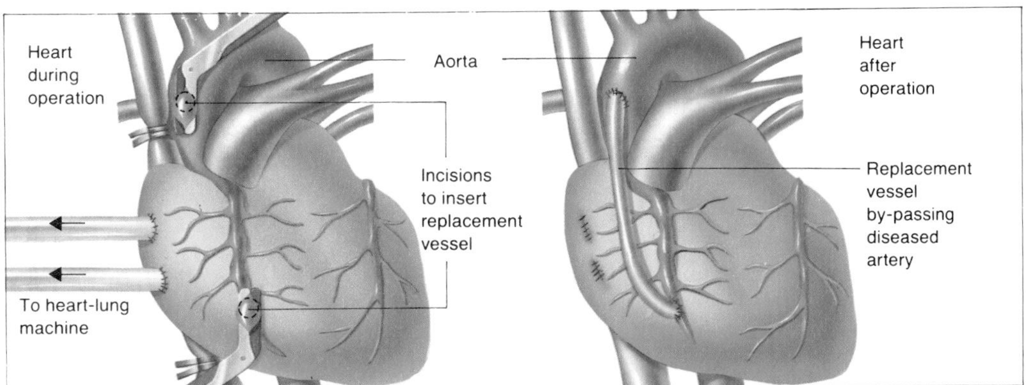

Coronary artery disease can be treated surgically by rerouting the blood through a by-pass. In this operation, a section of saphenous vein from the patient's leg is used as the replacement blood vessel.

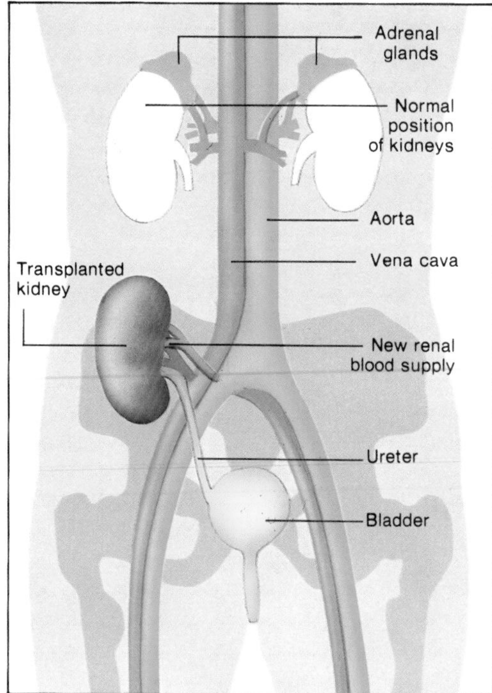

A kidney transplant is one of the most successful types of transplant operations. The new kidney, from a donor, is positioned at the top of the pelvic girdle and turned upside down to facilitate connections with the renal blood supply and the ureter. The adrenal glands are left in their original positions.

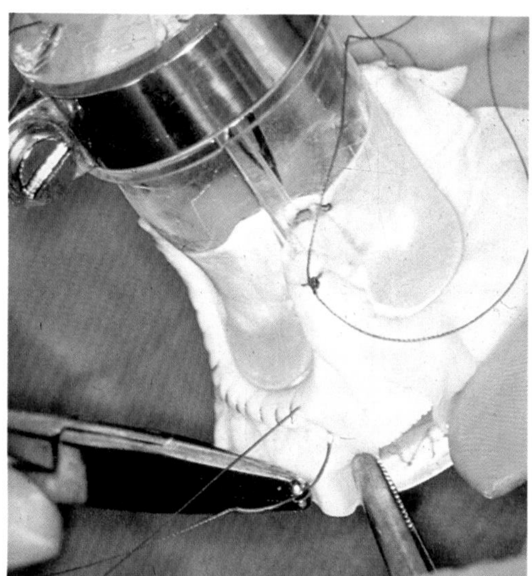

An artificial heart valve is stitched into position using many small sutures (stitches), which have to be strong enough to withstand the pressure inside a pumping heart.

and prenatal care minimize obstetric difficulties. Common gynecological operations include D and C (dilatation of the cervix and curettage of the uterus) for diagnostic or screening purposes, or for the removal of small growths (polyps) in the uterus; the removal of fibroids; removal of the uterus (hysterectomy); and surgery to treat cancer of the uterus or cervix.

The cardiac (heart) surgeon has derived particular benefit from technological advances, especially in the development of the heart-lung machine, which takes over the functions of the heart and lungs of a patient undergoing surgery so that the heart can be operated on while stopped; in the use of computers to aid monitoring; and in techniques that involve cooling the patient to slow down metabolism during an operation.

Transplant surgery involves the replacement of a diseased or failed organ (such as kidneys or the heart) with a healthy one, usually taken from a donor who has just died. By the early 1980's, heart transplants were still comparatively rare, although there had been some remarkable successes. Kidneys and bone marrow can, however, be transplanted from a living donor. The chief difficulty in transplant surgery is ensuring that the new tissue is not rejected by the recipient, whose natural immune response to foreign tissue can be as acute as it is to agents that cause allergy or disease. This difficulty can be largely overcome by careful matching of the tissue types of donor and patient, and by using special drugs that suppress the patient's immune response. (The use of these drugs is itself dangerous, however, in that the patient is thus left without any natural defenses against infection.)

Replacement (or "spare part") surgery avoids the problem of rejection by using inert plastic or metal devices to replace or strengthen natural ones. Some arteries, veins, heart valves, and joints can be replaced with artificial equivalents. Replacement of limbs or parts of limbs has been possible for a long time, but the sophistication of artificial limbs has reached such a degree nowadays that it is

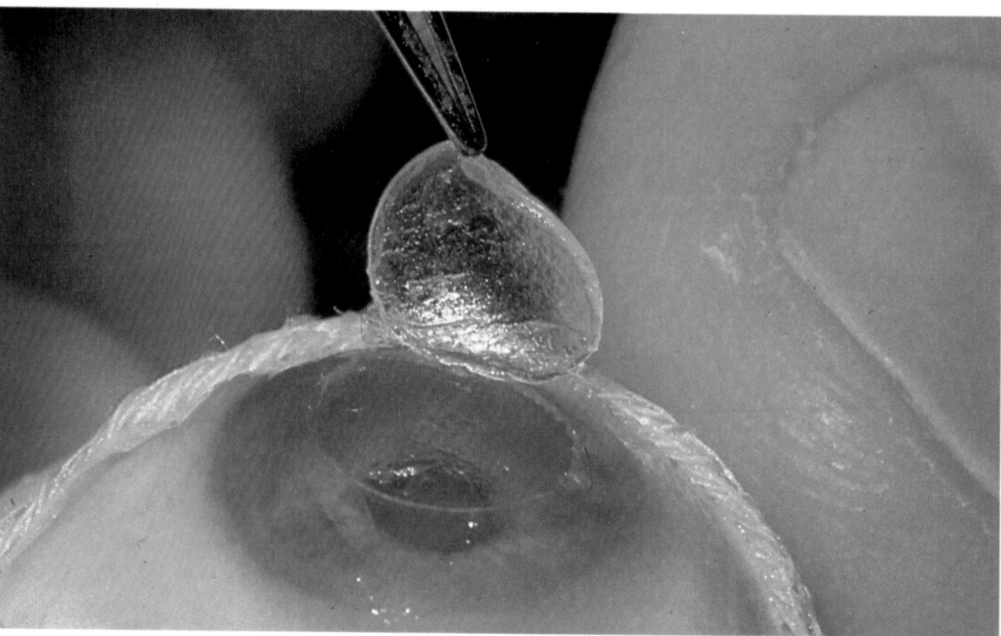

Specialized surgery on the eye includes cornea transplants. This photograph shows the donor's cornea being removed.

possible to use the nervous impulses in the remaining portion of the damaged limb to control the battery-operated replacement (prosthesis).

A plastic surgeon is concerned with the reconstruction and cosmetic repair of damaged surface tissue and bone, whether for aesthetic or psychological reasons, or after damage caused by burns or other injury.

An ophthalmic surgeon deals with the eyes, especially with the removal of cataracts (opaque patches in the lens), replacement of a damaged or diseased cornea by a corneal graft, or with the repair of a damaged or detached retina. Microsurgical techniques and advances, such as the medical use of lasers, particularly benefit ophthalmic surgery. They are also important for operations on the minute and delicate organs of the ear.

Removal of the tonsils and adenoids is a common ear, nose, and throat (ENT) operation, as is surgery to treat certain inner ear infections. Specialists in ENT surgery also remove tumors in the sinuses, mouth, larynx, and throat.

Common major operations

Most major operations are abdominal, and the most common of these include appendectomy (removal of the appendix); removal of ulcerated parts of the digestive tract, all or part of diseased organs, and benign or malignant growths; and the repair of hernias.

Accidents—particularly road accidents—are another common reason for major surgery. Further types of major surgery include urinary tract, cardiovascular, thoracic, and neurosurgical operations.

Preparations for surgery

Before an operation, the patient is tested for any condition that might complicate the operation, such as high blood pressure. Solid food is restricted for a period before any operation that requires a general anesthetic, in case the patient vomits while anesthetized. Finally, premedication is given to relax the patient before the anesthetic itself is administered. Preoperative antibiotics may also be given to minimize the risk of internal infection, particularly if surgery is to be carried out on or near the gastrointestinal tract.

Meanwhile, sterile conditions are established in the operating theater, and sterile instruments and clothing are obtained. Members of the surgical team "scrub up" by washing their hands extremely thoroughly and wear sterile clothing, which includes gloves, face masks, hats, and overgarments.

The patient is anesthetized before entering the operating theater, usually by an intravenous injection of barbiturate. Anesthesia is usually maintained during the operation by means of inhaled gas and monitored throughout the operation by an anesthetist or anesthesiologist.

Operations are performed by a skilled and specialized team consisting of the surgeon (or surgeons), various assistants, an anesthetist or anesthesiologist, and, where special apparatus is being used, a technician to operate it. A surgeon may also require the presence of one or more specialists, from radiologists to pathologists.

Postoperative care is very important. After surgery, the patient is taken to a recovery room until the effects of the anesthesia wear off and he or she regains consciousness. If recovery is satisfactory, the patient is returned to the ward. If there are postoperative complications, however, the patient may need to be kept temporarily in an intensive care unit.

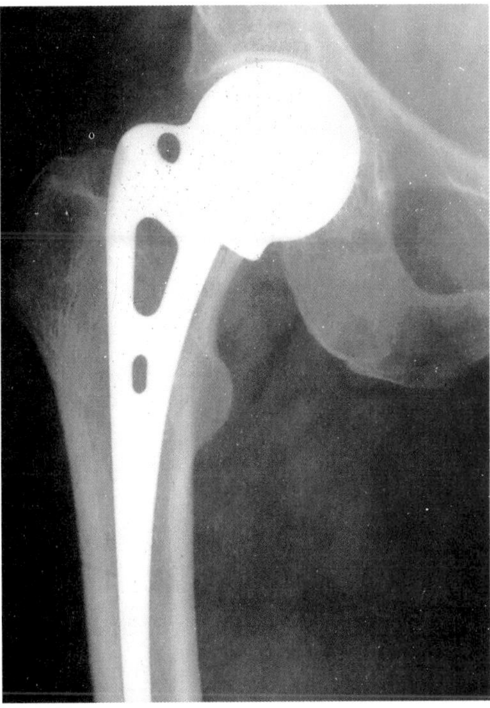

Orthopedic surgery includes the replacement of damaged or diseased joints. This X ray shows an "artificial hip," which comprises a metal pin fixed in the neck and body of the femur and a ball-and-socket joint that replaces the hip joint itself. The ball joint fits into the socket as the head of a normal femur fits into the acetabulum.

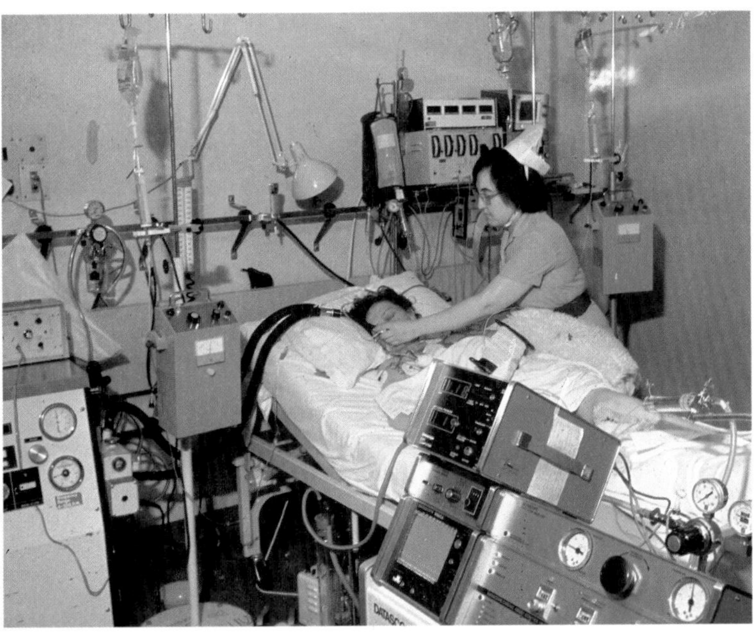

An intensive care unit monitors a patient's condition and helps to keep him or her alive during the recovery period after a serious operation.

Alternatives

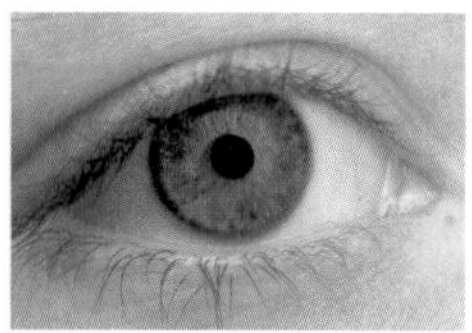

The iris of the eye is studied by the technique called iridology, as explained in the chart below.

Alternative therapies are, for the most part, still suspect in conventional medical eyes; indeed, several of them are commonly regarded as no more than quackery—except by the patients who seem to benefit from them. The medical profession, however, is properly cautious, secure in the knowledge that it has science and proven safety records behind it; physicians' reservations are deeply felt. Yet overall, in both physicians and public, there is a growing awareness that conventional medicine does not hold all the answers, and techniques such as osteopathy have become recognized medical practices.

Drug treatment in particular has contributed to this disquiet because—although drugs are a strong weapon in the fight against disease and pain—many have harmful side effects.

Furthermore, drugs are often used to control symptoms rather than to prevent or cure disease. Drug treatment, however, like surgery, has the advantage that it can be understood in conventional scientific terms, and this is crucially important to those trained in that tradition, because the mysticism and ritual that seems to surround some alternatives makes them unacceptable to a scientist from the start.

Iridology claims to interpret the color and condition of segments of the iris in terms of the state of health of various parts of the body. This simplified chart is for the right eye (the left-eye chart is basically a mirror image of this one). For example, by studying the right-hand sector of the eye at the four o'clock position, an iridologist can possibly diagnose ill health in a person's back or spine.

Iridology chart (right eye)

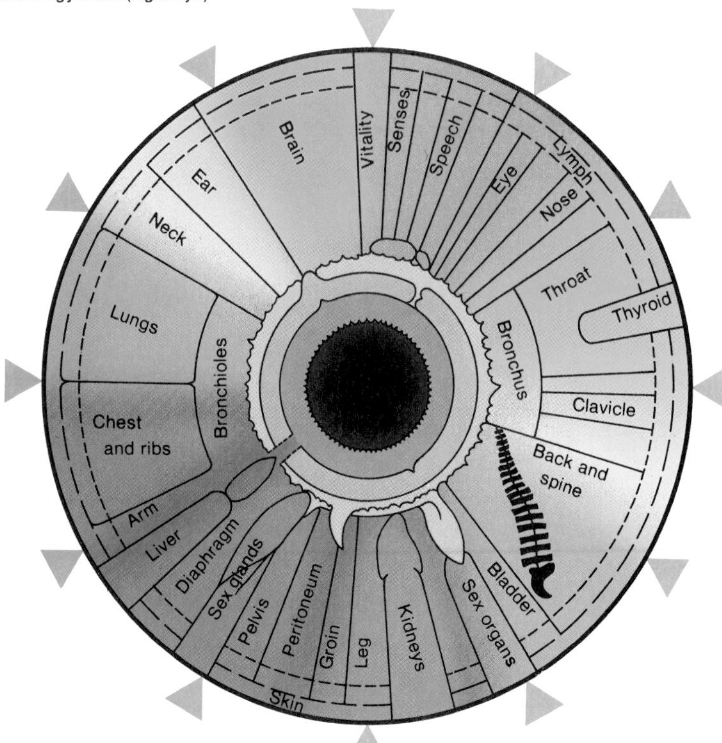

The alternative approach

There are so many different alternatives that to regard them as a whole can be of only limited value. One characteristic many share, however, is that the interrelationship, or coordination, between the healer, the patient, and the method used is much closer than is usual in orthodox medicine. Although the variety of alternatives is vast, their modes of action can be broken down into three major categories.

The first category includes techniques that manipulate the body's "energy"—a characteristic that is difficult to understand, but which certainly seems to exist. It has been effectively excluded from Western medical concepts, but in some Oriental philosophies it is known as "prana" or "chi," which translates best as "life force."

The second category works on the physical body as conventional drugs and other treatments do. These therapies either alter the structure of the body—as does osteopathy, for instance—or alter the chemicals within the body, as occurs in orthomolecular therapy or herbalism.

The third category has a mental or psychological approach. Examples include biofeedback, or—on a paranormal or psychic level—faith healing.

Acupuncture

Acupuncture is one of the oldest forms of medical treatment and has been practiced in China for centuries. Classical acupuncturists believe that the body remains healthy so long as its energy or life force *(chi)* flows freely along well-defined channels known as meridians. Blockages in these channels are the cause of ill health, and the insertion of needles into points along these channels or the application of heat at these points (moxibustion), allows the energy to flow once more, encouraging the restoration of health.

Acupuncturists decide where to insert needles either by assessing the qualities of six pulses felt at each wrist, which represent the major organs of the body or, if they are treating pain, by needling points lying along the meridians that cross the painful area. Pain is often successfully treated by acupuncture but many other conditions can be helped too—notably hay fever and depression. Belief in acupuncture is not needed for it to be effective, although some people—for unknown reasons—do not respond to treatment. Techniques are still developing and recent advances include electrical stimulation of needles, ear acupuncture, and the use of acupuncture in anesthesia.

Homeopathy

Homeopathy originated in the 1750's when a German doctor, Samuel Hahnemann, noticed that if the effects produced by a substance taken by a healthy person corresponded to the sufferings of a sick person then this substance, homeopathically prepared, could provide a useful cure. His homeopathic preparations were made by repeatedly diluting and shaking the substance.

Why does this system work, even when the degree of dilution may be so great that the physical presence of the original substance is virtually undetectable? Many homeopaths believe that every substance has both physical properties and a characteristic "vibrational en-

Curative properties of mud and hot sand have been advocated for hundreds of years. Here, a group of people, completely buried except for their heads and feet, relax in the warm volcanic sands at the hot springs near Ibusuki in Japan.

ergy," which is enhanced by homeopathic preparation. Treatment is effected by a substance with a vibrational energy that corrects the distorted vibrational energy of the patient. The substance is usually chosen as a result of investigating both the symptoms and character of the patient, though some practitioners attempt to match up the vibrational energy of the remedy to the patient directly. This can be done using radionics or electrohomeopathy. Homeopathy has been used to treat all forms of illness and tends to work either very well or not at all.

Osteopathy

Osteopathy was developed in the 1870's by the American doctor Andrew Taylor Still, who felt that the physical integrity of the spinal column was essential for good health. Today, this is no longer generally believed, although osteopathic techniques are widely and usefully practiced. Osteopathic medicine emphasizes the importance of the muscles and bones of the body and their connecting tendons and ligaments. These parts of the body make up the musculoskeletal system, which osteopathic physicians believe has important interrelationships with all other body systems. Osteopathic physicians are specially trained in the detection and treatment of musculoskeletal disturbances. They use massages and other types of osteopathic manipulation to treat these disturbances. This form of therapy is a distinctly osteopathic approach to the problems of health and disease. However, osteopathic physicians also use all the medical, surgical, immunological, pharmacological, psychological, and hygienic procedures of modern medicine.

Orthomolecular medicine

Orthomolecular medicine was developed in the 1950's, with the aim of supplying patients with quantities of all the forty or so nutrients the body needs, on the assumption that a lack of any of these prevents the body from either working or healing itself effectively.

As well as adequate amounts of protein, fats and carbohydrates, minor nutrients, including vitamins and minerals, are also necessary for health. All of the substances used in orthomolecular medicine are found naturally in foods. The nutrients are either supplied by alterations to the diet or by dietary supplements. A range of methods, including blood and urine tests, hair analysis, and the use of questionnaires, together with information obtained directly from the patient by questioning or examination, help the practitioner to formulate the treatment. How much of any nutrient is required is difficult to decide. However, as the majority of nutrients used are harmless and without side effects—unless given in extremely large doses—there is a tendency for practitioners to err on the side of excess. Although this form of treatment can be used on its own, it is often even more useful when combined with other treatments, whether orthodox or not.

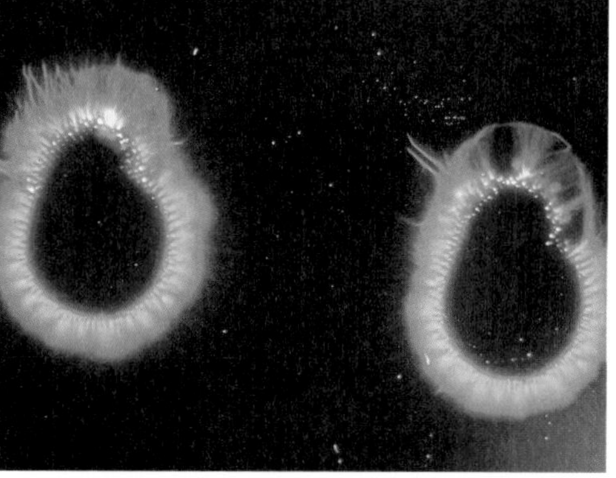

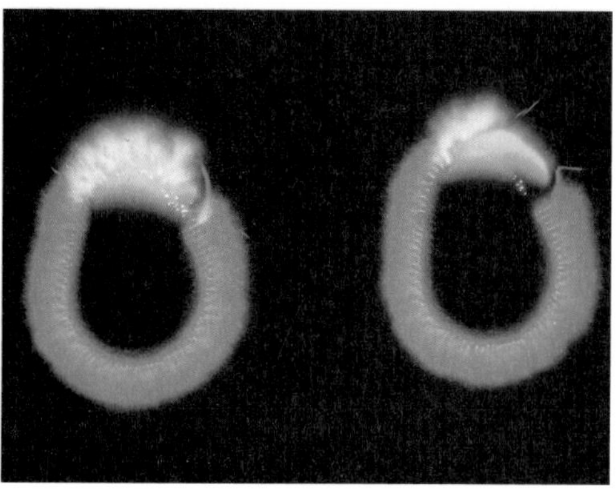

Healing by touch, or "laying on of hands," has been regarded with skepticism by some orthodox practitioners, who challenge its scientific basis. That physical changes do occur is demonstrated in these remarkable photographs, taken by Kirlian photography using an electrostatic field. The upper illustration shows the fingertips of a healer in their normal state; in the lower photograph, the fingers are in a state of healing.

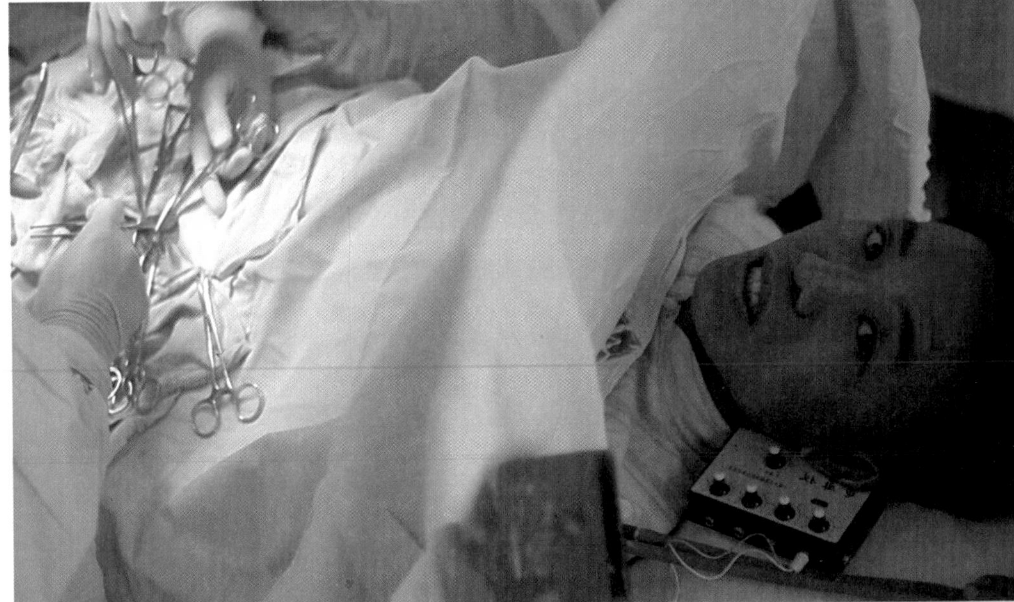

Acupuncture is an ancient discipline that finds increasing use today as a method of inducing anesthesia. Here, a fully conscious patient obviously feels no pain while undergoing abdominal surgery. Some dentists fill or extract teeth using acupuncture anesthesia.

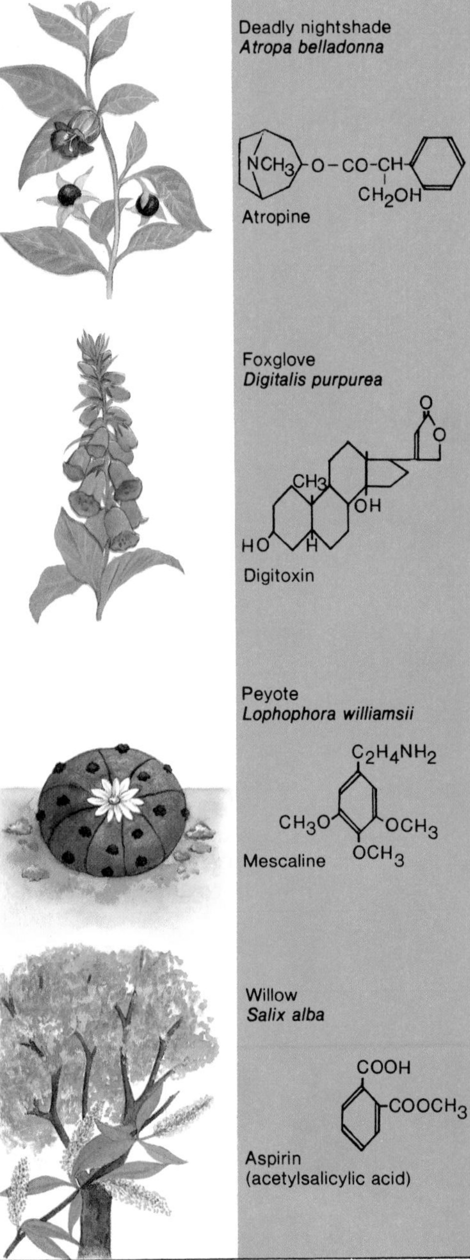

Medicinal plants have been used to treat illness, relieve symptoms, and affect the body or mind since ancient times, in societies at all levels of sophistication and in all parts of the world. In Western countries, refined pharmaceutical preparations tend to be favored, but some of these are, in fact, the active ingredients of traditional "herbal" remedies. For example, distillations of deadly nightshade (belladonna) were used as sedatives or antispasmodics; one modern drug obtained from belladonna is atropine, which has various medical uses, including the treatment of the spasms of asthma. Preparations of foxglove (digitalis) were employed as heart stimulants, and one derivative, digitoxin, is used for this purpose today. Peyote is still taken for its hallucinogenic properties by some North American Indians, and its derivative—mescaline—is also used as a psychedelic drug. Willow bark was employed in ancient times—for instance, by the Romans—as a dressing for wounds because it relieved pain and inflammation; its active ingredient resembles aspirin, which is widely used for pain relief today.

Hypnosis

Hypnosis is now an accepted part of medical practice, although it has passed in and out of fashion since it was first used clinically in the 1820's. A hypnotic state can be invoked in a variety of ways, but all aim to suppress the activity of the conscious mind. This relaxes the patient deeply, allowing the subconscious part of the mind to become more accessible. Through this access, the hypnotherapist can discover, explore, and remove forgotten mental or physical traumas that may be the root of the patient's disorder. The high degree of relaxation also allows the patient's body to heal itself, which is especially valuable in cases where relaxation is normally hampered by an overactive conscious mind.

Hypnosis can also be used in a form of behavior therapy. An idea, such as stopping smoking, is suggested to the patient under hypnosis, so that it continues to work through the patient's subconscious mind once the session is over and full consciousness is restored. Not everyone can be hypnotized, and there is great variety in the depths of hypnotic state that can be achieved in different people.

Most people experience an enhanced sensation during hypnosis—being hypnotized is not like being sent to sleep—although they respond automatically to the hypnotherapist's suggestions. A hypnotized subject would break from the hypnotic state, however, if an attempt was made to override the conscious will. Hypnosis is particularly useful if mental or emotional factors are important in a condition—for example, in an illness that is psychosomatic or induced by stress. It is also of value in the treatment of addictions.

Faith healing

Faith healing is as old as civilization and appears under many guises. As a general term, it is used (by uninformed observers) to cover any means of healing that claims to work by unknown forces that only certain people are able to utilize. It can be argued that such methods work by psychological suggestion based on confidence, beliefs, and receptivity of the patient and healer. However, this does not explain why such methods seem to work even when the patient has no faith.

Many healers work by lightly stroking or touching the patient, often while the healer enters a meditative or trancelike state. The healer's thoughts are directed toward the health and love of the person, and this seems to encourage the healing phenomenon—even when "projected" from a distance. It is possible for any illness to be helped by faith healing but in no specific case can success be guaranteed.

Alternatives evaluated

Contrary to many people's beliefs, alternative therapies are not without their dangers, because almost any treatment that is of value can do both good and harm. In alternative therapies, the most common unwanted effect (often termed a "flare-up") is the worsening of symptoms after treatment. Nevertheless, despite its temporary unpleasantness, this is a measure of the patient's sensitivity and usually indicates that treatment will succeed.

One fear shared by many regarding alternative therapies is that they are practiced by charlatans or quacks. Unlike conventional physicians, alternative therapists are not subject by law to a strict code of therapeutic practice. Uniform standards of training and practice are not established, although membership in a recognized organization goes some way toward providing this.

The future

As interest in alternatives grows, among conventional medical practitioners as much as the general public, the clear distinction between the two camps is disappearing. When drugs fail or surgery seems inappropriate, alternatives such as osteopathy may be suggested. And conversely, a homeopath or acupuncturist would recommend antibiotics to treat an abscess or an infected wound. Fair evaluation by each of the other techniques can only serve to advance medical knowledge, and this view is gaining favor in what is loosely called "the holistic approach." This involves all forms of treatment, according to what is thought likely to benefit the patient most.

Fact entries

Alternative therapies fall into three major categories, each with two subdivisions. The categories are concerned with energy, physical techniques, and psychological techniques, respectively. Acupuncture is based on principles of energy flow, as are techniques such as Reflexology, Shiatzu, and Acupressure. Vibrational energy is important in Homeopathy, and also in Radionics and Bach Flower Remedies. Physical techniques affecting the structure of the body include Osteopathy, Chiropractic, Massage, Alexander Technique, Yoga, and Rolfing. Physical techniques affecting body chemistry include Orthomolecular Therapy, Herbalism, Naturopathy, Special Diets, and Fasting. Hypnosis, Biofeedback, Meditation, and Encounter Therapy are psychological techniques based on normal mental processes. Paranormal psychology, in contrast, seems to be the basis of Faith Healing and variants such as Spiritual Healing, Therapeutic Touch, and Healing Pilgrimages. Many so-called "alternative" treatments are attractive because of their novelty or their "personal" style. It must always be remembered, however, that few offer any genuine scientific evidence for their effects, and most are suspect in conventional medical eyes.

Glossary

In the following glossary, small capital letters (for example, HORMONE) indicate terms that have their own entries in the glossary.

A

abscess An infected, often painful area in which pus forms. An abscess is most commonly caused by BACTERIA entering the body through a break in the skin or a cavity in a tooth.

acute An acute disease is one in which onset is sudden, and duration is comparatively short. A CHRONIC disorder, by contrast, lasts for a long time.

adenoma A BENIGN (noncancerous) TUMOR of a GLAND or similar tissue. An adenoma can occur almost anywhere in the body.

adipose tissue Fatty connective tissue; that part of the body where fat is stored.

albumin A PROTEIN present in blood PLASMA. As serum albumin, it helps to regulate water distribution in the body.

allergen Any substance that causes ALLERGY.

allergy An abnormal reaction to specific substances (ALLERGENS), such as pollen or certain foods.

amino acid Any of about 20 nitrogen-containing organic acids that constitute the building blocks of PROTEIN. When food is digested, the protein in it is broken down into amino acids that are then reassembled to form the particular types of protein required for the manufacture of muscles, red blood cells, and other body tissues. Most amino acids can be manufactured by the body, but eight "essential" amino acids are not synthesized by the body and must be obtained directly from protein in the diet.

amniocentesis The process by which a specimen of amniotic fluid is obtained through a small tube for analysis. Performed early in pregnancy, it is valuable in detecting fetal abnormalities such as SPINA BIFIDA.

amnion The thin membranous sac that encloses the fetus in the uterus. It is filled with amniotic fluid.

anaerobic Without oxygen; usually used to describe BACTERIA that live or function without free air or oxygen, such as the tetanus bacterium. It is the opposite of aerobic, which means living in or using oxygen.

analgesic A drug such as aspirin, acetaminophen, or codeine that relieves pain without loss of consciousness.

androgen A male sex HORMONE.

anesthesia Loss of feeling in part or all of the body either from natural processes or accidents, or deliberately by use of anesthetic drugs.

angina Spasmodic pain, sometimes producing feelings of suffocation. Angina pectoris, for instance, is a painful symptom of a heart disorder.

antibiotic An antibacterial drug made synthetically or obtained from living organisms, such as fungus or mold, that inhibits the growth of, or destroys, BACTERIA. Specific antibiotics can be used to combat specific PATHOGENIC bacteria.

antibody A PROTEIN in the blood that combines with an ANTIGEN so that it destroys or neutralizes that specific substance. Antibodies are key elements in the body's IMMUNE system.

antigen A foreign substance that stimulates the production of ANTIBODIES.

antitoxin A type of ANTIBODY that works against a specific TOXIN entering the body. Some are produced naturally in response to a disease; others are manufactured artificially from SERUM obtained from immunized horses or other mammals. Antitoxins are used to treat diphtheria and tetanus.

auscultation Listening with the ear or a stethoscope to sounds within the body to determine the condition of various organs, particularly the heart and lungs.

autoimmune disease A disease caused by excessive functioning of the IMMUNE mechanism so that sensitivity is created to certain of the body's own tissues.

axon A single, thin, long fiber that conducts nerve impulses away from a nerve cell. Most axons are covered with MYELIN.

B

bacterium A tiny, single-celled organism that may be shaped like a rod, sphere, or spiral. Most bacteria are harmless; those that cause disease are described as PATHOGENIC.

barium meal A preparation of barium sulfate in water swallowed by a patient to be X-rayed for intestinal disorders, such as ULCERS or TUMORS. X RAYS cannot pass through the barium, so the relevant organ—usually the stomach or intestine—shows up clearly on the developed X ray. A barium enema may be given to X-ray the rectum or lower intestine.

benign A term used to indicate a disorder that is neither recurrent nor progressive. It is the opposite of MALIGNANT and is usually applied to noncancerous TUMORS.

biopsy Removal of a small piece of tissue from the living body for examination and diagnosis, often in cases of suspected CANCER. A biopsy may be performed during an operation or during a preliminary investigation. For example, a section of a lump in the breast—which may be a CYST or a TUMOR—may be removed under anesthetic. The specimen is then frozen, cut into slices, stained and studied under a microscope. If the lump is BENIGN, the operational incision is sutured; if it is MALIGNANT, an operation to remove it may be carried out immediately.

blastocyst A stage in embryonic development following the stage of CLEAVAGE that forms the MORULA. The blastocyst is a small cluster of cells that forms within the morula, from which the fetus, amniotic sac, and placenta develop.

blind spot A small area in the retina of the eye, where the optic nerve enters, which is insensitive to light.

blood count A laboratory procedure by which the concentrations of red and white blood cells and platelets are determined. The concentration of hemoglobin (the oxygen-carrying chemical of the blood) is also obtained.

blood pressure Usually refers to the pressure of blood in the main arteries. A sphygmomanometer—an instrument consisting of a dial or column of mercury and a hollow rubber cuff—is usually used to measure blood pressure. The cuff is wrapped around the upper arm and inflated to stop the blood flow. Air is slowly released until a tapping sound can be heard (with the aid of a stethoscope). This is caused by a spurt of blood being forced through the artery. A reading at this point indicates SYSTOLIC pressure. The cuff is further deflated until sounds disappear, the reading at this point indicating DIASTOLIC blood pressure. Normal pressure for young adults is about 120/80mm of mercury (systolic/diastolic) or less.

bowels A general name for the intestines.

bronchoscope A tubelike instrument inserted, under anesthetic, through the mouth and down the trachea. A light and system of lenses and mirrors enable examination of the trachea and bronchi; alternatively, the bronchoscope may be used to remove secretions or tissue samples.

C

Caesarean section Surgical delivery of a baby through an incision in the abdomen and uterus.

calculus An abnormal stonelike deposit, which may consist of mineral salts, especially calcium, CHOLESTEROL, PROTEIN, or urea. Calculi, or stones, form most commonly in the urinary bladder. If they obstruct the normal flow of body fluids, they can cause pain and malfunction of the parts affected by the blockage. Treatment is usually by surgical removal.

calorie Equivalent to one kilocalorie, a calorie is a unit of heat used in measuring body METABOLISM. A calorie is the amount of heat required to raise the temperature of one kilogram of water one degree Celsius.

cancer A disease that results when cell division gets out of control, leading to the development of MALIGNANT CELLS. Cancer cells multiply in an uncoordinated fashion to form a TUMOR. By the process of METASTASIS, cells may then travel from the primary (original) site via the bloodstream or lymph vessels to form secondary cancers elsewhere in the body.

candidiasis A fungal infection caused by *Candida albicans.* Also known as thrush, candidiasis commonly occurs on nails, skin, and in the mouth, vagina, and gastrointestinal tract.

carbohydrate With PROTEINS and fats, carbohydrates are one of the three main constituents of food. Carbohydrates occur as sugars and starches, the latter being converted to sugars during digestion. Carbohydrate-rich foods include bread, potatoes, rice, and all sweet foods. If more carbohydrates are consumed than are used as energy, the excess is stored as fat.

carcinogen Any substance that contributes to the development of CANCER.

carcinoma A CANCER originating in the epithelium, the tissue of the skin, MUCOUS MEMBRANES, and organs or glands, such as the lung, breast, prostate, or thyroid. Carcinomas are the most common form of MALIGNANT TUMOR.

cardiac Of the heart.

cardiovascular Of the heart and blood vessels.

cauterize To destroy damaged or abnormal tissue by burning.

cell The basic unit from which all living tissues are built. Some simple microscopic organisms, such as amebas, are single-celled; the human body consists of about one hundred million million cells. Each cell consists of a variety of specialized structures, the largest of which is the cell NUCLEUS, which contains 23 pairs of GENE-carrying CHROMOSOMES. Sex cells (sperm or ova) have only half the number of chromosomes in their nuclei but combine at fertilization to create a new cell with the full complement. Body cells replicate by a process called MITOSIS, which is the basis of cell division.

cerebral palsy A form of paralysis characterized by jerky or spasmodic movements, resulting from damage to MOTOR control centers in the brain. It may result from birth injury or damage to the fetal brain before birth. The degree of disability varies considerably.

cholesterol An organic compound chemically related to vitamin D and the sex hormones, found in all body tissues, particularly the brain and spinal cord. A key element in the body's chemical processes, cholesterol regulates the passage of substances through cell walls, maintains water balance, and performs other functions not yet understood. Cholesterol is manufactured principally in the liver and is also found in various foods, such as egg yolk, meat, and milk. Excess cholesterol is thought to be a contributory cause of heart and blood vessel diseases.

chromosomes Threadlike bodies contained within the NUCLEUS of every CELL. Usually occurring in pairs, chromosomes consist mainly of nucleoprotein, a combination of protein with DEOXYRIBONUCLEIC ACID (DNA), and are the sites for GENES.

chronic A chronic disorder is one which lasts for a long time without any marked change. It is the opposite of an ACUTE disorder.

cilia Minute hairlike threads that beat or lash rhythmically to keep mucous fluids flowing in a constant direction, for instance, out of the lungs.

cleavage A stage in embryonic development when the ZYGOTE undergoes repeated MITOTIC division to form the MORULA.

collagen Fibrous PROTEIN that forms the fibers of connective or supporting tissues of the body. Collagen is found in cartilage, bone, the inelastic material of tendons, and the elastic part of skin. Collagen (or connective tissue) diseases are a group of diseases, such as rheumatoid arthritis, characterized by inflammation of the connective tissues.

colostrum A milky fluid produced by a mother's breasts during the few days just before and after the birth of a baby. Colostrum is not true milk but is rich in PROTEINS and ANTIBODIES, which protect against infection.

cone A specialized cell of the central part of the eye's retina, responsible for color distinction and detailed vision.

congenital Present at birth.

corpus luteum The yellow body that develops from an ovarian FOLLICLE after a ripened ovum has been released. The corpus luteum produces the HORMONE progesterone to prepare the uterine lining for a fertilized egg. If FERTILIZATION occurs, the corpus luteum enlarges and continues to produce progesterone for several months; otherwise, the corpus luteum shrinks and gradually degenerates.

cortex The outer layer of an organ, such as the brain,

kidney, or adrenal gland.

culture medium A substance, such as agar jelly or gelatin, on which microorganisms, such as bacteria, are allowed to grow for identification or analysis.

cyst A lump consisting of a liquid- or semiliquid-filled sac without an opening. Cysts occur most commonly in the breast, ovary, and skin. Most are BENIGN, but because some may become MALIGNANT or interfere with the body's functioning, their removal may be advised.

D

dementia A general term for mental disorder involving deterioration of the brain and its functions.

dendrite A thin, branched fiber that receives and conveys impulses to the nerve cell of a NEURON.

deoxyribonucleic acid (DNA) A long-chain compound found in the NUCLEUS of all CELLS. In humans, the DNA molecule is made up of four basic building blocks, called nucleotides, joined together in two long intertwining helices. DNA contains a set of "instructions" for reproducing other cells of the same kind as the original cell. It also contains the genetic information required for sexual reproduction.

desensitization Removal or reduction of a person's sensitivity to a specific substance, most commonly in the treatment of ALLERGY.

diagnosis The process of identifying a disease or diseases. Many factors must be taken into account when making a diagnosis—for instance, the findings of physical examination, previous medical history, and perhaps the health of other members of the family.

dialysis A method of separating substances in solution by passing them through a semipermeable membrane. This process is carried out naturally by the kidneys, and artificially by a kidney dialysis machine.

diastole The relaxation and dilatation of the heart after each contraction or SYSTOLE. It is during the diastole stage that the chambers of the heart fill with blood. In BLOOD PRESSURE readings, the diastolic pressure is the lower of the two figures.

differentiation Changes in structure or function of CELLS, tissue, or organs during embryonic development. Cell differentiation may manifest itself by the appearance of particular visible structures, such as muscle striations, or the production of chemical substances, such as enzymes. Tissue differentiation usually involves the grouping of cells of various types to form different tissues, which in turn may develop into a specialized organ.

dilatation (or dilation) Widening of an organ or part of it. The term is commonly used with reference to the pupil of the eye or to the neck (cervix) of the uterus.

Down's syndrome Also known as mongolism or trisomy 21, Down's syndrome is a CONGENITAL abnormality resulting from a chromosomal defect called trisomy, in which a Down's syndrome child has 47 chromosomes rather than the normal 46.

E

electrocardiograph (EKG) A machine that records electrical activity in the heart, producing a recording (electrocardiogram) in the form of a trace on paper or on an oscilloscope.

electroencephalograph (EEG) A machine that amplifies and records electrical activity in the brain. The resulting trace is called an electroencephalogram.

embolism Obstruction of a blood vessel by foreign material (embolus). The embolus may be a blood clot, clump of BACTERIA, air bubble (air embolus), or similar obstruction that is carried through the blood until it lodges in a blood vessel and blocks the blood flow. The consequences vary, depending on the size of the embolus and the part of the body deprived of blood. Embolism is one cause of STROKE, in which a part of a blood clot lodges in an artery supplying the brain. Deprived of their blood supply, brain cells starve and die (infarction), and a stroke results. Other areas that may be affected include the heart, lungs, and arteries of the legs.

endorphins Peptides with a relatively low molecular weight that occur naturally in the body and bind to the same receptor sites in the brain as do morphine compounds. Their name derives from the original description of them as endogenous morphines. They are believed to be part of the body's natural protection against pain, and it is postulated that their action may explain the fact that some pains can be temporarily ignored if a person is distracted, for instance, by another pain. They may also be involved in the apparent "addiction" of some people to certain activities, such as long-distance running, which may encourage the body's production of endorphins, producing the so-called "runner's high."

endoscopy Examination of parts of the body by means of inserting a lighted instrument through one of the body's natural orifices or through a small surgical incision. Instruments include a BRONCHOSCOPE and sigmoidoscope. Endoscopes may incorporate lens systems for viewing or photography, or devices for tissue sample removal (BIOPSY).

endothelium A membrane consisting of narrow, flattened cells that line the blood vessels, heart, and lymph vessels.

enzymes A large group of naturally-produced PROTEINS that act as catalysts in specific biochemical reactions, particularly in METABOLISM.

epinephrine A HORMONE produced by the adrenal GLANDS. It stimulates heart action, constricts certain blood vessels, and relaxes bronchial tubes and other smooth muscle. When the body is under stress, production is stimulated, thus preparing the body for emergency "flight or fight" action. Epinephrine obtained from animals or produced synthetically can be used to treat bronchial asthma and some allergic conditions.

epithelium A layer of tissue that covers external and internal body surfaces.

F

fertilization The union of sperm cell and egg cell. Although many million sperm are released into the vagina at ejaculation, only one penetrates and fertilizes the ovum. Once fertilized, the ovum's membrane is reinforced and the ovum becomes impenetrable to further sperm.

fibrinogen A PROTEIN manufactured in the liver and released into the blood, where it acts as a clotting agent when a blood vessel is damaged. Together with another substance—thrombin—fibrinogen produces long threads of fibrin that create a mesh that traps blood corpuscles to form a blood clot.

fibroid A normally benign TUMOR that grows in the muscle and connective tissues of the uterus or vagina. One single large tumor or several smaller ones may develop. A large fibroid may cause the uterus to press on neighboring organs, particularly the bladder, or may interfere with normal menstrual functioning. In such cases, surgical removal of the fibroid(s) may be required.

fimbria A fringelike projection, particularly the one at the opening of each Fallopian tube, close to each ovary. Fimbriae are covered with CILIA, which lash backward and forward, sweeping a matured ovum released by the ovary into the Fallopian tube.

fluoride A compound of the chemical element fluorine. Fluorides help to maintain calcium deposits in hard tissues of the body. The addition of fluorides to water supplies seems to help prevent tooth decay. Fluorides may also play a role in the prevention and treatment of osteoporosis.

follicle A small cavity or sac that produces secretions. Follicles have various forms. Hair follicles are tiny cylindrical depressions from which single hairs grow; they are linked to sebaceous GLANDS. In the ovary, each ovum, or egg cell, is contained within a membrane, which with the ovum constitutes an ovarian or Graafian follicle.

G

ganglion In the nervous system, a ganglion is a cluster of NERVE cells where nerve fibers connect to create a center of nervous activity. Ganglion also describes a type of swelling or CYST that contains fluid. Most ganglia of this type are connected to a tendon or membrane at a joint, usually at the wrist. Usually painless, a ganglion may be removed by surgery if it is troublesome.

gangrene Death of tissue caused by lack of oxygen, usually because the blood supply has been stopped. It may be caused by burns, frostbite, injury, obstruction of blood vessels, or vascular disease. Wet gangrene is characterized by an offensive, watery discharge and is easily infected. In dry gangrene, infection does not occur, instead, circulation is cut off gradually, the affected part becoming dry and mummified. Amputation may be necessary as a result of either type.

gastrulation An embryological term referring to the complex rearrangement of CELLS that occurs within the BLASTOCYST following CLEAVAGE. This rearrangement involves the migration of cells whose descendants will form future internal organs in their approximately final positions within the embryo. The pattern of movement varies among different animals, but in human beings, cells either migrate inward to form the mesoderm and endoderm layers or they remain on the outside to form the ectoderm layer.

gene The basic unit of inheritance, composed of molecules of DEOXYRIBONUCLEIC ACID (DNA) and located on the CHROMOSOMES of each CELL. The genes determine and pass on all the characteristics an individual inherits, for example, color of eyes and hair and shape of facial features.

gland A CELL or organ that produces and releases substances needed for the normal functioning of the body. There are two kinds—those with ducts (exocrine glands), which carry their secretions to specific regions inside or outside the body (examples being salivary glands, mammary glands, and sweat glands); and those without ducts (endocrine glands), which release their secretions (called HORMONES) directly into the bloodstream, an example being the thyroid gland.

H

hematoma An accumulation or clotted lump of blood in tissue, usually associated with bruising after an injury. Some are quite minor and may be reabsorbed by the body; others may be serious. A subdural hematoma is one that occurs under the skull following a head injury. This type may press on the brain and require surgical treatment.

hemorrhage Bleeding. Where blood loss is rapid and large, shock results and may be fatal unless blood is replaced by means of a transfusion. Hemorrhage may result from injury, complications of childbirth, from an ULCER or TUMOR, the rupturing of a blood vessel, or from bloodclotting abnormalities.

hemostat An instrument that stops bleeding by clamping a blood vessel.

hereditary Inherited genetically from one or both parents.

herpes Inflammation of the skin accompanied by the formation of small blisters, caused especially by two types of virus: *Herpes zoster* (chickenpox and shingles) and *Herpes simplex* (cold sores). An unusual feature of this condition is that although ANTIBODIES are produced after the primary infection, so that there should be no recurrence, the virus lies dormant and may reemerge in response to some strong stimulus. The process is not fully understood, nor is it clear what the stimulus might be.

hormone Any of several substances present in very small amounts in the blood and producing specific effects in the body. For instance, the hormone insulin controls the way in which the body uses glucose. The endocrine GLANDS produce most of the hormones essential for normal body functioning, their activity being governed by the action of the nervous system under the control of the hypothalamus and by the pituitary gland. Some hormones are produced by other tissues: for instance, the placenta produces sex hormones during pregnancy, and the stomach and intestines produce hormones that aid digestion.

hydrocephalus A rare condition usually present at birth, in which there is abnormal enlargement of the head due to the accumulation of cerebrospinal fluid in the brain cavities. Often found in babies suffering from SPINA BIFIDA, it may also occur as a result of brain TUMOR or meningitis. Mild cases may clear by themselves; more severe cases require surgery to drain the fluid and pass it into the bloodstream.

hypertension Abnormally high BLOOD PRESSURE.

I

immunity The ability to resist infectious disease. Immunity to certain human diseases varies according to individual inherited differences in antibody output. The chief source of natural immunity is the lymphatic system, which manufactures ANTIBODIES in response to specific alien proteins (ANTIGENS). Interferons—proteins that curb the spread of viruses—also provide natural immunity. Immunity may be active or passive. Natural active immunity is the immunity that the body creates by the production of antibodies so that one attack by a disease may produce lifelong immunity against that disease thereafter, artificial active immunity is that conferred by vaccination or immunization. Passive immunity is temporary. It occurs in the case of a newborn infant who acquires antibodies from the mother before birth, which provide a natural immunity that lasts only a few months. Or it can be provided artificially by the use of SERUM.

immunization The procedure by which acquired IMMUNITY to disease is induced in a person.

induction (of labor) Artificial stimulation of labor before it begins naturally, usually by rupturing the amniotic sac or by the use of drugs, such as OXYTOCIN.

inoculation The introduction into the body of live, weakened, or dead germs to produce IMMUNITY against infectious diseases, such as diphtheria, measles, poliomyelitis, or smallpox; a type of IMMUNIZATION.

insulin A HORMONE produced by the small groups of cells in the pancreas known as the islets of Langerhans. Insulin controls the metabolism of sugar (glucose). Insufficient production of insulin results in diabetes mellitus.

J

joint The point where two bones articulate or fuse. Joints may be immobile, as in the skull, or movable, as in the limbs.

K

keratin A tough fibrous PROTEIN that makes up the horny tissues of the body, such as fingernails, hair, and skin.

kilocalorie *See* calorie

Krebs cycle (citric acid cycle) A complex cycle of enzyme-controlled natural biochemical reactions by which pyruvic acid is broken down in the presence of oxygen to carbon dioxide. It is the final stage in the oxidation of CARBOHYDRATES.

L

lacrimal Of or relating to tears, which are produced by the lacrimal GLANDS sited just above the eye.

lanugo Fine, downy hair that covers the fetus. Most of it disappears before birth.

ligament A band of tough, flexible tissue that supports body organs or keeps bones in place. Damage to a ligament causes a sprain—the overstretching of a ligament attached to the bones of a joint. Ligaments can also be torn in an accident.

lipids Fatty substances, one example of which is CHOLESTEROL, stored in the body. They are needed as sources of available energy, but an excess is associated with obesity and tissue disorders, such as arteriosclerosis.

lipoma A fatty benign TUMOR occurring most commonly in the armpit, or on the forearm, back of the neck, or trunk.

lymph The colorless fluid of the lymphatic system. It contains white blood cells known as LYMPHOCYTES, stored in the LYMPH NODES. At the base of the neck, the two main branches of the lymphatic system merge with two veins so that lymph becomes incorporated in the bloodstream.

lymph nodes Small masses of spongy tissue found throughout the lymphatic system, especially in the armpit, neck, and groin. The lymph nodes contain LYMPHOCYTES, act as filters for BACTERIA and waste debris, and produce ANTIBODIES. Lymph nodes are stimulated by infection, and, in such circumstances, may become swollen and painful.

lymphocyte A type of white blood cell formed in the thymus and bone marrow and found in the lymphatic system. Lymphocytes are concerned with the production of ANTIBODIES and IMMUNITY.

lymphoma A general term for new tissue, which may be MALIGNANT, growing in the lymphatic system.

M

malignant Tending to grow progressively worse; potentially life-threatening. Malignant usually refers to cancerous TUMORS as opposed to BENIGN tumors. A malignant tumor, or CANCER, invades surrounding tissue and must be removed surgically or treated with radiotherapy or drugs at the earliest possible stage.

medulla The inside of certain organs, such as bones and GLANDS, as opposed to the surface CORTEX.

melanin The brown or black pigment that occurs naturally in the lowest layer of the epidermis. It gives coloring to parts of the body such as the hair, skin, and iris of the eye. It is derived from an AMINO ACID, tyrosine, through ENZYME action. If the enzyme is absent, the person has no melanin pigment and is described as an albino.

meninges Three membranes that cover the brain and spinal cord. They are the pia mater (internal), the arachnoid, and the dura mater (external).

metabolism All the chemical processes by which life systems are organized and maintained, involving the breakdown (catabolism) and building up (anabolism) of complex substances, the assimilation of nutrients, and the release of energy. Metabolic rate describes an individual's energy output. Basal metabolic rate describes this output in an individual at rest.

metastasis The movement of CANCER cells from one part of the body to another.

micturition An alternative term for urination.

mitosis The process by which a CELL replicates to produce two daughter cells, each identical to the parent. This is the method by which the body grows, and is also the way it generates new cells to replace those lost as a result of injury or normal cell death. During mitosis, each CHROMOSOME is duplicated, then the resulting duplicates separate and migrate to opposite sides of the parent cell. A new nuclear membrane develops around each set of chromosomes, and a new cell wall forms between the NUCLEI. In this way, mitosis produces two daughter cells with the same chromosome constitution as the parent cell. Meiosis is a similar but more complex process of cell division in which the daughter cells end up with only half the total number of chromosomes of the parent cell and so become gametes (sex cells), either sperm or ova.

mole A small, pigmented area of skin, sometimes raised above the level of the surrounding skin. A mole present at birth is usually called a birthmark.

morula A stage of embryonic development following CLEAVAGE. After fertilization, the ZYGOTE undergoes continuous cell division to produce a small bundle of cells—the morula. In turn, the cells of the morula become separated to form an outer wall (the trophoblast) and a cluster of cells (the BLASTOCYST).

motor Having to do with, or causing, motion. Motor NERVES carry impulses from the central nervous system to muscles to make the latter contract.

mucous membrane Mucus-secreting tissue that lines most of the inner cavities and passages of the body, such as the digestive tract, the respiratory tract, the urinary tract, and reproductive tract. Although similar in structure, mucous membranes perform different functions. Those of the nose warm and moisten air; those of the trachea (windpipe) trap dust and dirt; while those of the stomach contain special GLANDS concerned with digestion and prevent stomach acids from harming body tissues.

myelin A white, fatty material that covers most AXONS, or impulse-carrying fibers, of NEURONS. Diseases such as multiple sclerosis result from myelin abnormalities.

N

narcolepsy An irresistible tendency to fall asleep at any time or place, not caused by normal tiredness. It is most usually the result of brain damage in the region of the hypothalamus, perhaps as a consequence of infection, brain tumor, or head injury.

narcotic Any substance that produces stupor, sleep, and relieves pain. Narcotics include opium and opium-derivatives such as morphine. Popularly and legally, the term also refers to an addictive drug used illegally.

necrosis Death of CELLS, tissues, or part of an organ in an otherwise living body. Necrosis may occur after severe burns or other injuries, or because the blood supply is cut off for a long period, as in GANGRENE.

neoplasm A new and abnormal growth or TUMOR that may be BENIGN or MALIGNANT.

nerve Any of the cordlike bundles of sensory fibers or NEURONS along which nerve impulses travel.

neuron A NERVE cell, including the cell body. DENDRITES carry incoming impulses to the nerve cell; the AXON carries impulses away.

nucleus The central body of a CELL. Surrounded by cytoplasm, the nucleus contains CHROMOSOMES and the materials required for cell division and heredity.

O

occlusion Closing or shutting off—a blockage anywhere in the body. In coronary occlusion, one of the arteries supplying blood to the heart is blocked by a blood clot or similar obstruction. The term also applies to the mouth's "bite"—the way in which the teeth of the upper and lower jaws fit together.

optic chiasma The arrangement of nerve fibers where the optic nerves of both eyes join and cross, in front of the limbic system.

ossification The process of bone formation.

oxytocin A HORMONE produced by the pituitary gland that stimulates uterine contractions. Synthetic oxytocin is sometimes used to stimulate labor (INDUCTION).

P

pacemaker A small knot of tissue in the right atrium of the heart that triggers the heartbeat. If this natural pacemaker fails to function properly, however, its function can be taken over by an artificial electronic device known as a cardiac pacemaker, which may be inserted surgically. It acts by stimulating the heart with tiny electrical impulses.

pathogen The scientific name given to any microorganism that causes disease.

percussion A method of physical examination that involves tapping the body surface with quick, sharp blows of the fingertips to cause vibration in internal organs, particularly the heart and lungs. Unusual sounds may indicate the need for further investigation.

peristalsis Slow, wavelike motions of organs of the body, such as the esophagus, intestines, and Fallopian tubes, which push along the contents of the tube or duct. It is affected by coordinated, sequential involuntary contractions of smooth muscle.

phagocytosis The process by which a specialized cell (phagocyte) engulfs or ingests other small particles, particularly bits of foreign matter, such as dust, or pathogenic BACTERIA. It is an important mechanism in the body's defenses against infection.

phenotype The outward physical appearance of an organism determined by genetic and environmental factors.

physiotherapy The treatment—usually to assist recovery from accidents or surgery—of bone, joint, and muscle disorders by physical means, such as massage and aided exercise, or other techniques, such as heat treatment (diathermy), ultrasound, or electrical stimulation.

plasma The liquid part of blood, without the blood cells.

platelet A minute, colorless blood cell that helps blood to clot.

polyp A TUMOR of the MUCOUS MEMBRANES, usually occurring in the nose, uterus, or colon. Polyps are seldom MALIGNANT but may cause obstruction.

prolactin A hormone of the pituitary gland that stimulates milk production in the female breasts.

prostaglandins A group of hormonelike substances in the body that perform a variety of actions. Not all their functions are fully understood, but they stimulate or relax smooth muscle, may regulate CELL behavior and the blood flow in the kidneys, and contribute to the action of HORMONES. Following medical studies, some prostaglandins may become valuable drugs to be used, for example, in induction of labor, treatment of peptic ULCERS, and relief of inflammation.

protein A complex chemical compound built of long chains of AMINO ACIDS that forms an essential part of every living CELL. Hair, muscles, and skin are largely protein, and protein also makes up part of CHROMOSOMES, ENZYMES, blood PLASMA, and hemoglobin. Synthesis of protein by the body is essential not only for the growth and repair of tissues but also for the continuation of life processes.

psychoanalysis A technique of investigating and treating certain mental disorders, which was developed by Sigmund Freud and is practiced now by Freudian, neo-Freudian, and other psychoanalysts.

psychotherapy A general term for all forms of nonmedical treatment of mental illness, typified as the "talking cures." At its most general, the term can mean simply treatment of the mind. More specific usage, however, tends to restrict it to non-Freudian (that is, non-psychoanalytical) techniques.

R

rabies A lethal VIRAL disease transmitted to humans by the bite of an infected (rabid) animal. Dogs, although the best known, are not the only source. The virus travels from the bite along the NERVE fibers to the brain. Symptoms include muscle spasms, convulsions, and extreme excitement, as well as a fear of drinking—which gave the disease its original name: hydrophobia. Although usually fatal, rabies has an incubation period of one month to a year, and treatment with injections of rabies vaccine at an early stage usually prevents the disease from developing.

ribonucleic acid (RNA) A substance found in all living cells that directs the CELL to manufacture specific ENZYMES and other PROTEINS by regulating the assembly of AMINO ACIDS.

rod A cylindrical structure in the retina of the eye. Rods distinguish only shades of gray but are sensitive to faint light, enabling us to see in dim surroundings.

rubella Also known as German measles, a mild VIRAL infection characterized by a pink rash spreading all over the body, sometimes accompanied by headache and mild fever. Although not normally a problem, rubella contracted by a woman during the first three months of pregnancy can cause serious birth defects, such as cataracts of the eyes.

S

saline A solution containing salt. In medical usage, this refers to a weak solution of salt, at approximately the same concentration as body fluids.

sarcoma A MALIGNANT TUMOR in connective tissue.

septicemia Blood poisoning in which BACTERIA or other germs are present in the blood and cause illness. Since the introduction of ANTIBIOTICS to treat infection, septicemia has become far less common.

septum A wall or division between two cavities, as in the nasal septum, which divides the nostrils.

serum The clear, yellowish fluid that separates from blood after clotting. Serum is PLASMA without FIBRINOGEN, and contains ANTIBODIES. The term is also used to describe blood fluid containing antibodies that is used to provide temporary immunity. Examples are antivenins, used to counteract the venom of a snake bite, and ANTITOXINS.

shock An emotional or physical reaction to a traumatic event. The term is used most commonly to describe emotional shock. More serious, and potentially fatal, is clinical shock, which is a common consequence of physical TRAUMA, such as can occur in an accident or major surgery. Clinical shock can cause death from reduced blood supply to the brain and vital organs.

sinus A hollow space or cavity, generally in bone. The term commonly refers to the paranasal sinuses, the membrane-lined cavities in bones around the nose. Sinusitis refers to inflammation of these sinuses.

spina bifida A CONGENITAL malformation of the spine in which some of the vertebrae fail to fuse correctly to create the channel that normally protects the spinal cord. As a result, the cord may be malformed and lack certain nerves. Complications of the most severe cases include HYDROCEPHALUS and meningitis (inflammation of the MENINGES).

steroids Naturally occurring or synthetic HORMONES. Natural steroids include the sex hormones—progesterone and estrogen.

stroke A THROMBOSIS affecting the brain. The term can also describe the result of any injury that blocks the blood supply to part of the brain, causing symptoms such as paralysis.

symptom An obvious change in the body's appearance, feelings, or functions, indicating an underlying disorder.

synapse A junction between NERVE cells where nervous impulses are transmitted from one cell to another.

syndrome A collection of SYMPTOMS or other signs that characterize an illness.

systole The rhythmic contraction of the heart that pumps blood through the circulatory system. Relaxation of the heart is called DIASTOLE.

T

thrombosis The OCCLUSION or blockage of a blood vessel by a blood clot (thrombus). If thrombosis occurs in an artery leading to an arm or leg, tissue NECROSIS or GANGRENE may result. Thrombosis in an artery of the brain or in a neck artery leading to the brain causes a STROKE. A coronary thrombosis is a thrombosis in an artery that supplies the heart.

toxemia A condition caused by the absorption into the blood of poisonous (toxic) substances. Toxemia of pregnancy, however, refers to a metabolic disturbance which, if left untreated, may develop into eclampsia.

toxin A poisonous substance that can be produced in the body by PATHOGENIC microorganisms, such as BACTERIA. An ANTITOXIN may be produced naturally by the body to neutralize their effects, or prepared synthetically for the same purpose.

trauma In psychological terms, an emotional SHOCK that leads to disordered thoughts or behavior. The term is also used for a physical injury, such as an accidental or surgical wound.

tumor A swelling on or in a part of the body, caused either by abnormal tissue growth or from a collection of fluid. Tumors may be BENIGN or MALIGNANT.

typhus A group of infectious diseases caused by various *Rickettsia* microorganisms and spread by infected lice, fleas, rats, and mice. The disease is endemic in parts of the Third World.

U

ulcer An inflamed open sore on the skin or on the MUCOUS MEMBRANES lining a body cavity. Ulcers may be caused by infection, injury, disturbances of the nerve or blood supply, or by acid (as in peptic ulcers).

unconscious A term used in Freudian PSYCHOANALYSIS to describe the aspect of personality of which the conscious mind is unaware. C. G. Jung developed the separate concept of the collective unconscious, which describes the part of the personality that is influenced by "collective" memories and instincts common to all mankind, probably through cultural and social upbringing. The patterns of these influences are reflected in Jungian "archetypes," usually represented as pairs of symbols with opposing characteristics, such as good and evil. In the relationship between the conscious mind and the unconscious, Freud identified three divisions, which he called id, ego, and superego. Jung, in contrast, saw the relationship as having four modes—thinking, feeling, sensation, and intuition—cut across by two tendencies, also opposed, called introversion and extroversion.

urine test One of the oldest and still most valuable DIAGNOSTIC tests available to doctors. The examination of urine is used to detect diseases such as diabetes, diseases of the bladder and kidneys, jaundice, and other disorders of body chemistry, that cause specific changes to urine composition.

V

vaccination A means of making an individual immune to an infectious disease, such as smallpox, by injecting (or, in some cases, by swallowing) a VACCINE. The vaccine stimulates the immune system of the body to produce ANTIBODIES that neutralize the ANTIGENS, so producing IMMUNITY.

vaccine A preparation containing weakened or killed viruses introduced into the body to produce IMMUNITY against a specific disease by causing the formation of ANTIBODIES. Vaccine may be prepared in various ways. VIRUSES may be killed by heat, sound waves, or chemical treatments. Alternatively, a living—but weakened—germ can be used.

vasopressin A HORMONE secreted by the pituitary gland and having the function of regulating the water content in the body. Medically, its chief use is the control of excessive urination that occurs in diabetes.

vernix A greasy substance that covers and makes waterproof the skin of the fetus in the uterus.

villus A microscopic, threadlike projection from an internal body surface. The small intestine is lined with thousands of villi.

virus Any of a group of minute PATHOGENIC agents that occupy the borderline between living and nonliving organisms. They can survive only by penetrating the living cells of another organism. Viruses show no lifelike activity unless introduced into a living CELL; once this has occurred, however, they control the processes of the invaded cell. Viruses are responsible for numerous diseases, including HERPES and RABIES.

W

wart A harmless but unattractive growth formed on and rooted in the skin. Common warts tend to occur on hands, fingers, knees, and face, and are most common among children. They are caused by a VIRUS and are contagious but easily removed.

weal A temporarily swollen area on the skin that may result from ALLERGY, drugs, or minor injury.

X

X-chromosome One of the two sex CHROMOSOMES in the cells of human beings (the other is the Y-chromosome). A person with two X-chromosomes in each pair is female.

X rays A form of electromagnetic radiation with high energy and short wavelength and with the ability to penetrate soft tissues. X rays are invisible, but they affect photographic film and so can be used to "photograph" the interior of the body and its structures.

Y

Y-chromosome One of the two sex CHROMOSOMES in the cells of human beings. A person with one Y-chromosome and one X-chromosome in each pair is male.

Z

zona pellucida The membrane that surrounds a fertilized egg cell; it disappears before the egg becomes implanted in the lining of the uterus.

zygote The fertilized egg CELL formed from the union of a female egg cell (ovum) and a male sex cell (sperm). It is the first stage in the development of an embryo, and is followed immediately by CLEAVAGE as the cells start to divide.

Index

Q

R

S

T

Credits

The following have provided photographs for this book: Cover photo—Manfred Uselmann, H. Armstrong Roberts; Michael Abbey/Science Photo Library 43; Aerofilms Ltd. 140; Simon Anderson/Science Photo Library 70; ©Bill Aron, Photo Edit 109; Bettmann Archive/BBC Hulton Picture Library 141; Biology Media/Science Photo Library 94; Brightman Art Library 2; Dr. J. Burgess/Science Photo Library 116; Camera Talks 47; Gill Clark 113, 114; R. Clark/M. Goff/Science Photo Library 8; Colour Library International 60, 68, 73, 117; E.H. Cook/Science Photo Library 100; Gene Cox/Science Photo Library 37, 41; Dr. R. Damadion/Science Photo Library 89; Dr. R. Dourmashkin/Science Photo Library 90; Sarah Errington/Alan Hutchinson Library 74, 89; Mary Evans Picture Library/©Sigmund Freud 112; Lawrence Fried/The Image Bank 84; Lowell Georgia/Science Photo Library 77; Glaxo Pharmaceuticals Ltd. Speke 77; GLC 69; Dr. M. Gorman/Science Photo Library 15; Henry Grant 65; Eric Grave/Science Photo Library 13, 17, 21, 33, 97; Sally & Richard Greenhill 55, 56, 57, 59, 71, 78, 93, 95, 98, 115, 116, 127; Guy's Hospital, London 45; Dr. Howells/Science Photo Library 80, 123; Alan Hutchinson Library 126; Keystone Press Agency 70; Clive A. Lawton/Board of Deputies of British Jews 63; David Leah/Science Photo Library 53, 92, 120, 122; London Scientific Fotos 17, 21, 27, 29, 31, 35, 37, 39, 49, 76, 82, 86, 91, 93, 110, 111; M. Macintyre/Alan Hutchinson Library 66; The Mansell Collection 110; Dr. J. McFarland/Science Photo Library 101; Dr. Thelma Moss/Science Photo Library 125; NASA/Science Photo Library 94; Ohio-Nuclear Corporation/Science Photo Library 35; Optical Information Council 107; Martyn Page 68; Photo Researchers Inc./Science Photo Library 99; Puttkamer/Alan Hutchinson Library 83; St. Andrew's Hospital, Northampton, England 114; St. Stephen's Hospital 79; Dr. G. Schatten/Science Photo Library 99; Science Photo Library 19, 22, 94, 96, 102, 103; Science Source/Science Photo Library 110; David Simpson/Alan Hutchinson Library 105; Shaun Skelly/Silvestrius 84; Tony Stone Associates, London, 2, 10, 11, 39, 42, 53, 54, 55, 56, 57, 58, 61, 64, 65, 66, 67, 81, 87, 88, 110, 121, 123, 124, 125; G. M. Villermet/Institute of Ophthalmology 106; John Walmsley 9, 61, 62, 81; John Walsh/Science Photo Library 119; John Watney Photo Library 113; C. James Webb 104; Robin Williams/London Scientific Fotos 51.